PRAISE FOR *Modern Medic*

This book is a must read. Dr. Nijhawan gives us a laser focused view on the path ahead for real health care reform. This isn't just public policy, this is the path ahead for every thoughtful consumer for their own journey.

The most important audience for this book is the 500 Americans who constitute our congress, cabinet and other critical leadership,… and the 300 other million Americans who might have some concerns about how their health care works. This book is a brilliant view that no one else has offered. This is how to make real health care reform.

This book is a seismic shift in thinking. Finally, how real health care reform should work. Any business wanting to cut health care costs 30-50% must read this book, because this is the foundation for how to make real health care reform work. We have to align incentives, develop Dr. Nijhawan's insight into life ecology, and explore how to really develop long lasting health change. This book is just a delightful look at the path ahead.

John E. Whitcomb, MD
Medical Director of Patient Access, Aurora Health Care

I highly recommend Dr. Nijhawan's new book. By far, it is one of the most comprehensive overviews of the state of medical care in this country. He brings an acute understanding from a personal clinical level of practicing medicine. More importantly Dr. Nijhawan critically integrates all of the elements of the "perfect storm" which has led us to the highest cost health care system with poor value outcomes. His personal and political analysis offers insight and understanding into one of the most complex issues facing Americans today.

Kathryn Havens, MD

We are in a health quandary. At a time when we need to invest in health, our system rewards disease management promoting "rescue" care that is often ineffective and potentially harmful. True health care recognizes the bio-pscyho-social and spiritual needs of unique humans to find their own health. Unfortunately, helping someone become healthy is not financially supported within the current medical model. Dr. Nijhawan takes an insightful approach to explain how we got to this challenge and what we can do to overcome it. He creatively shows how we can place value towards true health care which can reduce cost and improve quality. This book describes a captivating vision for positive change.

David Rakel, MD
Director, University of Wisconsin Integrative Medicine
Associate Professor, Dept. of Family Medicine
University of Wisconsin School of Medicine and Public Health

MODERN MEDICINE

is Killing You

START YOUR HEALTHCARE REVOLUTION NOW!

MODERN MEDICINE
is Killing You

START YOUR HEALTHCARE REVOLUTION NOW!

NIRAJ NIJHAWAN, MD MS

L·E·O PUBLISHING

MADISON, WISCONSIN

L·E·O PUBLISHING

Life Ecology Organization, LLC
660 W. Washington Ave., Ste. 304
Madison, WI 53703

For more information www.mmkills.com
To contact Dr. Nijhawan directly: raj@mmkills.com

LEO Publishing ISBN-13: 978-0-9843372-0-0
ISBN-10: 0-9843372-0-2

Library of Congress Cataloging-in-Publication Data has cataloged the following edition as follows:

Nijhawan, Niraj.
Modern medicine is killing you : start your healthcare revolution now! /
Niraj Nijhawan.—1st ed.
p. cm.
Includes bibliographical references.
ISBN-13: 978-0-9843372-0-0
ISBN-10: 0-9843372-0-2
1. Medicine—Philosophy.   2. Alternative medicine.
3. Self-care, Health.   I. Title.

R723.N55 2010   610'.1
QBI09-600226

Printed in the United States of America
10 9 8 7 6 5 4 3 2 1

TABLE OF CONTENTS |

ACKNOWLEDGMENTS

There are many people who have supported me on this 20 year journey. First and foremost, my wife, Tamara Schlessinger, whose strength, intuition, and love have helped me to become a much better person. I thank my parents, Ved and Nina Nijhawan, for providing me the security and freedom to be myself. Thanks to my kids for keeping me on my toes and grounded. Thanks to Drs. Kampine, Warltier, and DeMets, who provided me the opportunities and skills to become a scientific thinker within the realm of medicine. Thanks to my wife, Jim Morrissey, and Roan Kaufman for their extensive editing and book development help. Thanks to Myron Eshowsky for his support and introducing me to Roan. Thanks to Drs. Whitcomb, Rakel, Havens, and Streckenbach for reviewing the manuscript with the medical eye. Thanks to all the following people for their editing help and support: Lori and Philip Schlessinger, Heidi and Mike Goodrich-Blair, Brian Leitzke, David, Elsa, and Marielle Allschwang, Gina Kent, Sean Short, Vi Hammelman, David Malkenson, Steven Markiewicz, Nancy Conway, Sally Turner, Larry Schlessinger, Jane Zepp, Jason Bacon, Tom and Sandy Miskelly, Alexandra Stanculescu, Brian and Jeanne Lisse, Rob Witt, Barbara L. Anderson, Sonia Gholson, Debra Yatchak, Dan Hopkins, David Saltzman, Ann Mayer, J Li, Lisa Viscardi, Liz and Kyle Kobriger, Cindy Wick, Chris Van Mullem, Ginger Klinger, Steve Klinkhammer, Barb Torgerson, Erlinda Beebe, Asa Burton, Meghan Halder. Finally, my thanks to Kristyn Kalnes for her design work.

FOREWORD

What follows is the result of my unexpected 22 year journey through the American healthcare system. The various roles I've held as a physician have yielded a surprising discovery: modern medicine causes more harm than societies realize. Why is modern medicine so harmful? Very simply, modern medicine lacks the accountability and incentives for producing the best health outcomes possible. Poor accountability and incentives have allowed the development of three major forces which worsen health.

Now, you may say, "<u>Modern Medicine is Killing You</u>? Isn't that a bit of an exaggeration?" One statistic will make this idea more real. The Japanese experience a life expectancy of 82 years, which is 4 years greater than the life expectancy in the United States. To understand the significance of this seemingly small difference we must multiply the 4 years by the number of people in the United States, which is approximately 300 million. Relatively speaking, the Americans are losing 1.2 <u>billion</u> life-years compared to the Japanese!

But what does this figure mean? We can break it down simply. For example, part of the 1.2 billion life-years shortfall could be explained by 5 million children who lost their lives before the age of 5 instead of reaching their potential of 85 years. This would account for 400 million life-years lost, calculated by multiplying the 80 years of life lost by each of the 5 million kids. Another 10 million adults might have died at 50 years of age instead of 90 and thus account for another 400 million life-years lost. Finally, 20 million 70-year-olds might have died when they could have reached 90 years of age, accounting for another 400 million life-years lost.

Why were these years of life lost? Either society didn't do a good job of *preventing* the loss of life, the healthcare system failed to treat ailing patients appropriately, or the healthcare system actually worsened the patient's situation. This book explains how society and the healthcare system are failing you by not being held accountable for truly excellent outcomes. If you are an American, do not make the mistake of thinking this is only a problem for the uninsured. Regardless of your socioeconomic status, you have the possibility of being harmed by ineffective systems and incomplete awareness of the keys to health and healing. We're all in this together in more ways than you may realize.

My medical roles have included: training as a medical resident, learning how to perform medical research, designing and conducting medical trials as a clinical scientist, leading a medical department, helping to build medical departments with different types of healthcare providers, and participating in various healthcare reform movements. I've been inside the healthcare system and can provide powerful examples of its most fundamental failures.

The ideas in this book have been presented hundreds of times to a range of audiences, including consumers, medical students, medical residents, physicians, and even healthcare CEOs. This experience has allowed us to distill the ideas down to key concepts in plain language that will unlock the healthcare system puzzle for you.

The average person without a medical background may be overwhelmed with the amount of available healthcare information. Many people are intimidated by medical decision-making and the healthcare system in general. Healthcare has seemingly become so complex. This book will provide you the tools and confidence to see through the fog and make intelligent decisions about your own healthcare as well as the healthcare reform debate.

You only need a few key ideas or thinking tools to take control of your healthcare finances, healthcare planning, and the healthcare system itself. You will be surprised at how quickly you can become an intelligent partner in healthcare decision-making as opposed to simply accepting what your healthcare providers hand you. Your healthcare providers are flying more blindly than you realize! We are confident that you can be a powerful advocate for a revolution in the way the medical community delivers healthcare as well as a revolution in the development of your own healthcare plan.

The current American healthcare reform debate is misguided because it ignores the stunningly poor performance of the American healthcare system. The debate also ignores the more fundamental *causes* of this poor performance. This book presents solutions for a broken American healthcare system that are derived from extensive evidence. We recommend nothing short of a restructuring of the American healthcare payment system as well as the implementation of powerful healthcare science and accountability infrastructures.

Let's look at an analogy to understand how misguided modern medicine is. Imagine you are using a ladder to climb a wall as the paradise of wonderful health and healing is on the other side. How frustrating would it be to discover that your ladder is broken. Worse, someone keeps trying to knock you off the ladder as you climb it. Horror of horrors, you then discover that after all your effort to climb the ladder, the ladder was placed against the wrong wall! Instead of the paradise of health and healing, you are greeted by the desert of chronic disease! Such is the current state of modern and especially American medicine. In their current form, these systems are literally killing you either directly, or indirectly through inadequate care.

A couple quick notes of clarification: We intentionally do not footnote the references within the text. The reason is to encourage you to study the other references in addition to the articles pertaining to a specific point. You will hopefully realize how much evidence lies behind our concepts. Additionally, this book will often to refer to "we", meaning the authors. Though I am the primary author, there are many who have helped with this work over the past decade, whether by listening to me or suggesting clearer ways to express the ideas. At this point, this is a collective work. Please refer to the Acknowledgments to meet some of my family and friends who have taken this journey with me. Hopefully by the end of this book, you will want to join us!

INTRODUCTION

The healthcare system is reducing how long you live. It is soaking up your income. Almost all the current healthcare reform bills being considered by the American Congress badly miss the mark because they misdiagnose the core problems within the healthcare system. This book will empower the individual to protect themselves from the healthcare system both physically and financially as well as optimize their own health and healing. We will present evidence that will prove that modern medicine is remarkably ineffective at producing the best health outcomes possible. We will emphasize the American healthcare system as the best example of modern medicine's failures, but the key ideas in this book will help any healthcare system or individual throughout the world to optimize their health and healing.

Please do not think that the primary American healthcare problem is one of insurance coverage. It is currently the spring of 2010 and the American healthcare reform debate is focused on the battle between coverage for all versus who is going to pay for this extra coverage. There is also fear of a government take-over of healthcare. *These concerns completely miss the most important elements of a comprehensive healthcare reform discussion!* The issues of coverage and who pays should be dwarfed by the question, "How do we produce the most effective healthcare systems in the world?" Only a comprehensive debate will produce an effective set of solutions for a healthcare system that is much more ineffective than you may realize.

Ironically, if we held the American healthcare system accountable for cost and health outcomes performance, we could eliminate the national embarrassment of 50 million uninsured citizens, not worry about spending more to pay for this coverage, improve our average life expectancy, and *still* put more money back in people's pockets.

Dad's Tragedy

Imagine that your Dad developed chest pain, went to the cardiologist, and ended up getting a bypass surgery to fix a heart blockage. He undergoes the procedure and you hear that he made it through the surgery. You visit him a week later. At first glance, you're relieved; it appears that he did quite well. He's breathing without oxygen support and he requires no medication to support his heart. He appears to be doing so well that he's getting ready to leave the ICU. Suddenly you feel nauseated as your greeting of Dad is met with a blank stare. He doesn't recognize you. Something happened to Dad. Dad had surgery to fix his heart but in the process he suffered a stroke.

Was it even worth it to have the surgery? What's the use of living longer if you've lost who you are? Is this not a kind of death? Then you start reading (you're quite inquisitive) and get the sense that coronary (heart) procedures, amazingly, do not extend one's length of life overall! Why bother? The cardiology and cardiac surgery communities state that their procedures reduce patients' chest pain and improve their activity tolerance. In the meantime, you read that medication therapy for coronary artery disease is just as good as more aggressive interventions including surgery. Why didn't the medical community realize the side effects of the aggressive medical procedures as well as utilize less dangerous but equally effective heart disease treatments? Why has the medical community used aggressive coronary artery procedures for 30 years and created thousands of tragedies like your father's?

It gets worse. Not only is there no extension of life from most of the heart blockage procedures, but, as you've sadly experienced, there is a significant incidence of neurologic injury including loss of memory, confusion, and even stroke. These all lead to a significant deterioration in the patient's and their family's quality of life. It took the healthcare system 20 years after starting to use these procedures to realize that these major side effects were occurring. Sadly, the medical community could have detected these problems much sooner if it was held accountable for the best health outcomes possible.

There's even more! The medical community also began to realize some twenty years ago that certain lifestyle changes such as exercise; a stricter diet including more fruits, vegetables, and whole grains; and group therapy could reduce chest pain and improve activity tolerance. Rather than suggesting lifestyle modification as THE intervention for coronary artery disease, the medical community has simply continued performing hundreds of *thousands* of very aggressive cardiac interventions such as bypass surgery, balloon procedures, and heart artery stents at a cost of hundreds of billions of dollars.

Well, tragedy on top of tragedy, Dad develops a terrible infection in his chest wall at the site of the surgery. The infection requires multiple additional surgeries to get things cleaned up but, unfortunately, your father eventually dies when the infection takes hold of his whole body. Given what you have learned you are both heartbroken and furious.

Believe it or not, this story is an accurate reflection of the current manner in which modern, and especially American, medicine currently function. Most Americans and the American healthcare system have been operating with the attitude "Do everything possible for my loved one, Doc", without completely understanding the true risks and benefits of "doing everything". There are multiple problems with saying "Do everything". Understanding these problems will change your attitude about modern, and especially American, medicine.

Boosting Your HQ, the Three Root Causes of Ineffective Healthcare Systems

The healthcare system is reducing your life expectancy in three primary ways or what we will refer to as the Three Root Causes of an ineffective healthcare system. Understanding these Three Root Causes will boost your **Healthcare Quotient or HQ**. Similar to your intelligence quotient or IQ, which represents your general ability to solve problems, your HQ will represent knowledge or wisdom in making the best choices for your own health rather than simply accepting what the medical community suggests.

As your HQ rises throughout this book, you will become more confident and assertive in your own healthcare decision making. You will become an equal partner with your healthcare providers and the healthcare system as a whole. As a result of a rising HQ, you will become healthier and wealthier. You will literally increase your life expectancy, your quality of life, and the amount of money in your pocket!

The Three Root Causes of an ineffective healthcare system specifically include:

1. **Modern medicine is unintelligent.** Modern medicine is surprisingly unscientific in its healthcare decision making. The result is that the healthcare system wastes resources at a remarkable rate resulting in higher taxes and relatively stagnant incomes. Modern medicine also worsens your health by using technology that is more harmful than good, as well as by not having the resources to apply innovative approaches to health and healing. Chapters 1, 2, and 3 explain Root Cause #1. Understanding Root Cause #1 will especially boost your HQ by teaching you healthcare *scientific thinking*. With this scientific thinking HQ boost, you will force healthcare decision making to be much more intelligent. A smarter approach to medical technology will make you healthier <u>and</u> wealthier.

2. **Modern medicine is overrated.** Modern medicine tends to focus on care that uses medical technology but it turns out that lifestyle and especially life effectiveness are far more powerful predictors of health and healing than most people realize. We call these scientifically confirmed forces "Life Ecology Factors". The combination of false hope for medical technology's impact on health outcomes and ignorance of Life Ecology Factors means the healthcare system is misguided in producing the best health outcomes possible. Modern and American medicine are not the main reason you are living longer, by far! Understanding and applying the Life Ecology Factors concept to your own life will provide you a second HQ boost. This HQ boost has an even greater likelihood of improving the quality and length of your life!

3. **Modern medicine is dangerous.** American medicine, in particular, has become so complex that it injures and kills patients at a remarkable rate. Stunningly, the American healthcare system has become one of the top killers of people alongside heart disease and cancer! This section will also boost your HQ by causing you to be much more vigilant when engaging the healthcare system for necessary care.

In summary, modern medicine is doing too much of what they shouldn't do and not doing enough of what they should do. That's a lethal combination!

With an understanding of the Three Root Causes for American and modern medicine's ineffectiveness in hand, you can be much more motivated, creative and effective in constructing your own health program. The result will be better health including less disease; a longer, higher quality life; AND more money in your pocket. This book will take you through a fascinating journey of science and personal discovery and provide you with the key HQ tools to protect yourself both physically and financially.

The Current State of Affairs

Earlier we made the statement that current healthcare reform bills being considered by Congress "badly miss the mark." That may seem like an exaggeration but that's how thoroughly society is misunderstanding the problems within the American healthcare system and the problems with modern medicine in general. It is ironic that we are misdiagnosing the problems within healthcare systems just as they misdiagnose the best ways to heal you. Meanwhile, the real disease within the healthcare system, and even you, festers.

It's politics as usual in Washington as they continue to lack the political willpower for meaningful reform as suggested in this and other books/proposals. The focus, instead, is on delivering more coverage and spreading out the costs. Reform debate must produce a healthcare system that performs much better. The Democrats focus on covering more people and the Republicans would rather keep government uninvolved but there is *little in the current Congressional movement to truly force the system to work better*.

Societies will continue to be haunted by an ineffective healthcare system without an understanding of the real problems and necessary reforms. The goal of this book is to educate you to be so skeptical of the healthcare system that you will be compelled to launch personal and societal healthcare revolutions. This book will provide any person with the tools to powerfully participate in the healthcare reform debate AND take action right now to better their own healthcare program.

This book may make physicians seem incompetent. The reality is that most physicians are truly intelligent and caring. They simply do not have the tools or a system to deliver the best patient care possible. Societies must now work themselves out of their modern medical messes. Healthcare systems are deep in to their dysfunctions. We need to stop tinkering at the margins and get to the heart of the problem.

Much of this book may overwhelm and anger you, but we are confident that together we can produce the best healthcare systems in the world due to our plentiful resources and ingenuity. The healthcare systems and patients just need the correct accountability and incentives to start moving in the right direction.

Why Another Healthcare Book?

The vast majority of healthcare reform books and proposals do not get to the real problems inside healthcare systems. Most books are focused on the symptoms of the problem, not the cause. Over the past few years several excellent books have addressed the litany of problems within the American healthcare system, but these issues are merely the symptoms of the chronic disease afflicting our healthcare system. It's certainly important to be aware of the symptoms so that we can convince ourselves to tackle the underlying problem, but we have to ultimately cure the disease itself.

Imagine you started developing general symptoms such as fatigue and pain. The medical system responded by providing you with medications that boost your energy and take away your pain. Unfortunately, the *cause* of the fatigue and pain was ignored. Things are fine for a while, but then the symptoms return more strongly and it now appears that you had cancer that has advanced further. Now the symptoms cannot be completely suppressed unless the underlying problem of the cancer is treated.

So, what is the "cancer" within the healthcare system and what are the resulting symptoms? The symptoms of the diseased healthcare system include high costs, too many uninsured people, too much paper work and wasted time, and too many errors. The underlying *disease* or cancer within the system is a combination of poor science, incomplete healthcare programs, inefficiency, and system complexity. The result is a system that wastes your resources and worsens your health, literally either killing you directly and/or allowing you to die prematurely.

In contrast to other books, we will take our analysis of the healthcare system disease a step further by describing the Three Root Causes of the disease. Only with an understanding of the fundamental causes of the problem can we treat the disease and prevent it from returning.

The most vital, inspiring ideas about health, healing, and healthcare system reform have not yet been distilled down in one place for the typical consumer. With only three key concepts you can transform your approach to your own healthcare as well as force the healthcare system to perform better. You can help to launch personal and societal healthcare revolutions.

Why Haven't We Launched a Revolution in Healthcare, Especially within American Healthcare?

With the healthcare system being in such a mess, we started asking ourselves, "Why would people put up with this situation?" Here are the conclusions we have come to:

- People feel we are living longer primarily because of modern and American medicine.

- People feel Americans have the best healthcare system in the world.

- People in the United States are grateful they do not have to wait in line for a surgery like they do in Canada.

- People would much rather have a free market healthcare system versus a government run system as in England.

- People believe the American healthcare system provides more access to healthcare technology and that this is a good thing.

You will be amazed to find that all these assumptions are wrong! We are *not* calling for a single payer or nationalized healthcare system within the United States, but we *do* want Americans to stop making excuses for a system that is failing them. Once you learn the critical health and healing facts including the Three Root Causes of poor healthcare system performance, you should be ready to take control of your healthcare destiny and benefit from:

- A better understanding of the how and why of your healthcare choices
- Better choice of healthcare providers
- Wider selection of healthcare strategies including a variety of alternative healing systems
- Better service
- A better quality of life
- More money in your pocket

Sound too good to be true? This is much easier to achieve than you realize. You just need some key knowledge and thinking tools and you will be armed with the confidence to take control.

What This Book Will Teach You and What Actions You Can Take as a Result

Let's talk about the goals of this book and what specific actions you can take. It doesn't matter what your life situation is, whether you are insured or uninsured, wealthy or not, educated or not, you WILL get something useful out of this book.

We will be providing you with the tools to understand the health care reform debate as well as the keys to increasing the length and quality of your life. You will experience an HQ boost with each of the following concepts or tools as detailed in this book:

- Healthcare scientific thinking
- The difference between technological advancement and scientific advancement
- The neglected power of self healing and the framework called Life Ecology Factors
- The systems effect compared to the individuals that make up the system
- The parallels between the healthcare and financial system failures
- The power of a functional free market
- The perfect storm of lost checks and balances that allowed the healthcare mess to develop
- The components of a comprehensive healthcare reform

The above concepts/tools will motivate you to:

- Restructure your healthcare plan to produce better and more satisfying healthcare results including a longer and better quality of life as well as more money in your pocket.
- Compel your legislator toward much more bold and complete healthcare reform legislation which will force better healthcare system performance, also resulting in greater health and wealth for you.

Let's Launch a Constructive Healthcare Revolution

Despite the disheartening or even maddening information in this book, we are optimistic about the healthcare results that we can achieve once we set our minds to it. We should not blame anybody for our health-care mess. We are all responsible for either contributing to the mess or allowing it. Now we need to co-create our way out of it. This book is not a cynical approach, nor is it antagonistic. This is ultimately a very hopeful and proactive approach to fixing our healthcare systems as well as our personal health and healing program.

As you work your way though the evidence in the following chapters, you will start to understand the Three Root Causes of ineffectiveness within healthcare systems. You will also be able to explain how the American healthcare system could be <u>the worst</u> in the world! You say, "Wait a minute, modern medicine is unintelligent, overrated, harmful AND Americans have the most ineffective healthcare system in the world?" Does that seem hard to believe?

Well, think about Dad's story and ponder the following facts. Americans have the most expensive healthcare system in the world, costing over $8,000 per person per year. This figure is two to three times more than any other developed nation and yet, Americans on average do not have <u>any</u> superior health outcomes to show for this expense relative to other nations! In fact, the United States has the *worst* life expectancy and infant mortality of *any* of the thirty richest nations. Its performance as a healthcare system *in general* is towards the bottom of the wealthiest nations (Fig. 3.1). It is also a myth that Americans have better access to healthcare, as we will fully describe in Chapter 3.

How is it possible that Americans spend so much and have so little to show for it? There are basically three reasons for this that we will describe in the next five chapters. Get ready for an eye-opening tour of modern healthcare decision-making and the *real* science of health and healing!

Part I

ROOT CAUSE #1 :

MODERN MEDICINE IS UNINTELLIGENT

Chapter One

Scientific Thinking Will Boost Your HQ

One of the primary aims of this book is to help you understand healthcare scientific thinking in order to increase your HQ. You would imagine that the healthcare system is scientifically advanced, but it is not! You would think that healthcare science is a complex subject, but it is not! Your healthcare providers are quite possibly poorly developed in their scientific thinking whereas you can get up to speed quickly on a *scientific* approach to healthcare decision making.

Poor scientific thinking is literally killing hundreds of thousands of people either directly or indirectly due to premature death related to missed healthcare opportunities. Using scientific thinking, you will be able to understand most of the healthcare system's mistakes and inefficiencies and be motivated to take control of your own healthcare decisions. Time to get healthier and wealthier!

My Story—Anesthesiology Residency, Witnessing the Explosion of Medical Technology

After medical school, I completed a residency in the medical specialty of anesthesiology/critical care. This provided me with an inside view of the incredible technology being developed and utilized for patient care. This book will come down pretty hard on the use of technology by the healthcare establishment but please, be clear, this does not mean that we do not believe in the possibilities of technology. As an anesthesiologist, I live in a world of technology. I use technology on a regular basis, and I can attest to the beneficial impact of technology upon health outcomes. In other words, we do not have a bias against technology, but we do have a problem with the unintelligent or undisciplined use of medical technology.

The field of anesthesiology is a perfect example of technology at its best. Death rates from anesthesia have dropped from one in a thousand patients receiving anesthesia all the way down to one in a million! This remarkable improvement in safety is, in part, due to three important technologies. The first was the measurement of blood oxygen levels through the skin (called pulse oximetry) which has allowed for an earlier detection and treatment of dangerously low blood oxygen levels. A second important operating room technology has been the ability to measure carbon-dioxide being exhaled from your lungs (called end-tidal capnography) which allows an earlier detection of inadequate artificial breathing for a patient who is not themselves breathing because of an anesthetic sleep. Finally, another technology has been so-called "decision-making systems" for dealing with emergencies in an organized manner analogous to that of the airline industry. Recall technology means any application of knowledge not simply physical technology.

The airline industry and the field of anesthesiology have produced remarkable improvements in safety in part through continuously improving decision-making guidelines. Decision-making guidelines produce a more standardized approach to complex situations which in turn allows a systematic discovery of better approaches to managing emergencies. Creating systematic and standardized approaches to emergencies also allows clear-mindedness during a crisis as well as accountability for healthcare providers to do the best job possible. We do have modern medical success stories, but there are also many stories of failure that often go ignored.

The Vital Importance of a Disciplined Approach to Medical Technology

One of the key ideas we are conveying is that while there might be occasional medical technology success stories, there are also many problems created by the unintelligent, misguided, and error-prone usage of this technology. We must stop this as soon as possible and hold healthcare systems accountable to a higher standard; that standard is scientific discipline. In the meantime, you are becoming sicker and poorer because of the healthcare system's ignorance of science.

Recall Dad's story. It was initially exciting when he was getting his heart fixed and being "saved" by a coronary procedure. Then poor Dad, you, and your family were subjected to one serious problem after another until he finally died from a problem created by the healthcare system. Tragically, the medical procedure didn't accomplish its promise *and* the medical community possessed an equally effective *and less expensive* heart care option that they did not even consider. Dad's story is really the story of modern and especially American medicine, but it doesn't need to be this way. That's where you and scientific thinking come in.

Scientific thinking allows us to scrutinize major healthcare decisions and also evaluate the multitude of minor decisions made during the course of any medical treatment. Big or small, these choices can add up to a huge amount of waste and worsened health outcomes. Thus, all medical decisions affecting you or your loved one need to be approached with the highest level of intelligence possible. The healthcare system currently has a low HQ, meaning it produces much worse results compared to the resources it expends. You must take control by boosting your own HQ and becoming at least an equal partner in healthcare decision making. The purpose of this and the next chapter is to provide you the first HQ boost by teaching you scientific thinking.

Anesthesiologists often encounter the sickest of the sick. We see firsthand the impulse to apply technology haphazardly in dire situations simply because doctors feel pressured to do everything possible for patients and their families. On reflection, we need to ask ourselves, "Was it truly beneficial to do everything possible?" Again, recall Dad's story. It was harmful to him to do the maximum possible in his situation. This is the idea being conveyed by the Three Root Causes of poor healthcare performance on the part of modern and American medicine.

The following questions will challenge the notion that we should do everything possible just because we believe it's in the best interest of our family. At the same time, these are the very questions you should ask your healthcare providers in order to be much more discerning about your future healthcare decisions.

Does the Proposed Treatment or Test Provide More Benefit Than Harm?

How would you feel about doing everything possible for a loved one if you knew there was a good risk that the proposed medical intervention could actually make them worse off? Don't you feel that your healthcare provider should ensure that any technology they use is <u>actually</u> beneficial and doesn't cause more problems than benefits down the line?

This dilemma is the basis of Root Cause #1. The problem we face is that modern and American medicine are relatively <u>unintelligent</u>, *(Fig. 1.1)* The medical community often uses advanced technology but is generally ignorant about whether this technology is *actually* improving, *if not worsening,* our health. This ignorance stems from a failure to properly utilize scientific thinking. Failure to apply scientific thinking is the reason your father suffered. Neither Dad nor his healthcare providers asked or answered the essential question as to whether there was NET benefit meaning the total benefits exceeded the total side effects. In Dad's case, the treatment not only failed to provide a benefit, it also produced harm and ultimately death. Such is the power of the technology the healthcare system wields.

Is the Proposed Treatment Truly the Best Healing Option Available?

Many people would reconsider the demand to "do everything" if they realized that doing a lot of things technologically can be a distraction

FIGURE 1.1 | THINKING TOOL — "DANGERS OF DOING TOO MUCH"

- New medical technology might actually hurt you more than help you (Root Cause #1, Chapters 1,2, and 3)
- Technological care causes false hope which distracts from self healing approaches to health (Root Cause #2, Chapter 4)
- Doing too much creates confusion and a greater likelihood of errors (Root Cause #3, Chapter 5)

- Wasted resources means less resources for better technological care (Root Cause #3, Chapters 5)
- Wasted resources also means less resources for valuable less-technological medical care including prevention (Root Cause #3, Chapters 5)

- Wasted resources means less investment on self healing approaches to health (Root Cause #3, Chapter 5)
- There is a risk of being hurt financially and creatively (Root Cause #3, Chapter 5)

from what really works. This is the idea behind Root Cause #2: modern medicine is <u>overrated</u> *(Fig. 1.1)*. Dad suffered from this problem as well. We *knew of* lifestyle <u>interventions</u> that could have helped with Dad's chest pain, removing the need for much more aggressive and dangerous treatment such as bypass surgery. The medical community did not have the proper accountability and incentives to apply all the knowledge at its disposal. The medical community started using a treatment on your father without proving its RELATIVE benefit, meaning the proposed treatment was better than all existing options let alone the least risky! The healthcare system was not only unscientific but also misguided in delivering health and healing.

Does the Proposed Treatment or Test Provide More Benefit Compared to the Overall Risk of Entering the Healthcare System?

The healthcare system has become quite complex. As a result, patients are potentially subjected to numerous medical errors. This is rarely factored into the cost of "Do everything Doc". Every time you demand that the healthcare system do something without truly understanding whether it is scientifically the best course of action, you are playing Russian roulette with you or your loved one's health. The stunning truth is that the American healthcare system itself has become one of the top killers of people. Its lethal record is right up there along with heart disease and cancer. *(Fig. 1.1)* And so, we come to the idea behind Root Cause #3, that Modern medicine is <u>dangerous</u>.

Once again, your dad's story is pertinent here. Not only did he fail to receive benefit from the proposed treatment but he also suffered a hospital-acquired infection that ultimately killed him. It's quite ironic that, as of 2009, Medicare will not reimburse hospitals for any care related to a hospital-acquired infection because this problem is deemed an error. Unfortunately, there are more errors where that one came from.

What If We Realized That Our Treatments and Tests Often Produce More Harm Than Good?

Would you feel the same about doing everything possible if you knew that you were paying approximately $8,000 <u>extra </u>per family *every single year* for healthcare that isn't serving your true needs? Shouldn't we KNOW that there is more healthcare benefit than harm being derived from our precious dollars? What is unfortunate is that the loss of your dollars may have been occurring without your awareness through a combination of progressively higher taxes and lower incomes spent on useless medical technology as well as wasteful bureaucracy.

Do you see now that it's not as simple as "Doc, do everything possible"? The practice of doing everything may actually accelerate the illness and possibly the death of your loved one. At the very least, the medical interventions may create even more misery, decrease your quality of life, and waste precious financial resources. We summarize the potential problems with doing "everything" in the "Dangers of Doing Too Much" *(Fig. 1.1)*.

Looking at it in a different way, doing too much of the wrong thing WILL hurt you for reasons corresponding to the three Root Causes of poor healthcare performance:

Root Cause #1—"Modern Medicine is Unintelligent"

The healthcare system uses technology unintelligently re-sulting in "doing too much". Unintelligence stems from a failure to apply scientific thinking. As a result of poor scientific thinking, the healthcare system's choice of care often provides much less benefit than is hoped for. Doing too much results in wasted resources which means we can-not pay for medical care that IS beneficial. Worse still, our chosen care might actually harm more than it helps, another danger of doing too much. Root Cause #1 means the health-care system causes unnecessary injury to hundreds of thou-sands of patients by doing too much.

Root Cause #2—"Modern Medicine is Overrated"

As a result of the false hope we place in medical technology we have become distracted from healthcare approaches that are much more powerful. Root Cause #2 represents another category of the "Dangers of Doing Too Much". In the case of Root Cause #2, a greater frequency of health problems and less timely recovery than necessary results because the medical community is often not healing you as effectively as you are capable of.

Root Cause #3—"Modern Medicine is Harmful"

One of the Dangers of Doing Too Much is that we create a complicated clinical environment and generate more waste. Complexity results in many types of mistakes which hurt patients by the hundreds of thousands. Waste harms patient indirectly by the medical community not being able to af-ford care that IS valuable. Root Cause #3 is yet one more danger of doing too much.

As you can clearly see, doing everything possible encourages multiple risks to your health. I have witnessed the barrage of tests being ordered and medications being given and people being poked and prodded. I have participated in these rituals myself, having been taught to do so based on the theory of the day. Then I discovered that theory is not good enough. The current version of the healthcare system has been progressively making you sicker and poorer for the past 60 years. You need to stop the damage by turning the tables through an understanding of scientific thinking. Scientific thinking will help you understand how it is possible for the three Root Causes to have appeared and why you must take action *NOW!*

In fact, we will see that the last 60 years of "modern medicine" have been a relative failure as our tools and technology have far exceeded our ability to intelligently incorporate these tools in the medical program. As a result, we have created tremendous waste and destruction. Right now healthcare technology is innocent until proven guilty – it needs to be guilty until proven innocent, as we will soon demonstrate repeatedly.

Thinking Tool—Science and Scientific Discipline

Immediately after completing a four-year medical residency in the area of Anesthesiology/Critical Care, I had the good fortune to receive a medical scientist training grant. I acquired an additional degree beyond my medical degree, a master's degree in clinical research. As a result of the medical scientist training, I learned the techniques of science as applied to medical care.

What I soon discovered was quite shocking. Since healthcare science is so difficult to accomplish, the so-called scientists within healthcare performing research were actually being remarkably unscientific! The medical community simply was not using the best science tools available. The result has been the creation of numerous "Dad" types of errors on a large scale. Remember, I'm not some economist analyzing the healthcare system, I'm a physician who actually witnessed many of these scientific misadventures over the past twenty years! I also became a healthcare scientist and was frustrated by the lack of resources to study our healthcare decision making scientifically. We will provide you multiple examples of scientific failure in this and the following chapter.

Scientific Thinking

Let's discuss a critical matter, science. In the process, you will acquire the tool of scientific thinking which will provide you a significant HQ boost. Then you can apply your higher HQ to your own healthcare decision-making resulting in better health outcomes and greater financial security. Specifically, a higher HQ will mean you will be able to confidently ask the most significant healthcare questions. These questions as well as your understanding will allow you to produce the best healthcare results for the lowest cost and risk. Incredibly, this approach is not currently used by the healthcare system! Instead you are unwittingly exposed to the "Dangers of Doing Too Much" *(Fig. 1.1)* because of the system's poor scientific discipline.

What is science? Reflect on that for a moment. What is the goal of science? Our simple definition is: Science is the acquisition of knowledge regarding what causes what. In turn, this knowledge can be utilized for simple enjoyment or practical purposes. Obviously, the stakes for the use of science are much higher when it comes to your health and financial security.

This brings us to an important concept within the realm of science, the scientific method. The purpose of the scientific method is to ensure that our understanding of what causes what is accurate. The scientific method asks, "Is this connection real? Does A really cause B?" *(Fig. 1.2)* and then proceeds to confirm that A does truly lead to B.

By utilizing the scientific method we can truly benefit from the knowledge of a causal connection instead of wasting time and resources as well as risking our health by heading down the wrong healthcare pathway. Scientific thinking helps us to decide whether we are taking the best pathway for our health and healing meaning the treatment or test is producing more

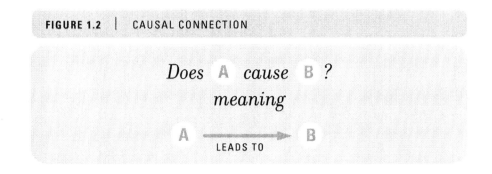

FIGURE 1.2 | CAUSAL CONNECTION

Does A *cause* B ?
meaning

A ⟶ B
LEADS TO

health benefit than harm. If we are wrong in thinking that the treatment or test produces net benefit, we refer to it as healthcare causal confusion.

This is the goal of the scientific method: to make sure that A *is* leading to B. Factor A might represent a disease factor, like fat in the diet, causing outcome B, such as heart disease. In another sense, factor A could represent a surgery, diagnostic test, or medication. The question then would be: "Do these tests/treatments prolong or improve the quality of one's life (B)? Is there a true connection?"

An example of healthcare causal confusion would be thinking that a surgery (A) directly improves a patient's health (B) when, in fact, it does not. Another example would be to believe that a diagnostic test (A) results in less cancer related death (B) when, in reality, there is no difference compared to simply waiting for symptoms of the disease to develop and *then* treating the patient. Another example of healthcare causal confusion is incorrectly believing that a particular new medication (A) treats high blood pressure (B) better than less expensive and less dangerous medications already in use.

Let's review why you should care about science and the scientific method. Recall the "Dangers of Doing Too Much" *(Fig. 1.1)*. If we do not PROVE that our proposed treatment improves our health then we may be mistaken and therefore taking on too much risk. As you will see, you cannot simply trust your healthcare providers and the healthcare system to make a scientifically correct decision because they themselves may not have the understanding and/or tools to do this! It's up to YOU to understand science and the scientific method or YOU are physically and financially at risk every time you engage the healthcare system for services. With the tool of scientific thinking in hand, you will be able to ask the most important, penetrating questions that will help you decide whether the proposed test or treatment is truly worthwhile.

In an era where we have tremendous financial strain, it is critical to truly *know* whether tests, medications, and/or surgeries provide a net health benefit for patients. If they do not, the healthcare system risks wasting resources that could have been used for much greater impact or, even worse, we take steps backwards and actually worsen our health.

So, a scientific approach to health and healing is the smart, logical thing to do. Otherwise we are acting blindly and potentially making our health worse, as in the example of Dad's heart surgery. Scientific thinking is such a common sense approach that by the end of the discussion, during this and the next chapter, you will be perplexed as to why we haven't been delivering healthcare according to these principles.

Next, we'll make science and its role in healthcare come alive for you and then evaluate how well modern medicine is *actually* performing scientifically. Once you have the tool of scientific thinking under your belt, you'll be amazed at how the world around you will look differently AND you will become healthier and wealthier!

Recall that the goal of science is to ensure causal accuracy, which means A is truly causing B *(Fig. 1.2)*. In particular, we are interested in whether new treatments (A) or tests (A) are causing health improvement (B).

VITAL POINT: This book will frequently refer to the "Science Triangle" *(Fig. 1.3)* in order to illustrate the interplay between A, B, and two important forces that create causal confusion: bias and confounding factors (C). In the Figure we refer to "The Truth" and "An Illusion". In this case, The Truth is that there is NOT a connection between A and B, but we have the impression or some evidence that there IS a connection. We would call this causal confusion. Even though the Truth might be that there is no connection between A and B (The cross-out of the line between A and B) there are two forces that can bypass the truth:

confounding factors (C) and bias. The goal of science, specifically the scientific method, is to eliminate these two pitfalls of truth. Once we avoid the pitfalls, we can know the truth in terms of whether A is really causing B. The image of this triangle will help you absorb scientific thinking by presenting it visually.

Let's first discuss confounding factors (C) in broad terms. Confounding factors are other life factors, whether environmental or human, that are causing A <u>and</u> causing B. For example, was the proposed surgery (A) causing the improved health (B) or did the surgery cause a dramatic improvement in lifestyle (C), which was the true cause of improved health (B). The surgery gets too much credit because of causal confusion.

The problem with healthcare causal confusion in applying medical technology is that we can unnecessarily waste billions of dollars and potentially cause more harm than good. With an analysis at <u>one point in time</u> it *looks* like A is causing B. This type of study is referred to as an observational study. More precisely, this is a *retrospective* observation where the A and B have already occurred. A *prospective* observational study is when only A, but not B, has occurred. This prospective observational tool is more powerful at discovering the truth because it is more clear that A occurred before B and thus much more likely to have caused the latter. Since, prospective studies are better at uncovering the truth they are considered more scientific. Unfortunately, most of healthcare thinking is dominated by the weaker (because it's easier) tool of retrospective observational studies. Later, we will expand on the confounding factors concept and provide examples of retrospective compared to prospective studies.

The Problem of Bias

The other force that creates causal confusion, in addition to confounding factors, is called "bias". As Figure 1.3 indicates, bias, in effect, causes a bypassing of the truth. There are several types of bias which can all create the illusion that A is causing B.

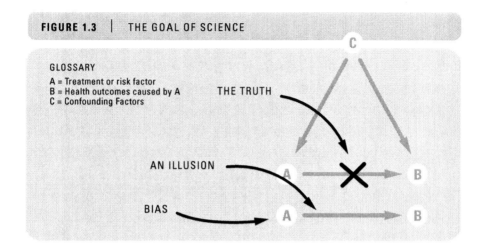

FIGURE 1.3 | THE GOAL OF SCIENCE

GLOSSARY
A = Treatment or risk factor
B = Health outcomes caused by A
C = Confounding Factors

One type of bias is **selection bias.** This occurs when we mistakenly or intentionally cherry-pick patients that are more likely to respond to a therapy. Selection bias unfairly makes it seem that an intervention or treatment (A) is causing improved health (B) when, in fact, it will not for the average patient.

Another type of bias is **assessment bias.** This takes place when we intentionally or unintentionally select studies that we choose to believe while ignoring the others. Assessment bias can result from either focusing on a study that happens to demonstrate a new treatment or test's benefit, or by placing the new treatment in the best light. The latter can be achieved by tossing out the studies that show no benefit or even reveal harm.

For example let's imagine we perform four studies. Studies #1 and #3 show no benefit from the new therapy; Study #2 demonstrates that the treatment actually makes the patients *worse off;* and only one of the four studies, Study #4, shows any benefit. The truth appears to be that there is NO connection between A and B or, even more troublesome, that A makes B worse.

What if we started with Study #4 and just stopped there and stated that the therapy works? Well, first we would be wrong. Second, we would waste a lot of resources on the new treatment. Third, patients could be made sicker on average. These are resources that could have been used for treatments that really *did* work. Even worse, what if we stopped the studies that weren't showing the results we desired? These are all examples of assessment bias. Let's examine some real world examples of bias.

Doesn't it seem like everything causes cancer? Every other day we hear conflicting advice: coffee's bad for you, then coffee's not bad or even good for you! We're advised that living next to a power line is bad for you, but later we're told that experts aren't sure if there's an effect. The risks seem to change every day. In a recent *L.A. Times* article, there were approximately fifty variables that were implicated in causing cancer within a two year period! It seems that everything causes cancer if you look hard enough! Why is that the case?

Cancer rates will fluctuate up and down every time the medical community studies a new group of people simply due to chance or random movement. The rate of coffee drinking also fluctuates up and down by chance. So, just by chance, you would *expect* the coffee rate and the cancer rate to *both* go up or down independent of each other in one of the studies. Now here's the problem; most people do not realize that there may have been many studies that showed no connection between coffee and cancer. Academic or university programs are in the business of publishing interesting results, so they will tend to present their study's results as if there is a stronger connection between a risk factor or treatment (A) and the health outcomes (B) than there actually is.

You see, professors at academic institutions want to get promoted and become tenured for the sake of security. The way they get promoted is to publish interesting findings. They do not benefit from telling you that their paper does not establish a causal connection, or that it may not contribute anything to our understanding of a problem! In fact, some experts have called for the elimination of these types of studies because they sow confusion. Of course, suppression of these types of studies may be going too far, but we cannot simply broadcast the results of an individual study to the public without explaining that we have NOT fully established whether a risk factor such as coffee (A) is truly causing a disease such as cancer (B).

So, the more you look at a problem, the more likely it becomes that some risk factor will show up randomly as if it is causing the problem. This includes, for example, coffee causing cancer. In other words, a study may seem to show that something is causing cancer when, in fact, it does not. If you looked at the risk factor and its connection to cancer 10 times, 9 times the risk factor will appear to have no correlation with cancer. Confusion is created when one time, in the population being measured, the risk factor is higher and the problem of concern is also occurring more frequently. These two things are moving in the same direction by coincidence. So, the factor (A) is either blamed or praised for its role in changing the health outcomes (B) when, in fact, there is no real connection whatsoever!

In contrast, a scientific appraisal takes into account all the studies performed thus far, *together.* In the case above, 9 times out of 10 there was no connection so we are much closer to the truth by indicating that the factor does not cause cancer. So you can see that the scientific approach is an alternative to the fear mongering way of using a single research study as if it is a scientific analysis and then broadcasting it in the media. You have just taken one big step towards understanding scientific thinking!

Here's a funny example of the head spinning caused by bias as quoted in *The Lancet*, a well-known British medical journal:

> *"In October of 2002, women who were moderate drinkers received good news. Their risk for breast cancer was not raised (higher) but the bad news is that smoking at an early age is now implicated as a risk factor for breast cancer. However, after they enjoyed guilt-free drinks, without cigarettes mind you, for only a few days, on November 13 the message was reversed! Alcohol did increase the risk for breast cancer after all, but smoking was declared as innocent. The press release proclaimed: Alcohol, tobacco and breast cancer, the definitive answer. A reader was driven to complain in the letters page of the Guardian. 'So let me get this*

right, alcohol is not good anymore, and if you smoke within 5 days of your period, that's bad news too. Oh no, that was a couple weeks ago, smoking is okay now. Do you think it would stop being bad for us if we just forget about them for a bit?"'

Unfortunately, much of the research that drives medical decision-making is the type of weak, deceptive analysis we just described. These slice-in-time studies are referred to as "observational". These studies are NOT scientific; they only serve as early clues. Their results should not be presented by themselves as some sort of "truth" without the context of all the other similar studies.

Bias can be introduced by mistake or intentionally. Examples of intentional bias include removing studies that do not favor the outcome one desires. Bias introduced by mistake includes the above examples of performing a study and then not explaining the results relative to all the other studies of the same matter. Another bias can be a theory about health and healing that we have been convinced of and we change our medical practice before we study the matter scientifically. Shortly, we will describe *how* we need to study our healthcare options scientifically. Scientific discipline is costly and time-consuming, but there is simply no substitute.

In the absence of a sound, scientific analysis of our proposed treatments and tests, we could end up wasting money and causing more harm. This waste and harm is magnified by the expense and danger of the medical technology the medical community utilizes. Thus the consequences are much worse if society does not introduce new medical technology with scientific discipline.

As long as we're worrying about things that cause disease such as the recent cancer example, let's discuss another example of bias that has sown fear throughout society: the belief that fatty foods cause heart disease. A fascinating article in the well-known journal, *Science*, concluded that after spending a couple hundred *million* dollars on large scientific trials, scientists have realized a huge mistake on the part of society: fat does NOT cause coronary heart disease. For some 50 years, society was force-fed (pun intended!) this notion that high fat consumption leads to heart disease. By shunning fat, we've shifted to more of a carbohydrate-based diet. A carbohydrate-intensive diet has lead to several unintended consequences including increased incidences of obesity, coronary artery disease, cancer, and diabetes.

Where did this theory and bias that fat causes heart disease gain momentum? Quite simply, it stems from the famous Framingham Heart Study that began in 1948 and is still ongoing with its third generation of participants. This study, based in Framingham, Massachusetts, has collected and analyzed data from a large group of people since its inception. The results of this study led to the development of the theory that high levels of fat in the diet caused heart disease. Here's how the reasoning went: "Increased cholesterol causes more coronary artery disease by plugging up certain heart blood vessels. Well, increased fatty foods *probably* cause an increase in cholesterol levels, therefore fatty foods *probably* causes an increase in coronary artery disease." "Probably" is not good enough. "Probably" is not scientific. We became *biased* in favor of this theory and started to act as if it was true. Even our national recommendations for diet changed to fit the theory. So, we took off with this notion and never looked back. Now, 30 or 40 years later, there is a growing realization that in following this theory we made a disastrous public health care mistake.

Consider the basic science regarding fats and food. There are three calorie building blocks of food: fats, carbohydrates (also known as "carbs"), and proteins. Guess what happens when we reduce our fat intake? Our body still requires the same amount of calories and has only two categories to pick from: carbs or proteins. Many in this society have chosen carbs, a disaster that has led to many health problems and, ironically, has increased the incidence of heart disease. This disaster has resulted from a combination of increased calorie intake since people get hungrier faster on a more carbohydrate-based diet, carbs are often processed grains that are much less healthy for you, and carbohydrate-based foods are often accompanied by other troublemakers such as high-fructose corn syrup.

As we stated, most of the medical studies we have are these so-called "observational studies". In fact, the situation is so bad that some scientists (*The Rise and Fall of Modern Medicine*, J. Fanu) have called for the virtual elimination of epidemiology departments (the ones that perform these slice-in-time observation studies) because they create such confusion and anxiety.

The following is a very important point. As we will demonstrate to you, most of our healthcare decision-making is based on either a lack of science or the use of observational studies, which are not very scientific. We do not believe that Fanu's suggestion is the answer. Epidemiology departments are still important for discovering certain health patterns but we must clearly label these discoveries as VERY PRELIMINARY. Furthermore, we must then follow up with scientific discipline to prove if there is a real connection or pattern.

Recall our heart surgery example and Dad. If there was bias for using a new technology or new surgery, like Dad's intervention, what would protect the patient and society as a whole from that bias? Could you imagine a bias towards doing the surgery if it meant fame or glory and earning a handsome financial reward? Of course! Were there scientific discipline checks and balances to neutralize bias over the past 50 years? You be the judge as you read this book.

Thus far, we have discussed one major category of problems that confuses our understanding of the world, bias. Again, if our understanding of the health world is wrong then we stand to worsen our health and waste our resources. Wasting our resources causes financial strain which in turn further worsens our health.

Confounding Factors, the Other Impediment to the Truth

The other group that interferes with a discovery of the truth is Confounding Factors. Let's go back to our Science Triangle (*Fig. 1.3*). To review, if we perform an analysis by gathering information regarding many patients at one point in time this is called an observational study.

We are observing a large group of patients, NOT performing an experiment where we decide that some patients get the risk factor or treatment and some do not. We have already discussed one set of problems with observational studies, bias. We can cherry-pick which studies or patients we select and this can make the connection between A and B seem more real than it is. That's the reason the bias arrow points to a line (A causes B) indicating a false connection *(Fig. 1.3)*. We were able to find a study that showed a connection when most studies did not show a connection. The A to B with a cross-out through it is the truth i.e. there really isn't a connection between A and B. Rather, bias has created the illusion of a connection.

Confounding factors are even more interesting and confusing than bias. You see, the absolute conundrum with confounding factors is that you can have multiple studies that ALL show a connection between A and B and in fact there *isn't* a connection. You might say, "Give me a break, how can we know the difference?" Recall that with bias if we did multiple investigations and studied ALL the results together, it would become apparent that A wasn't really causing B. But, with confounding factors (C), if C is always present with A, then we are not sure if 1) A is causing B or 2) A is causing C which is causing B, or 3) C is causing both A and B *(Fig. 1.4)*!

Again, if we don't get this right then the medical community may introduce healthcare mistakes and you will suffer physically and financially. We must be scientific and know the <u>truth</u> about whether the proposed treatment is benefiting us. We cannot take pot shots and *hope* that the new treatment will improve our health *overall*. There will definitely be health costs *("Dangers of Doing Too Much"*, *Fig. 1.1)* of any therapy, so you better make sure the benefits justify the physical and financial costs.

Here's another example. Imagine we are studying a new type of surgery and, once again, think about our tragic tale of Dad. The surgery in question is cardiac surgery for coronary heart disease. Looking at Figure 3, "A" represents the cardiac surgery. "B" represents health outcomes such as living longer, having less chest pain, and having more

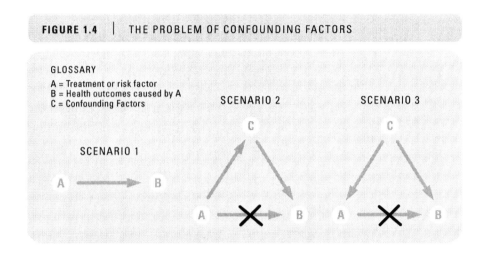

FIGURE 1.4 | THE PROBLEM OF CONFOUNDING FACTORS

GLOSSARY
A = Treatment or risk factor
B = Health outcomes caused by A
C = Confounding Factors

SCENARIO 1

SCENARIO 2

SCENARIO 3

tolerance of activity. "C" represents potential confounding factors.

It turns out that the first study or two do have some positive outcomes for patients who receive the surgery. The big question is, "Was it the surgery or some other factor (C) that really deserves credit?" Now, let's try and imagine some possible confounding factors in this situation:

1. **Better medical care than usual** (*Fig. 1.5*)—The confounding factor could be the surgeon. The surgeon may take extra special care of the patient well beyond what he/she would normally be able to do with every patient. They could use all the best medical know-how, keep a constant vigil on their patient, and respond quickly to any signs of early problems. The confounding factor would be superior medical care.

2. **Lifestyle changes** (*Fig. 1.6*)—The confounding factor could be the patient who is understandably inspired to make profound changes in their lifestyle. With this confounding factor it is the disproportionate selection of compliant patients that caused the better health outcomes in the treatment

group not the surgery itself. As we will discuss in Chapter 4, lifestyle has a much more powerful effect than almost anyone gives it credit for. For many interventions, lifestyle changes may be the actual cause of health improvement. The confounding factor would be better self healing as a result of improved lifestyle.

3. Patient highly compliant with the medical program

(Fig. 1.7)—Similar to the surgeon confounding factor, the patient may have been selected for being highly motivated and therefore much more likely to be compliant with the medical therapy. Again, the confounding factor is the better use of medical therapy and NOT the surgery that caused better outcomes.

4. Self healing including the placebo effect *(Fig. 1.8)*—

Another powerful confounding factor is the patient's own healing ability activated by something referred to as the placebo effect. The placebo effect is when a patient's health improves independent of a direct effect of the medical intervention. We will soon discuss the placebo effect in greater detail.

Given all these potential confounding factors and the risk of healthcare causal confusions as well as the danger and cost of aggressive interventions, shouldn't we *know* if there is more benefit than harm from our proposed intervention? The medical community almost never knows for sure. The medical community is unscientific meaning relatively unintelligent. Doesn't this surprise you?! Why have Americans in particular been placed in the position of playing Russian roulette when they obtain medical services?! Again, it's a function of the wrong accountability and incentives as we will expand on later.

FIGURE 1.5 | MEDICAL CARE AS A CONFOUNDING FACTOR

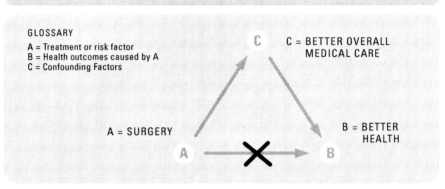

GLOSSARY
A = Treatment or risk factor
B = Health outcomes caused by A
C = Confounding Factors

C = BETTER OVERALL MEDICAL CARE

A = SURGERY

B = BETTER HEALTH

FIGURE 1.6 | LIFESTYLE CHANGES AS A CONFOUNDING FACTOR

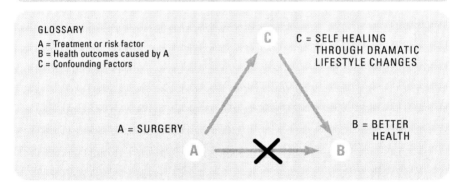

GLOSSARY
A = Treatment or risk factor
B = Health outcomes caused by A
C = Confounding Factors

C = SELF HEALING THROUGH DRAMATIC LIFESTYLE CHANGES

A = SURGERY

B = BETTER HEALTH

FIGURE 1.7 | BETTER COMPLIANCE AS A CONFOUNDING FACTOR

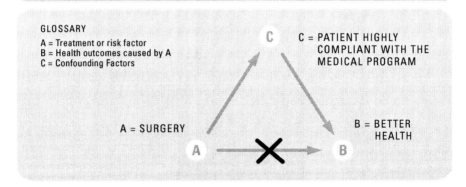

GLOSSARY
A = Treatment or risk factor
B = Health outcomes caused by A
C = Confounding Factors

C = PATIENT HIGHLY COMPLIANT WITH THE MEDICAL PROGRAM

A = SURGERY

B = BETTER HEALTH

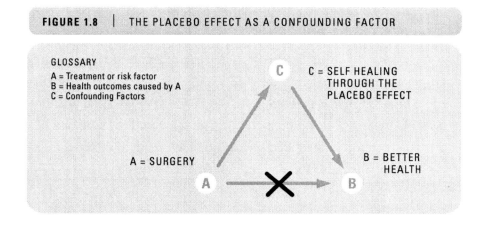

FIGURE 1.8 | THE PLACEBO EFFECT AS A CONFOUNDING FACTOR

GLOSSARY
A = Treatment or risk factor
B = Health outcomes caused by A
C = Confounding Factors

C = SELF HEALING THROUGH THE PLACEBO EFFECT

A = SURGERY

B = BETTER HEALTH

The Placebo Effect, a Special Type of Confounding Factor

In the above list of confounding factors, we ended with the placebo effect. The placebo effect is defined as an improvement in one of the patient health outcomes *independent* of the treatment being studied. For example, a patient receives an antidepressant medication and their state of mind improves. It turns out that this medication does no better than a sugar pill on average in scientific studies. Thus, the patient improved because of their belief and hope tied to the medication. They basically self healed!

The placebo effect is both an interesting confounding factor and a window into the power of self healing. Therefore, also think of the placebo effect as a preview of a very important concept, self healing, the focus of Root Cause #2, (Chapter 4). Very interesting studies of the placebo effect have been performed starting in the 1950s and 60s. In one particularly classic study patients were randomly assigned to one of four experimental groups. The first group received an oral blood pressure medication, a second group received an intravenous (IV) version of the same medication, the third group received a dummy pill also referred to as a sugar pill or placebo by the oral route, and finally, a fourth group received the placebo through the IV route.

The authors of this study analyzed these four groups to see their ability to treat blood pressure. The results were quite interesting. Both the IV groups, IV placebo and IV medication, lowered the patients' blood pressures *equally* while the oral route of BOTH the blood pressure reducing medication and placebo did *nothing*. So we conclude that the way the medication was delivered is what mattered for lowering the blood pressure, not the medication. Isn't that amazing! How could this be? It is simply because the patient believed that the more aggressive approach (intravenous injection) was quite effective. In this belief, they relaxed and reduced their blood pressure. We will extensively discuss the evidence for the power of self healing in Chapter 4 and the placebo effect is but one pathway to unleashing this ability.

Other studies have shown that the more invasive a treatment is, (i.e. the more there is a big to-do or a big ceremony), the more powerful the placebo effect. So it makes sense that hope for healing will be enhanced the more the patient witnesses all the preparation for the "event" of the surgery or intervention. Also important is belief in the treatment on the part of the healthcare provider and the patient. This also fits because if the patient has belief, they will relax their way into better healing. If the healthcare provider also conveys a sense of belief about the procedure, this will naturally enhance the patient's optimism about the healing that is in store for them.

Of course, there has been great belief on everyone's part in the value of medical technology and surgery. Surgeries and other types of interventions are highly ceremonial in their performance. Ceremonial means there is a lot of preparation and the feeling of a significant and important medical intervention. This ceremony stirs up great hope for the arrival of medically derived healing. Thus, surgeries and interventions undoubtedly have a substantial placebo effect, but why pay so much and risk so many of the "Dangers of Doing Too Much" when there are much less expensive ways to tap into this power as we will elaborate later?

How does the placebo effect work? As we will describe at length, people have a remarkable ability to self-heal. No medical technology can compare to our own belief and the resulting ability to heal. The trick is to get out of our own way so we can use our inner healing powers. State of mind has much to do with this. The more we are relaxed, the better we heal ourselves. So you can imagine how the placebo effect works. The patient's body is self-healing because it is relaxed in the knowledge that help is on the way as a result of the surgery or intervention that both the patient and healthcare provider believe in.

Summary of the Causal Confusion Problem

We've discussed what problems can create causal confusion. Causal confusion means we make the mistake of thinking that treatment or test (A) is causing benefit (B). If we are wrong in our healthcare understanding, we risk heading down the wrong pathway for our healthcare interventions with all the "Dangers of Doing Too Much" *(Fig. 1.1)*. You may be physically and financially harmed IF the medical community does not protect you from bias and confounding factors. It requires scientific discipline to eliminate bias and confounding factors, as we will soon describe.

In this chapter we provided several examples of how bias functions and we provided an outline of how confounding factors can cause problems. In the next chapter, we will provide more powerful examples of confounding factors and bias in action.

What you will discover is that the healthcare system is highly un-disciplined from a scientific perspective. You may think that the healthcare system is scientifically advanced but, amazingly, it is not. The healthcare system is technologically advanced but NOT scientifically advanced. This is a distinction YOU will start to understand better than the healthcare system as you continue absorbing scientific thinking and elevating your HQ!

The healthcare system has put the cart before the horse. Western societies have experienced an explosion in the use of medical technology over the past 60 years. Unfortunately, technological advancement without scientific discipline in healthcare means we constantly risk the "Dangers of Doing Too Much" similar to Dad's case. As this book will prove to you, the healthcare system has made this mistake <u>millions</u> of times. The result is a multifold healthcare disaster making you sicker and poorer by the day in ways that are hard to imagine or even <u>see</u>! There are literally tens of thousands of cases like Dad's out there! It is vital that you hang in there through the next chapter and get healthcare scientific thinking under your belt. It is literally a matter of life and death for you as you dance around a minefield of expensive and dangerous medical technology.

You will be amazed at how quickly you can become smarter than the healthcare system and you're almost there! Time to keep boosting your HQ and then enjoy the fruits of greater health and wealth.

Chapter Two

Technological Advancement Without Scientific Advancement is Harmful to Your Health

The truth shall set you free. That biblical statement could be no more true in describing the essence of science and what we will cover in this chapter. In the complex world we live in, what you don't know *will* hurt you, especially in the realm of healthcare. One cannot simply leave it to the experts without keeping the experts honest by some measure. Let's continue helping you master healthcare scientific thinking and then have some fun applying your new thinking tool with one example after another. You will literally become smarter than the healthcare system, become much more selective in your use of medical technology, and, as a result, grow healthier and wealthier. One side note, there are quite a few examples to follow but if you get to the point where you agree with the statement, "Modern medicine is unintelligent because it is relatively unscientific" then feel free to move on to Chapter 3.

Let's introduce another healthcare story to help you understand the tragedies that can be created when the medical community utilizes medical technology without scientific discipline. Your mother is suffering from the symptoms of menopause including hot flashes, reduced energy, and difficulty sleeping. Her healthcare provider suggests that she should follow a course of medication called "long-term hormone replacement therapy", also know as HRT. Sadly, as with Dad, the therapy was much less ineffective than the medical community thought. In this case, the medication was not significantly reducing the symptoms of menopause just as Dad's cardiac surgery was deemed ineffective for most heart-blockage patients. Worse, the medication was also causing breast cancer in many women including, unfortunately, Mom. The connection between the medication and Mom's breast cancer is quite strong since there is no family history of such disease. She is understandably devastated by the news that she "must have" a radical mastectomy (breast removal). Unbelievably, some years after your mother underwent this gruesome procedure, the radical mastectomy *itself* turns out to be proven *unnecessary*. Scientific studies revealed that a much more moderate procedure was just as effective. You are heart broken and outraged since your mother suffered from years of depression after the horribly disfiguring breast surgery. She was never the same. This could all have been avoided if the experts were more scientifically disciplined. Time for you to take control.

The goal of this chapter is to further teach you the tool of scientific thinking. You will find this to be an eye-opening experience with many practical implications. Immediately, you will become a powerful partner in healthcare decision making. In a nutshell, you will take a big step towards becoming smarter, healthier, and wealthier. Furthermore, you will start to understand why more complete healthcare reform is a must. You will more clearly understand the mistakes of the healthcare system. It's time to start avoiding tragedies like your mother's and father's. Let's learn about the most powerful pathways to health and healing.

So far we have tackled one adversary of scientific accuracy or truth, bias. We also started to touch upon the other trouble makers, confounding factors. In this chapter we'll delve further into confounding factors and provide a few more examples of bias in real life. By the end of this chapter you will have the tool of scientific thinking under your belt and then be able to better see the ways in which the healthcare system is failing you.

Let's take a slight detour and talk about what can be done about all the bias and confounding factors we are about to expose. Eliminating bias and confounding factors is surprisingly both easy and difficult. The method is clear, but the execution requires time and resources. Again, the alternative to a scientific approach to healthcare decision making is mistake after mistake and progressively worse health outcomes and wasted wealth. A non-scientific approach makes you sicker and poorer. You must get the tool of scientific thinking under your belt in order to protect yourself. Furthermore, we as societies must make much greater investments in health outcomes science infrastructures to ensure that we only utilize medical technology when it has been proven to be of value. The latter is one of the strongest recommendations of this book.

How To Be Scientifically Disciplined

Let's talk about eliminating confounding factors, one of the two big problems causing interpretation mistakes or causal confusion. In Figure 2.1, we illustrate a connection between a particular medication and a good health outcome using an arrow. A is a medication, and B is the health outcome. In this case, the health outcome is a reduction in symptoms related to menopause such as hot flashes. It turns out that the medication we are studying does not *actually* reduce menopause symptoms. To confuse matters, one study reveals that the group with higher usage of this medication DOES also have less menopause symptoms AND has less heart disease related death! What could have caused this inaccurate study result? If we mistakenly believe this study's results, we risk overusing the technology of a new medication which, in turn, can be costly for both your health and finances. It turns out that in our medication example there are at least three confounding factors that could have created the confusion.

We will provide you with some real examples of these three confounding factors to make scientific thinking come alive. We will call the first confounding factor C1 which will represent the subject's income and education level. These, in turn, have an effect on health outcomes because of a combination of access to better healthcare as well as better health behaviors. The access to healthcare is improved by virtue of greater financial resources as well as greater ability to acquire medical

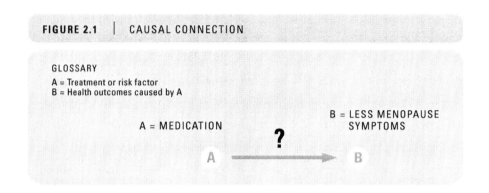

FIGURE 2.1 | CAUSAL CONNECTION

GLOSSARY
A = Treatment or risk factor
B = Health outcomes caused by A

A = MEDICATION

?

B = LESS MENOPAUSE
SYMPTOMS

A ⟶ B

knowledge. For example, the women experiencing the symptoms of menopause that are being evaluated for a study may take advantage of the best medical care available. What if one of these healthcare options reduced hot flashes? How would we know that it was actually the medication and not one of the many other medical and health behavior steps being taken that was actually reducing the hot flashes?

The second confounding factor, C2, might be a patient who has excellent self healing ability. As we will discuss extensively in Chapter 4, there are several body-wide chemicals or phenomena (we will call these inner-body elements) that in excess can cause damage to the body resulting in disease. These elements include glucose, cholesterol, blood pressure, stress hormone, and inflammation. One of these elements, the immune system, is a problem for health if it is depressed or insufficient. There are several behaviors or states of being (what we will call life ecology factors) that, in turn, have a powerful effect on the level of inner-body elements. These life ecology factors include good sleep habits, a great mental attitude, and regular exercise. It turns out, in our mock case, that self healing ability also reduces the symptoms of hot flashes. So another question, as with C1, is whether the patient's self healing is causing the reduced hot flashes or is it the medication being studied? What if the medication is just going along for the ride? This is the problem with observational studies that look at patients at one point in time. We cannot be sure if it is the treatment or test (A) that is caus-

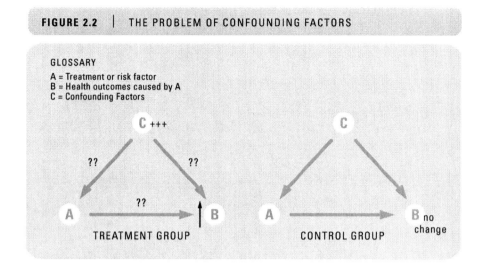

FIGURE 2.2 | THE PROBLEM OF CONFOUNDING FACTORS

GLOSSARY
A = Treatment or risk factor
B = Health outcomes caused by A
C = Confounding Factors

ing the improved health (B) or if the patients who have A also happen to have a factor C that is really causing the improved health.

Finally, in our example study, there happens to be a third confounding factor, C3. C3 represents the taking of specific supplements. It turns out, coincidentally, that these supplements themselves reduce hot flashes. Again, we have to ask the question, "If patients receiving the new medication for menopause symptoms experienced reduced symptoms, was it because of the medication or the supplements (C3)?"

To summarize, if the treatment group *(Fig. 2.2, left triangle)* has substantially more of one of many confounding factors (denoted as C+++) compared to the control group *(Fig. 2.2, right triangle)* AND B improves (less hot flashes) more with the treatment group, we cannot be certain that it is the new treatment (A) and not some patient confounding factor (C) that is causing improved health *(Fig. 2.2, question marks)*.

This following is a vital point about confounding factors and your health and wealth. *We have no way of knowing if the treatment actually causes a benefit unless we keep C equal in both groups.* For example, by chance, the treatment group has more people with excellent health habits *(Fig. 2.3)*. As we described earlier, it turns out that healthy habits such as

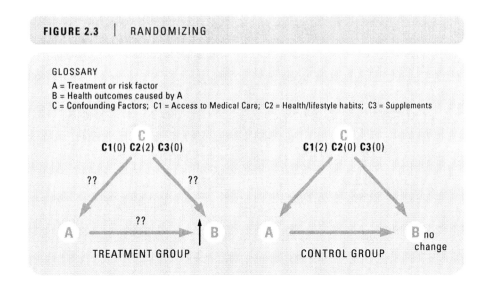

FIGURE 2.3 | RANDOMIZING

GLOSSARY
A = Treatment or risk factor
B = Health outcomes caused by A
C = Confounding Factors; C1 = Access to Medical Care; C2 = Health/lifestyle habits; C3 = Supplements

exercise and getting enough sleep happen to reduce the symptoms of menopause. Now we have a problem. We do not know if the reason for the reduced menopause symptoms was the medication or the healthier habits of the patients in the treatment group.

There is *no way* of knowing the truth about the real benefit of a treatment or test if the medical community only analyzes the matter with a one-point-in-time observational study. We should insist on the healthcare truth and science is the light that exposes this truth. When the medical community analyzes existing patients at one point in time rather than randomly assigning them to treatment or no treatment, we cannot know if the primary factor (A or treatment, test, health behavior, or risk factor) we are studying is causing the health outcomes or some other factor (C) is more responsible. This is vital. If we do not know the truth, we are flying blindly. Flying blindly with expensive and dangerous medical technology can be harmful to your health per the "Dangers of Doing Too Much" (*Fig. 1.1*).

Most of the medical community's healthcare decisions including the use of surgeries, other interventions, tests, and medications *are based on either no or weak science*. Society is constantly being exposed to the "Dangers of Doing Too Much" without knowing it! In other words, the medical community does not typically ensure that A is truly causing B. Thus, you are often being subjected to care that has certain cost and risk but uncertain benefit. This is not smart. You understandably trusted the healthcare system. *Time to get smarter than the healthcare system by continuing to boost your HQ*!

So how *do* we make sure it is a treatment or test (A) and not confounding factors (C) that is causing a patient's health improvement (B)? The key for virtually eliminating confounding factors is to perform a large clinical study with at least 80 to 100 patients randomly assigned to at least two groups. The first group might include people assigned to receive the treatment. The second group would include people who receive a dummy pill, a pretend intervention, or nothing at all. The latter is referred to as a comparison or control group.

For example, in Figures 2.3 through 2.5 we have a study with two groups, treatment and control. We list three confounding factors: C1, C2, and C3. In parentheses we indicate how many patients have which confounding factor. You will notice that as the number of patients increase from Figure 2.3 to 2.4 to 2.5, the confounding factors start to even out between the two groups. More specifically, as per our hot flash example *(Fig. 2.3)*, the first two patients who randomly get selected for the treatment group both have C2 meaning they possess better self healing ability and the first two patients within the control group happen to have more C1 meaning better access to medical care options.

As we continue accumulating and randomly assigning patients, Figure 2.4 shows that the treatment group patients happen to have more of C1, less of C3 i.e. supplements, and about the same number of patients with C2. In other words, if we stopped the study right now and there were better health outcomes for the treatment group (more B) then we wouldn't be sure if it was because of the treatment (A) or because of a greater amount of medical knowledge and access to medical care (C1).

With further randomization, the treatment and non-treatment groups start to have approximately the same amount of confounding factors *(Fig.*

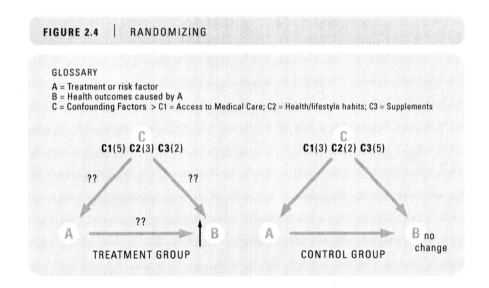

FIGURE 2.4 | RANDOMIZING

GLOSSARY
A = Treatment or risk factor
B = Health outcomes caused by A
C = Confounding Factors > C1 = Access to Medical Care; C2 = Health/lifestyle habits; C3 = Supplements

2.5). This equalization of confounding factors occurs predictably when there are nearly one hundred subjects in each treatment group. *Randomly assigning a large number* of study participants to the various comparison groups causes the confounding factors of each person to be evenly distributed between the two groups. As a result, Factor C will not be more substantially prevalent in one group than the other. NOW we can be certain that if the treatment or test group has better health outcomes (B) it is *because of* the treatment or test and not something else (C). This is what we mean by scientific thinking and being scientifically disciplined; eliminating bias and confounding factors so that we are much more certain that our treatment or test is truly causing health improvement.

Why does healthcare scientific thinking matter to you? Because there is a risk of YOU becoming the next victim of unintelligent care like your father! If we do not <u>know</u> that the proposed medical care or medical technology is *actually* beneficial then the medical community is quite possibly harming you by employing useless or potentially dangerous technology for your health. You should confirm the science behind every significant medical decision in your care because there is so much cost and danger built into technology utilized by the medical community.

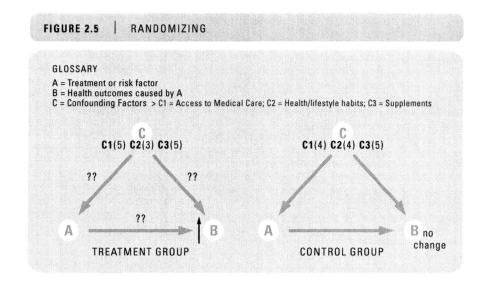

FIGURE 2.5 | RANDOMIZING

GLOSSARY
A = Treatment or risk factor
B = Health outcomes caused by A
C = Confounding Factors > C1 = Access to Medical Care; C2 = Health/lifestyle habits; C3 = Supplements

We've just described the method for removing confounding factors in scientific investigations of health matters, but we still have that pesky bias to deal with. We can eliminate confounding factors and still get tripped up by bias and make the wrong conclusions. The result? You guessed it, healthcare professionals draw the wrong conclusions and YOU get sicker and poorer.

Eliminating/Reducing Bias

In a research study, combating bias is where the concept of "blinding" comes in. To double blind means that the patient receiving the new treatment or test and the healthcare providers delivering the treatment or test are both unaware of whether the patient received or didn't receive the actual treatment. The patient is blinded so that the confounding factor of the placebo effect is not causing an overvaluing of the treatment's benefits. If the investigator cannot be blinded, the medical team assessing and caring for the study participants should be separate from the intervention team which might have an interest in seeing the treatment or test succeed for personal reasons. This, in effect, blinds the after-treatment assessment team and thus, double blinds the study.

The vital reason for blinding the patient is that improved health outcomes might be related to the confounding factor of self healing and not the treatment being studied. It is also critical to blind the intervention team to avoid the confounding factors of picking patients that are more motivated than the average patient in complying with the medical treatment plan as well as improving their life style in order to heal. Another confounding factor that is eliminated by separating the intervention team from the selection/assessment team is above-and-beyond medical care. With all these confounding factors, the treatment would receive too much credit and therefore be over utilized. There are multiple problems of excess treatments and tests including the "Dangers of Doing Too Much" *(Fig. 1.1)*. Doing too much will make you poorer and sicker!

Recall the multiple examples of assessment bias or cherry-picking of studies as discussed in Chapter 1. If we intentionally or unintentionally pick the best studies and the best results and ignore the ones that did not demonstrate a benefit or may have caused harm, we are creating a false impression of the connection between a treatment or test (A) and good health outcomes (B). Again, we would be creating harm because there is a risk of doing too much when there is not really a benefit being delivered by the proposed treatment or test. Unfortunately, this happens quite frequently.

That's why we argue for having independent agencies performing clinical research studies and not the company that is promoting its medical technology product. Independent agencies will not have a bias in favor of the new treatment or test and therefore be less susceptible to assessment bias. To use a silly example, imagine Kellogg's was studying their new Cornflakes and they performed a study comparing it to another cereal. It just so happened that in one of the many studies they performed, the participants reported better thinking ability. Kellogg's starts advertising that its cereal improves mental function even though most of its studies demonstrated no such effect. This is an example of bias which may seem outrageous but this is exactly what pharmaceuti-

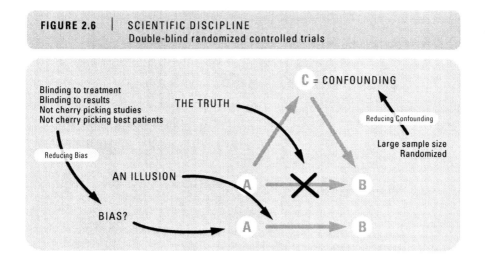

FIGURE 2.6 | SCIENTIFIC DISCIPLINE
Double-blind randomized controlled trials

cal companies are allowed to do!

In summary *(Fig. 2.6)*, the gold standard or most powerful scientific method for ensuring that our proposed treatments are truly beneficial is the double blind (patient and provider), randomized, large sample, comparison group (controlled) trial.

There you have it! You've got the tool of scientific thinking under your belt. When it comes to your own healthcare decisions, you can ask whether the proposed treatment or test has been verified with real science i.e. a double blind randomized controlled trial. If not, all things being equal, we should err on the side of treatments and tests that are less expensive, less complicated, and natural because they are less likely to cause us to be sicker and poorer. The latter is true because natural compounds have, in effect, been tested over thousands of years. Of course, this presumes the natural compounds are being consumed in modest amounts. We'll discuss alternative medical therapy more extensively in Chapter 4. Believe it or not, we're going to continue to further sharpen the scientific thinking tool in this chapter.

Now, guess what percentage of healthcare decisions are guided by double blind randomized controlled trials? The Figure is difficult to know with precision, but, it is safe to estimate that a very small percentage, around 5-10%, of healthcare decisions are based on strong healthcare science! The vast majority of our healthcare is not verified for TRUE benefit. Remember the list of the "Dangers of Doing Too Much"? *(Fig. 1.1)*. You still may not be sure about this science idea and may be apprehensive about rejecting treatments simply because the proposed treatment has not been validated by a double blind randomized controlled trials. Get ready for some real examples of what happens when we aren't scientific! These examples will complete the building of your scientific thinking HQ tool.

Confounding Factors in Action

Now that we know there is a tool for applying scientific thinking to our healthcare treatments and tests, let's get motivated to use this tool all the time. We're going to look at some real examples of healthcare decision making mistakes due to poor or deceptive science including an ignorance of confounding factors. In the process, we will expose the healthcare system as remarkably unintelligent. More complete healthcare system reform will be the next obvious step.

Recall the sad story of your mother's breast cancer. Her doctor most likely recommended to her to take the menopause medication based on positive results from a major study that came out of Harvard University Medical School. The Nurse's Health Study (NHS) was performed at Harvard and analyzed tens of thousands of patients. This study discovered that women receiving hormone replacement therapy (HRT) for menopause had a 30% reduction in heart attack related death. This sounded wonderful; reduce the symptoms of menopause AND reduce your risk of dying from a heart attack. Naturally, we were off to the races and millions of women spent billions of dollars on HRT.

Notice, we said tens of thousands of patients were *analyzed* in the NHS. Remember the key to scientific discipline and especially for eliminating confounding factors is a large number of patients *randomly assigned to treatment or non-treatment*. The Harvard Nurse's Health Study seemed impressive because it is *Harvard* and they studied *thousands* of patients. However, these patients were not randomly assigned to a treatment or non-treatment control group. *Many* healthcare providers overlooked this fact. They were so impressed by who did the study and how many people were analyzed that they became overly confident in the results and started prescribing HRT to many menopausal women, including your mother.

As time progressed, the medical community DID finally get around to performing a large and randomized controlled trial of HRT. This study was called the Women's Health Initiative (WHI). You are not going to believe what they discovered. Whereas the NHS demonstrated a 30% lower incidence of heart attacks amongst women taking HRT, remarkably, the WHI demonstrated that, in fact, HRT *increased* the incidence of heart attacks by 30%, strokes by 40%, and breast cancer by 26%! Furthermore, it didn't even reduce the symptoms of menopause such as reduced vitality, memory, and clearness of mind. The reduction of these symptoms was the reason for using the medication in the first place! Poor mom suffered unnecessarily just like Dad did. She did not receive the benefit promised by the treatment AND she developed a serious complication. Is it worth taking treatments and tests if we do not know *for certain* that there is net benefit? This is especially the case when we *know* there are multiple problems of doing too much.

We're not as smart as we think we are. Most healthcare decision making is based on a theory of the benefit being provided by the proposed treatment or test. Example upon example will prove that theory is definitely not good enough. This is especially true when it comes to the expensive and dangerous medical technology weapons the medical community wields.

Let's go to our tried and true science triangle to understand how we made such a large mistake in interpreting the NHS. If the double blind randomized controlled trial did not demonstrate a benefit but also revealed harm, what explains the results of the Harvard NHS? Could there be confounding factors that encouraged the medication to be used AND also reduced the incidence of heart attack related death? Remember, these patients were not assigned to treatment or no-treatment

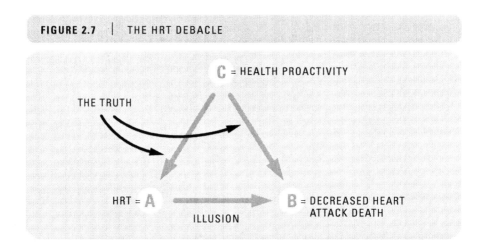

FIGURE 2.7 | THE HRT DEBACLE

C = HEALTH PROACTIVITY

THE TRUTH

HRT = A ➡ B = DECREASED HEART ATTACK DEATH

ILLUSION

groups. They were already using the medication and analyzed for their health status after the fact.

We already described some possible confounding factors in the beginning of this chapter with a similar story about a medication for hot flashes. It could be that the patients who selected HRT were already doing many other things to improve their health including reducing their heart attack risk ("health proactivity"). In the triangle *(Fig. 2.7)*, the confounding factor is the patient who is proactive about their health. They are "causing" the medication's (A) usage AND causing the better health outcome (B).

Our theory is that women who were proactive about their health were already doing many things that would improve their health outcomes including exercise, healthier diet, and other more powerful behavior that we will discuss in Chapter 4. All of these elements were decreasing heart-attack death and in many instances they also added HRT to their routine. Women and their healthcare providers decided, "Here's something that could be useful as part of my toolkit for optimizing my health." Therefore, HRT was simply a marker for the proactive woman rather than a cause of decreased heart attack related death in the average patient.

BUT, if we look at one point of time like the NHS *observational* study, both A and B go up and we can make the mistake of assuming that A is causing B. This obviously represented a BIG mistake for all those women who either received no benefit or, worse, those who experienced significant side effects AND no benefit, such as Mom's case. Are you starting to understand why it is absolutely vital to reduce/ eliminate bias and confounding factors?

Most importantly, the NHS study was an observational study much like all the studies "proving" that those 50 factors all caused cancer as discussed in the previous LA Times article. As we described in Chapter 1, factors A and B will fluctuate up and down independent of each other. On occasion, they will happen to move in the same direction. An academic department studying the matter will catch an instance where A and B happen to go in the same direction and say, "Hey, we see an interesting correlation." The investigators go ahead and publish the results without a summary of all the studies that showed no or the opposite conclusion! In reality, "the truth" is that there was NO connection based on the vast majority of studies already available. This is why observational studies are useless individually.

Sadly, almost all of our healthcare decisions are based upon such observational studies. Observational studies can include a report of just a few patients who received a trial surgery and happened to get better or even a large study like the NHS. Size does NOT matter, as we have just learned. We must demand the truth, not a collection of theories confused by bias and confounding factors, especially when there is so much sickness and poverty created by the use of unintelligent medical technology. There's too much at stake. The evidence in Chapter 3 will make it clear that Americans are experiencing a full fledged, but silent, modern medical healthcare disaster as a result of healthcare decision-making built upon poor scientific discipline.

Supplements Are Medications, Buyer Beware

Now let's turn to supplements. You must keep the following discussion in mind when you consider any supplements for your health, including vitamins and non-vitamin supplements. We'll analyze vitamins specifically. In the 1970s and 80s, we started learning that beta carotene (think carrots) and alpha-tocopherol (vitamin E) levels in the blood correlated with lower cancer rates. So we said, "Great, let's use beta carotene and vitamin E to improve our health" *(Fig. 2.8)*.

Luckily, the medical community decided to study this matter scientifically using a randomized trial. Lo and behold, when investigators randomly assigned a large number of patients to either a group receiving beta carotene or a group receiving a so-called "dummy pill", the beta carotene group actually *increased* cancer in smokers, and vitamin E did *nothing* for cancer, but *increased* stroke *(Fig. 2.9)*. In a separate analysis, vitamin C correlated with a 50% reduction in coronary artery disease related death in an observational study *BUT a scientific study* (i.e. randomized controlled trial), demonstrated no effect at all.

So what in the world was going on there? Why is it that these vitamins not only didn't cause better health but actually worsened outcomes? Here are some interesting questions to ponder. What could have caused the patients in the first studies to BOTH increase their beta carotene and/or vitamin E levels in the blood AND improve health outcomes (reduced cancer)? Go back to our trusted science triangle. What confounding factor (C) could have caused both an increase in these vitamin levels in the blood AND caused the cancer rates to go down in the original observational study per Figure 2.10?

A couple very strong candidates for the role of "C" are fruits and vegetables! Fruits and vegetables could cause the increase in beta carotene and alpha-tocopherol levels and certainly improve health outcomes such as cancer *(Fig. 2.11)*. Now cover Factor C with your hand in the same Figure and you can see how we made a mistake by assuming that because elevated alpha tocopherol and beta carotene correlated with lower cancer and that these vitamins in isolation would also create a benefit. WRONG! This is the kind of mistake we repeatedly make without scientific discipline. We will discuss the impact of diet on health outcomes at greater length in Chapter 4.

The take-home message is this: Be very careful about health short-

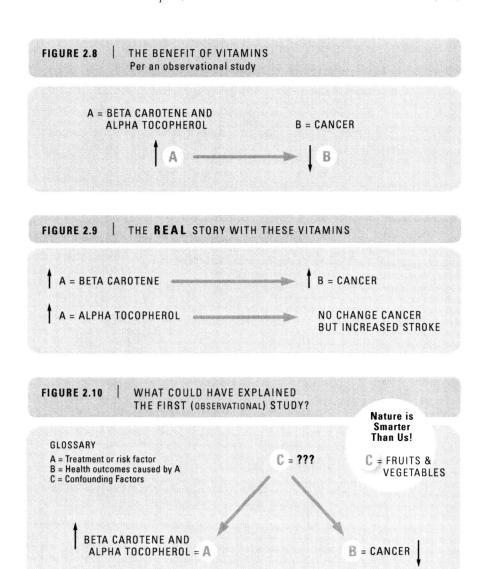

FIGURE 2.8 | THE BENEFIT OF VITAMINS
Per an observational study

A = BETA CAROTENE AND
ALPHA TOCOPHEROL   B = CANCER

A ⟶ B

FIGURE 2.9 | THE **REAL** STORY WITH THESE VITAMINS

A = BETA CAROTENE ⟶ B = CANCER

A = ALPHA TOCOPHEROL ⟶ NO CHANGE CANCER
BUT INCREASED STROKE

FIGURE 2.10 | WHAT COULD HAVE EXPLAINED
THE FIRST (OBSERVATIONAL) STUDY?

**Nature is
Smarter
Than Us!**

GLOSSARY
A = Treatment or risk factor
B = Health outcomes caused by A
C = Confounding Factors

C = ???   C = FRUITS &
VEGETABLES

BETA CAROTENE AND
ALPHA TOCOPHEROL = A   B = CANCER

cuts. Without double blind, randomized, controlled trials to validate the health benefits of a new medical treatment or test, you're gambling with your health. The odds are definitely not stacked in your favor with treatments that are not nature's own in their whole form. It's the vegetables, fruits, and other whole foods that are proven, not the artificially extracted components of the whole.

It is NOT as simple as taking the vitamin or supplement *just in case.* It's a gamble just like many of the medications, surgeries, scans, and diagnostic tests healthcare providers perform on you. Society must insist on greater scientific discipline on the part of the healthcare system. Society as a whole will reap the benefits of this discipline including better health outcomes and greater financial security.

In the reference section of this book, we will include multiple articles describing large-scale errors in introducing new medications. This includes such cases as problems with Celebrex, Vioxx, antidepressants, and others. We will also provide an updated, web-based, listing of additional mistakes made by the medical establishment.

Stepping Back for the Big Picture

Do you see the similarities between the mistakes made by the medical community in their interpretation of the benefit of vitamins as well as long-term hormones? Do you see why theories of what is happening may not only be wrong but harmful? Do you see how the medical community can make large errors in healthcare decision making without complete science to show them the actual value of the proposed treatment or test? This is why scientific thinking and scientific discipline are vital. Isn't it appalling that most of our healthcare decisions are not based on science while the medical community spends billions of dollars in the process? Meanwhile you play Russian roulette every time you engage the healthcare system!

Let's review what we are trying to teach you:

- There really are "Dangers of Doing Too Much" *(Fig. 1.1)* and therefore it is actually dangerous to say yes to treatments and tests "just in case" they might help.

- Because of the real possibility of harm, it is essential to confirm a real net benefit of the proposed treatment *with scientific* investigations.

- The extreme lack of scientific discipline within modern medicine makes it *unintelligent.*

What makes this situation particularly troubling is that the healthcare system has not been forced to track how well its patients are fairing as far as total health outcomes! Only recently has society forced this issue by demanding accountability for the incorporation of medical care that "experts" recommend. How expert can one be without the necessary tools? In the case of healthcare decision making, one of the most vital tools is scientific evidence. There is so little real scientific evidence that the experts are primarily making best guesses.

Let's pause for a moment and preview one of the major conclusions of this book. Our dominant model for healthcare reimbursement in this country is so-called "fee-for-service". This means, if your healthcare providers deliver a healthcare service, they get to charge a fee. Now, ask yourself this question, "In the absence of scientific discipline (whereby the medical community can prove that its proposed services *actually* improve health outcomes) AND the absence of accountability for how patients are fairing overall, what prevents the healthcare system from simply performing medical interventions indiscriminately? The risk of excess medical care is made worse by high profit. Root Cause #1 of a relatively ineffective healthcare system is that modern medicine is unintelligent (non-scientific) in its use of medical technology. Remarkably, Root Cause #1 only represents *one* of the powerful arguments for *eliminating fee-for-service.*

The alternative to a fee-for-service system is a fixed budget system whereby the healthcare system receives a fixed amount per patient per year adjusted for existing diseases. The argument against a fixed budget has been that care will be denied much like the managed care movement in the 1990's. If you realized the lack of scientific discipline behind almost all of our medical technology, you would see that restraint in introducing new treatments and tests **would be a** *good thing.* **There is much too much nervousness about being denied care. If you real-**

ized how blindly the healthcare system utilized medical technology, you may not be as nervous about restraint in care. In the absence of science, restraint is simply the smart thing to do until our health-care science catches up. Furthermore, this book will later outline the checks and balances required for an effective fixed-budget system.

To reiterate a VERY important fact, the VAST majority of medical interventions and tests that you are subjected to are not based on ANY truly *scientific* studies (meaning double blind randomized controlled tri-als)! Treatments and tests are primarily ordered based on your health-care provider's beliefs. These beliefs are derived from theories acquired during their training and reinforced by your healthcare providers' medi-cal association. These medical associations include an expert panel with intelligent healthcare providers and scientists who create healthcare decision-making guidelines with <u>very little science</u> to guide *them*!

No matter how intelligent *individuals* are within these expert panels or the healthcare system itself, health outcomes are too complex to de-cipher without proper scientific evidence. In other words, these medical associations are NOT collectively intelligent because they do not have the tools or scientific information to make their decisions accurately. One particular movement will highlight this fact but first, some histori-cal perspective.

More technology based medicine hit society starting in the 1950's as evidenced by the explosion in healthcare spending as a percentage of GDP or Gross Domestic Product, the total economy of a nation *(Fig 2.11)*. This medical technology has included thousands of new medica-tions, tests, surgeries, and procedures such as Dad's coronary interven-tion and Mom's hormone medication.

Suddenly, (if you can call 40 years later suddenly!), the medical community had an epiphany. It decided to start using *evidence* for its decision-making! This was literally 40 years after the medical technol-ogy stallion was let out of the barn. Just the term "Evidence based medi-cine" (EBM) tells you that the medical community was flying blind with many of its healthcare decisions before this "discovery". Frankly, things

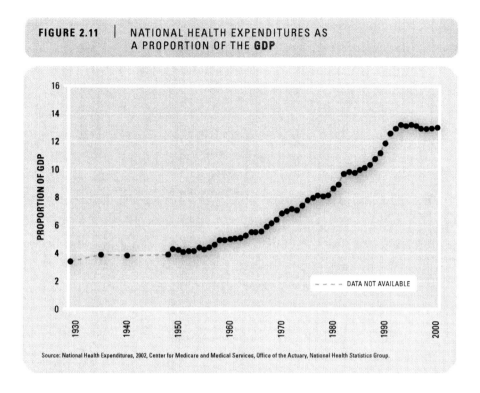

FIGURE 2.11 | NATIONAL HEALTH EXPENDITURES AS A PROPORTION OF THE **GDP**

Source: National Health Expenditures, 2002, Center for Medicare and Medical Services, Office of the Actuary, National Health Statistics Group.

have not changed much because of a lack of the right accountability and incentives as we will describe in the concluding section. The logical question would be, "How were we choosing treatments and tests without evidence?!" This has been going on for 50 years. This is absolutely unacceptable given the cost, danger, and distraction of the new technology the medical community was launching at people's disease.

Ok, back to the medical associations that are producing decision-making guidelines for your healthcare providers. These groups are, in effect, making *guesses* about the "best" practices that your healthcare providers need to follow. Even when these guidelines are indicated as "EBM", the recommendations are only as good as the evidence. We have so little quality *scientific* evidence that we are still at the level of guesswork not sophistication. It's literally the blind leading the blind!

What makes this situation even more horrifying is that there is not only a vacuum of accountability due to poor scientific discipline and poor measurement of our performance but there is also a powerful bias to perform many treatments and tests. The first cause of this bias is the ability of healthcare providers and medical technology companies to earn large sums of money by performing treatments and tests. Secondly, society mistakenly overvalues the overall impact of medical technology on health outcomes as we will analyze in Chapters 4 and 5. Thirdly, society did not consider the "Dangers of Doing Too Much" further exaggerating the value of medical technology in its mind. Finally, healthcare providers were also motivated to do everything possible as a result of a combination of wanting to please their patients as well as avoid being sued for even the most remote risk of poor health outcomes.

The medical associations that produced the medical guidelines are often infiltrated by individuals earning large sums of money from medical technology companies. These people serve as consultants for the medical technology companies whose products appear within these guidelines. In the absence of scientific discipline, who would bother to resist the introduction of new medical technology into the decision-making guidelines even if they were not receiving a conflict-of-interest payment from the technology company? What's the benefit of being honest? Occasionally, an individual speaks up because they can't tolerate the unintelligent use of medical technology. Yet, the forces encouraging the use of medical technology in any manner possible are quite powerful. Only now, given our dire financial straits and increasingly apparent poor performance as a healthcare system, do we have a captive audience for bold ideas and action.

We possess a dangerous combination with regard to the excess use of medical technology. First, there is a tremendous bias favoring the use of medical technology. This is most likely related to a belief in and fascination with technology. Secondly, there is tremendous cost and potential danger due to the complexity and invasiveness of medical technology. Finally, there is significant lack of scientific discipline to ensure that our proposed treatments and tests are more beneficial than harmful.

The Miserable State of Medications Science

The irony is that most new <u>medications</u> DO have double blind randomized controlled trials attempting to validate their health value. There is science, there are randomized trials, but these studies are contaminated <u>and</u> inadequate because of three significant problems we will describe next.

Problem #1 for Medications: False Science—The Effect of Assessment Bias

What if the person or group performing the study can generate recognition and profit through a positive result for their treatment or test? The investigator can simply pick out the studies that had positive results. We discussed this as *assessment bias* in Chapter 1. This is *false science* which means it has the look of science, but it has been intentionally or unintentionally biased. This type of bias can arise when non-positive studies (do not show the medical intervention to be helpful) have been removed or positive studies have received undue attention without a description of all the other non-positive studies.

If studies pose as real science, it causes us to put our guard down and believe that a medication is more beneficial than it really is. Despite our praise for the double blind randomized controlled trial as a critical tool for scientific discipline, please realize bias can still sneak in.

The evidence is clear that the pharmaceutical industry sponsored studies are significantly and disproportionately supportive of their own product. There can be several selection bias scenarios that produce these deceptive results. One scenario is that the medical technology company omits the trials that are not showing the desired results. This, in turn, inflates the value of their product. Another scenario is that the medical technology company designs the trial of their product to track multiple outcomes which allows them to focus on the set of outcomes that happen to show positive results.

Recall our discussion in Chapter 1 and how the treatment or test (A) and health outcomes (B) can coincidentally move in the same direction. Most people do not realize that bias is working in the background and we as a society risk overvaluing our treatments and tests.

Problem #2: Weak Science—Weak Comparisons Therefore a Low Bar

Recall that the goal of scientific discipline is to ensure that the treatment or test (A) is actually producing a benefit (B). In Figure 2.6 we confirm that the treatment or test is beneficial by comparing it to another non-treatment control group. By blinding the patient and provider to who received the treatment or test, we can eliminate bias. Furthermore, by randomly assigning a large number of patients to the two groups, confounding factors will be effectively equal between the groups. Thus, A is better than the comparison group IF the treatment group has a better outcome (B). Although we may have done an admirable job of eliminating bias and confounding factors, we must be even more scientifically disciplined!

Even if the new medication has been scientifically demonstrated to be effective relative to a "dummy" or sugar pill, as we discussed above, this by no means proves that the medication is worth adding to our toolkit. What if we compared the new medical technology or medication against *existing* treatment options instead of a non-treatment control group? This would be an even higher, (and more appropriate), bar for the new treatments to clear. This almost never happens. New medications almost always beat up on dummy pills and then prance around with their "effectiveness".

As a side note, even the placebo comparison is a weaker comparison than the name would indicate. Scientists obviously feel a need to subtract the placebo effect to understand the direct impact or health value of the new medication. The problem is that an accounting for the placebo effect is NOT really happening.

Recall that the placebo effect is proportional to our belief in the treatment. In turn, belief is fueled by our collective ideas of the world and the degree of ceremony surrounding a treatment. Furthermore, the more aggressive or invasive a treatment is, the more "ceremony" surrounds the intervention, further enhancing the placebo effect.

For example, if a treatment such as chemotherapy produces nausea then the patient will think that they are receiving an active medication. Now we have a problem because we cannot be certain if any health outcomes benefit (B) is from the treatment or the placebo effect, the latter resulting from the patient's self-healing. The side effects of the medication fuel the patient's hope of being helped by a medication. One way in which this hope can translate into self healing (the placebo effect) is by reducing their stress hormones which in turn allows the immune system to function better. A more effective immune system can often neutralize cancer cells. Therefore, if we want to *scientifically* determine that a medication is directly causing benefit, we must not limit the comparisons to dummy pills. Dummy pills do NOT produce a true placebo effect *unless* there is some active agent in the dummy pill creating the *perception* within the patient that they are receiving an active medication.

Comparison to an "active" dummy pill or existing active medication is virtually never done. This results in weaker medication science. Weak science means we do not know the truth and this means we are at risk for the "Dangers of Doing Too Much". We can and must do better than this! A much tougher and more logical test for a new treatment would be to compare it against either an existing therapy which will have just as much placebo effect as the new agent or some sort of active agent. This approach of comparing to existing treatment options is also referred to as proving <u>relative</u> benefit. There is yet a *third* problem in the way we add medications to the medical program.

Problem #3 for Medications: Non-Science— The Off-Label Use of Medications

Do you realize that as much as 30-70% of medications are used in an "off label" manner? These medications are used in a manner they were never tested for. The FDA has not approved the medication for purposes your doctor is using it for. In other words, a large percentage of medications are prescribed with no scientific discipline safety net. We're back to square one! Remember how Mom got hurt by her medication? In the reference section there are quite a few examples of the inappropriate use of off-label medications. Also refer to the reference section pertaining to the medical community's conflict of interest with regards to medication usage.

Just because your doctor has a gut feeling about the value of a medication, or they happen to have a few positive patient outcomes (don't forget about the placebo effect!), does not mean you will *directly* benefit from the proposed treatment let alone experience more harm than good. Remember, comparing a new medication to a dummy pill is NOT the same as comparing it to the placebo effect. We need to truly subtract the placebo effect by comparing medications to existing, active medications or natural substances. If we do not have PROOF that an artificial compound is better than the placebo effect why not utilize natural treatments which are usually less expensive, possess fewer side effects, and are just as effective at harnessing the placebo effect?

In summary, the current state of scientific discipline for new medication assessment is weak. The bar is set very low allowing for **thousands** of medications with little or no added benefit to enter our patient's cabinets! Does this make sense? Shouldn't we ensure that the new treatment is better than *existing treatment* options and NOT the low-bar comparison of a dummy pill?

Think back to Problem #2 above and the issue of weak science because of weak comparisons. The ALLHAT (Antihypertensive and Lipid-Lowering Treatment to Prevent Heart Attack Trial) study is a fascinating example of what happens when we DO raise the bar for newer medications. In the 1990s, Pfizer mistakenly funded the ALLHAT trial which was designed to compare newer groups of blood pressure control medications, also called antihypertensives, to an existing treatment option. Pfizer was obviously confident in their new class of medications. Interestingly, our own National Institute of <u>Health</u> would not fund the study. As a side note, in the conclusion section "Putting It All Together" we will criticize the lack of national funding for real science by presenting the research spending data. The ALLHAT trial studied several new classes of antihypertensives and compared them to the oldest class of antihypertensive medications around, the thiazides (a diuretic or "water pill"). Interestingly, the thiazides were also by far the least expensive.

Surprisingly, the oldest and least expensive medication proved to be superior to all the newest classes of antihypertensive medications. The thiazides were just as effective at controlling blood pressure AND had a much better safety profile. The newer classes of medications caused a significantly higher risk of stroke, heart failure, and heart attack! There simply was little incentive to use the medication that provided the best value because it was off-patent and nobody was strongly advocating for its use. Please study the reference section regarding the pharmaceutical industry's marketing, advertising, and lobbying power. This will be a recurring theme; how poor accountability and poor incentives allows the medical community to be scientifically undisciplined in its use of treatments and tests which frequently leads to the "Dangers of Doing Too Much" *(Fig. 1.1)*. We only needed the new blood pressure medications in very select circumstances.

Yet again, the new technology of medications was added to our toolkit without real scientific discipline. Billions of dollars were spent on these medications and for what? We didn't prove that the new medications (A) were causing better health outcomes (B) *relative to existing, less expensive treatment options.* Such poor scientific discipline and unintelligent healthcare decision making is the current state of modern medicine. Thus, you must master scientific thinking which is the HQ boost that will

allow you to ask intelligent questions about medical technology including medications that are being recommended for you health.

In the absence of science, the presence of much bias to do things,
and a powerful pharmaceutical industry promotion machine, who's
keeping an eye out for us? It's not the medical community. The government, specifically the Food and Drug Administration or FDA, is the last
one standing in this story. Unfortunately, the FDA is too weak to force
the medical community and the medical technology industry to introduce new medications with the highest level of scientific discipline.
Yet, we should insist on no less for the sake of our health and wealth.

On top of not being able to force the healthcare system to be scientifically disciplined, the FDA is handcuffed in filtering which pharmaceutical advertising is allowed on television. Direct to consumer advertising
on television is a tricky business. Television advertisement cycles are
typically completed, misinformation and all, before the FDA can stop
them. What's worse, the FDA review process was slowed down during
President Bush's recent term. Typically, damage of misinformation is already completed without any or minimal recourse. There have been many
claims against the pharmaceutical companies for deceitful advertising.

Thus far we have described the state of scientific discipline with
regard to medications based on a combination of false, weak, and absent science (Fig. 2.12). What makes this situation worse is the bias to
do things. The situation is worse yet due to the financial power of the
pharmaceutical industry. This financial power translates into an ability
to manipulate the science, as described above, and manipulate society
through slick marketing and advertising. Finally, the FDA is impotent in
forcing medications to be introduced with the highest degree of scientific
discipline as well as the utmost integrity in conveying the REAL relative
benefit of new medications. With no accountability for the healthcare
system's waste of your money and worsening of your health, the medical community can simply find some studies that happen to show some
positive impact of a proposed medication and then start broadly utilizing
a new treatment or test that might be ineffective or even harmful.

FIGURE 2.12 | THE MISERABLE STATE OF MEDICATION SCIENCE

FALSE SCIENCE

Confounding factors are neutralized by randomized controlled trials but bias is still a problem and therefore we are still making a mistake about the benefit of the new medication.

WEAK SCIENCE

Weak comparisons provide an illusion of benefit from the new treatment relative to what we already have at our disposal.

NO SCIENCE

Too many medications are being used in an off-label manner completely bypassing scientific discipline. Off-label medication usage can create problems.

THE BIAS TO DO THINGS

This is especially the case given little scientific discipline to counter it.

WEAK FDA

There is little agency power to demand scientific discipline from the medical technology companies.

THE PHARMACEUTICAL INDUSTRY'S MARKETING AND ADVERTISING MACHINE

Given the poor scientific discipline of the medical community, the bias to do things, and a weak FDA, the pharmaceutical industry has free reign and plenty of resources to control the message and the minds.

A Summary of the Attack on Science

Let's capture the above ideas in an image that will make it easier to remember the various science concepts *(Fig. 2.13)*. If the truth is that the new treatment or test provides no net and/or no relative benefit, then the forces that can bypass the truth and cause us to travel down the wrong healthcare pathway include:

- **Assessment bias**—the focus on selective studies that favor the treatment.

- **Not proving NET benefit**—by only demonstrating the benefits without analyzing or accounting for the side effects.

- **Not proving RELATIVE benefit**—here the problem is weak science because the medical community allows a weak comparison of the new medication to nothing, such as a dummy pill. A much higher scientific bar to jump over would be comparing the new medical technology to existing treatment which will itself have direct and indirect (real placebo effect!) effects.

- **Off-label use of the medication**—this represents NO science whatsoever as the treatment is used for purposes it hasn't even been studied for!

- **Direct to consumer advertising (DTC)**—this is a manipulation of the science by overemphasizing or mischaracterizing the benefits of a new medication while minimizing its side effects.

- **Observational studies**—this is a weak tool that drives healthcare decisions even though these studies are contaminated by bias and confounding factors causing them to be useless. Observational study results must, to the extent possible, be confirmed with double blind randomized controlled trials.

Are you starting to get the idea that modern medicine is flying blind? There can be no doubt that modern medicine is much less intelligent than it needs to be given the expense and danger of the medical technology forwarded by the medical community.

So we've hit medications pretty hard. Recall that in the beginning of the chapter, we described how little scientific discipline there is for almost all surgeries or interventions in general. In some ways, the story for medications is worse. Not only is there incomplete scientific discipline, there is also highly contaminated research posing as real science which causes consumers to drop their guard and waste even more of our resources and produce potentially worse health. Let's move on to the surgery/interventions category of medical treatments to examine their level of scientific discipline.

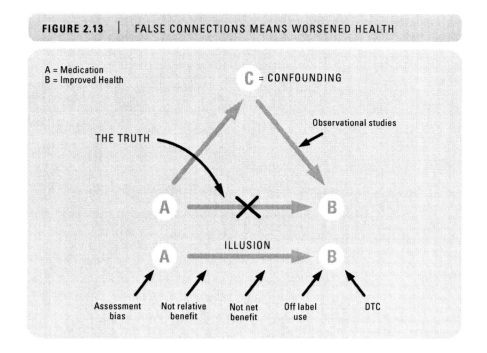

FIGURE 2.13 | FALSE CONNECTIONS MEANS WORSENED HEALTH

Surgeries/Interventions in General—Extreme Lack of Science

Let's get right to the bottom line for surgeries and interventions. There is almost no science to justify MOST surgeries, invasive procedures, or diagnostic tests. An interesting article makes the same point that, currently, society is only starting to *think* about *monitoring* surgeries or procedures. Western societies are not even talking about scientific trials, just *monitoring* them! When scientific analysis IS applied to surgeries and procedures, the results are often surprising. The problem is that the horse is already out of the barn; surgeries and other types of interventions achieve widespread use before scientific discipline catches up. This backwards approach to introducing new interventional treatments is making us sicker and poorer.

Now, it's time for some specific examples. Keep in mind that our goal is to establish how strongly a treatment, in this case a surgery (A), is connected to or causing an improvement in health (B). There is simply too much danger in doing too much for us to not know for certain that the surgery is *directly and substantially improving patients' health.*

We absolutely *must* study surgeries and procedures scientifically for several reasons. As we discussed earlier, the more invasive the therapy, the greater the placebo effect, which represents a significant confounding factor. This confounding factor leads us to overestimate the true value of the new treatment when in fact the procedure simply empowers the body to heal itself better. Also, interventions are expensive and absorb resources that could have been used for better interventional care. Wasted resources could also have been utilized for more proven, non-interventional medical care. Wasted resources could have been used for self healing approaches as we will discuss in Chapter 4 (Root Cause #2). Do not forget the possibility that interventions can just as easily make the patients health *worse* whether directly or indirectly. This will be discussed in Chapter 5 (Root Cause #3).

Coronary (Heart) Artery Interventions— Disaster Because of Poor Scientific Discipline

The left graph in Figure 2.14 shows how coronary artery disease (CAD) related death has been plummeting since the 1950s. Now if you ask almost anyone inside and outside the medical system what the reason is for the dropping heart disease related deaths, they will attribute it to modern medicine or more specifically coronary artery interventions such as bypass surgery (CABG) and balloon or stent opening of clogged arteries (also called angioplasty or PTCA). Let's put things in perspective with the following question: In what decade were coronary procedures such as CABG and PTCA introduced on a larger scale?

The answer: the early 1980s. If you look at Figure 2.14 again, death from CAD was already plunging for 30 years (left arrow, pointing upwards) *before* all those procedures came along (second arrow, pointing down). Now look at the right side graph on Figure 2.14. This represents a drop from 1965 to 1995 of a very important causal factor for coronary artery disease. Can you name the critical health behavior that dropped and thus reduced the CAD death rates?

The *right* graph in Figure 2.14 represents a significant drop in the smoking incidence and represents the answer to the previous question. This drop correlates exactly with the drops in CAD related death! So smoking and blood pressure control are the major reasons people are dying less from coronary artery disease, not surgery. In fact, the only thing you can say so far about CABG and PTCA is that these procedures look like they're "going along for the ride" and receiving undue credit. Again, common sense dictates that the more dangerous and expensive an intervention is, the more scientifically disciplined the medical community must be.

Recall that our goal *should* be to establish a strong causal connection between the cardiac procedure and both a net health benefit AND a relative health benefit. These can only be established with double blind randomized controlled trials that also track a broad range of side effects over a long period of time (NET benefit) as well as compares the intervention to existing treatment options (RELATIVE benefit).

It's interesting to note that the early studies of coronary procedures were NEVER performed with complete scientific discipline. They were not analyzed with double blind randomized controlled trials, with thorough side effects tracking and comparison to existing treatment. People argued that having a non-treatment comparison group was unethical.

This makes several major assumptions. The first assumption was that the medical community understood everything that was going on with heart attacks. A second assumption was that the medical community completely understood how its new medical technology was interacting with the body. A final assumption is that existing non-technological approaches for treating heart attacks were not as powerful as the new medical technology. Was it fair to make all these assumptions in the 1970s and 80s when we first started introducing these heart treatment technologies? The answer was clearly NO and should be a

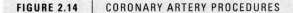

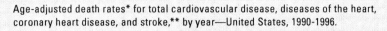

FIGURE 2.14 | CORONARY ARTERY PROCEDURES

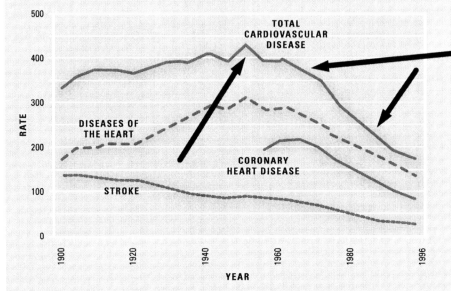

Age-adjusted death rates* for total cardiovascular disease, diseases of the heart, coronary heart disease, and stroke,** by year—United States, 1990-1996.

*Per 100,000 population, standardized to the 1940 U.S. population.
**Diseases are classified according to International Classification of Diseases (ICD) codes in use when the deaths were reported. ICD classification revisions occurred in 19190, 1921, 1930, 1939, 1949, 1958, 1968, and 1979. Death rates before 1933 do not include all states. Comparability ratios were applied to rates for 1970 and 1975.
Source: Adapted from data provided by the Natioanl Heart, Lung and Blood Institute, National Institutes of Health.

cautionary tale whenever there is resistance to being scientifically disciplined in introducing new medical technology.

Thus far in our exploration of coronary interventions we found:

- Coronary procedures received too much credit for the drop in heart attack death when in fact plunging hypertension and smoking rates are more than likely *the* major explanation.

- Coronary procedures were never studied in the most intelligent manner possible.

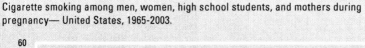

Cigarette smoking among men, women, high school students, and mothers during pregnancy— United States, 1965-2003.

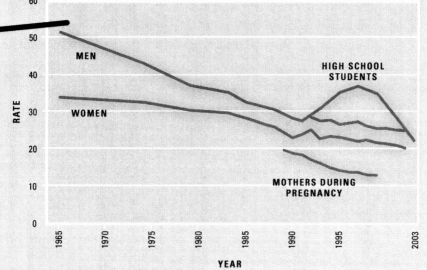

Notes: Percents for men and women are age adjusted. See Data Table for data points graphed, standard errors, and additional notes. Cigarette smoking is defined as: (for men and women 18 years of age and older) at least 100 cigarettes in lifetime and now smoke every day or some days; (for students in grades 9-12) 1 or more cigarettes in the 30 days preceeding the survey; and (for mothers with a live birth) during pregnancy.
Sources: Centers for Disease Control and Prevention, National Center for Health Statistics, National Health Interview Survey (data for men and women); National Vital Statistics System (data for mothers during pregnancy); National Center for Chronic Disease Prevention and Health Promotion, Youth Risk Behavior Survey (data for high school students).

- Scientific discipline becomes more necessary as our medical technology becomes increasingly complicated, invasive, and therefore dangerous and expensive.

The Scientific Discipline of Sham Comparison for Surgeries

Our contention regarding the unintelligent use of medical technology is that the human body is highly complex and sophisticated. It is arrogant for us to believe that we can discover a quick fix for a whole body-system that is malfunctioning. It is also arrogant to think that our sophisticated medical technology has covered all the bases and is providing more benefit than physical and financial harm. *The humble and wise thing would be to study all our interventions with scientific discipline including a so-called "sham" or pretend surgery comparison group.*

A sham comparison is when we randomly assign patients to either a treatment or non-treatment group. Recall that with medications, the non-treatment group was either a dummy pill or an existing medication. If the patient and healthcare providers don't know who actually received the active treatment, then we eliminate many sources of bias and confounding factors. Similarly with surgeries, we can create a comparison or control group where we give the patient the impression that they had the surgery by performing an incision and stitches only at the level of the skin.

Many have argued against sham comparison, especially for significant interventions such as coronary procedures. Yet, these are precisely the interventions that warrant a true scientific analysis because of their danger, the strong bias to do things, and the incredible susceptibility of invasive procedures to confounding factors. Given the tremendous risk from healthcare causal confusion and possible bodily harm, sham comparison is a must. Still not convinced? Please read on.

Confounding Factors for Surgeries and Other Interventions

Recall our discussion towards the end of the previous chapter regarding confounding factors as applied to surgery in general. Confounding factors means there is some other factor (C) that more truly and directly explains the health improvement, but the new treatment (A) is unfairly receiving credit. The problem with causal confusion is that we can waste many resources and risk much harm if the new treatment is not doing what we think it's doing. Furthermore, the wasted resources indirectly cause harm by causing us to miss out on truly beneficial medical care options.

There are many confounding factors that apply to surgery:

- **Selection favoritism** can be confounding because the patient appears responsive to the treatment when, in fact, this improved health is primarily due to better compliance with ALL aspects of the medical program *(Fig. 2.15)*.

- **The placebo effect** is a confounding factor since surgeries are such a big "to-do" and there is so much belief in the benefit of the surgery. As a result of belief, the patient relaxes and self heals which can be the primary reason for improved health (B) *(Fig. 2.16)*.

- **Life style changes** represent another confounding factor as the patient becomes inspired to improve their life style having been scared by their disease and then it's the life style changes that are the primary reason for the improved health (B) not the proposed treatment *(Fig. 2.17)*.

- **Intervention favoritism** is a final category of confounding factors when the patient receives above and beyond medical attention and treatment since they are subjects of the study. It can just as easily be this above average medical attention that caused the better health outcomes *(Fig. 2.18)*.

All these confounding factors can cause an overestimation of the true value of any surgery. Anyone undoubtedly has a story of a friend or loved one who had a heart procedure, or almost any other procedure for that matter, and they swear that the procedure is the reason they are living longer or doing better. The problem that most people overlook is healthcare causal confusion especially due to confounding factors. If it is something else that is causing their health improvement, why not tap in to that something else rather than spending tens of thousands of dollars and risk significant physical injury? If we do not study the benefit of surgeries in a scientific manner, then we risk causing much more physical and financial harm than benefit.

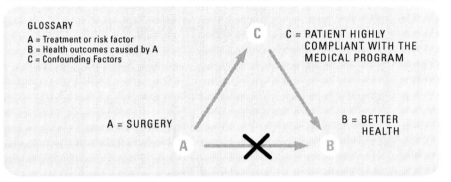

FIGURE 2.15 | SELECTIVE FAVORITISM
Better compliance as a confounding factor

GLOSSARY
A = Treatment or risk factor
B = Health outcomes caused by A
C = Confounding Factors

C = PATIENT HIGHLY COMPLIANT WITH THE MEDICAL PROGRAM

A = SURGERY

B = BETTER HEALTH

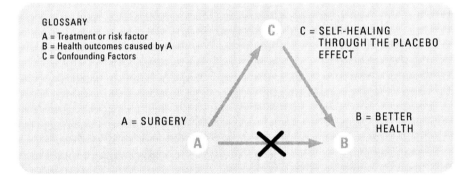

FIGURE 2.16 | THE PLACEBO EFFECT AS A CONFOUNDING FACTOR

GLOSSARY
A = Treatment or risk factor
B = Health outcomes caused by A
C = Confounding Factors

C = SELF-HEALING THROUGH THE PLACEBO EFFECT

A = SURGERY

B = BETTER HEALTH

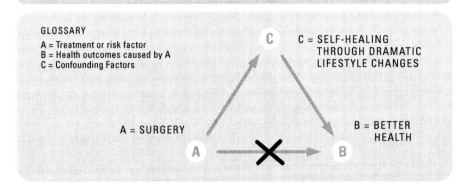

FIGURE 2.17 | LIFESTYLE CHANGES AS A CONFOUNDING FACTOR

GLOSSARY
A = Treatment or risk factor
B = Health outcomes caused by A
C = Confounding Factors

C = SELF-HEALING THROUGH DRAMATIC LIFESTYLE CHANGES

A = SURGERY

B = BETTER HEALTH

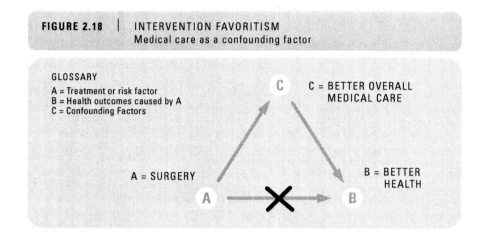

FIGURE 2.18 | INTERVENTION FAVORITISM
Medical care as a confounding factor

GLOSSARY
A = Treatment or risk factor
B = Health outcomes caused by A
C = Confounding Factors

C = BETTER OVERALL MEDICAL CARE

A = SURGERY

B = BETTER HEALTH

Continuing With the Cardiac Saga

An article written in a well-known cardiology journal approximately 15 years ago revealed an amazing discovery: we had the wrong understanding for how heart attacks occurred! The medical community made this mistake for 30–40 years; they got it wrong. Let's reiterate, *the medical community made a 30-40 year mistake regarding the basis for heart attacks!* We originally thought the plaque in the coronary artery kept building, in part due to elevated cholesterol levels, and that this plaque eventually led to a blockage of blood flow to the heart. We developed such a powerful bias against plaque in arteries, that we started scanning many hearts and opened up or bypassed *hundreds of thousands* of coronary arteries. Remember poor Dad?

It turns out that it was NOT the progressive closing of the coronary artery that caused the majority of heart attacks but rather the spontaneous development of a clot in a part of the coronary blood vessel system that did NOT have significant plaque as identified on a heart scan! This was true 85% of the time. So, we followed a theory that only worked 15% of the time, but applied it to 100% of the patients. This is a remarkable and large-scale example of a lack of scientific discipline. There was a bias to do things and the medical community, once again, spread the use of an overly aggressive intervention that didn't work in the majority of cases.

More than a decade ago, it became apparent that these coronary procedures did NOT prolong life on average. Further, it became clear that there were significant side effects from these procedures in addition to an incredible waste of resources that could have been applied to more effective medical and preventative care. Sadly, the medical community produced MANY tragedies like Dad's. In short, the indiscriminate use of coronary interventions has been a large scale healthcare decision-making disaster.

You probably heard a story of how a friend or family member had an angiogram or heart scan performed and the cardiologist discovered a blockage in the heart or coronary blood vessels. Thus, the cardiologist decided to open up these vessels with a balloon or stent or go around the blockage with a coronary bypass surgery. Your friend or loved one issued a sigh of relief at having survived a "near miss". If only this were true!

Now the reason you likely have a friend or family member that went through this discovery and intervention scenario is that *hundreds of thousands* of these procedures were/are still performed. *Amazingly*, as we stated earlier, the majority of these procedures produced little to no improvement in their heart condition or length of life. Your friends and family went through all the expense, stress, invasiveness, discomfort, and risk while often deriving no direct benefit! This is inexcusable. Such poor scientific discipline and large-scale medical errors are the result of poor accountability for health outcomes performance. *We must change this or suffer in ways that may not be apparent!*

Did the medical community study these coronary artery procedures with a sham comparison randomized trial? No! The medical community was not held accountable for the most intelligent method of introducing this complex medical technology. The medical community never studied those procedures scientifically. If they would have, we all would have realized what has now become conventional understanding: coronary artery procedures typically do NOT extend a patient's life. These procedures might reduce chest pain but there are other types of interventions that have been shown to be equally powerful for reducing chest pain, obviously less aggressive, and much less expensive! Why take on the tremendous risk and cost of aggressive interventions without exploring all the other alternative treatments?

In summary, the medical community had the wrong model or understanding of how heart attacks developed. This allowed the propagation of multiple highly invasive procedures on the basis of the wrong theory rather than scientifically proving that these procedures were truly beneficial. They had these really cool toys and they just had to use them!

Let's step back for some perspective. One of the fundamental concepts we are trying to convey is that there has been a remarkable absence of the proper accountability and incentives for modern and especially American medicine to produce the best health outcomes possible. Once again, we ask, "How does fee-for-service medical payment encourage a scientific exploration of all the alternative treatment options available besides medical technology?" This is a fundamentally flawed incentive, especially in the absence of the proper science check and balance.

On top of that, these are highly complex and gruesome procedures with many opportunities for severe complications including infectious disease, as Dad experienced. As a cardiac anesthesiologist, I was directly involved in many different types of cardiac procedures and their aftermath. As part of an international network of researchers, we started to uncover significant problems with coronary bypass surgeries including a significant incidence of brain injury, as experienced by poor Dad.

Patients who suffered brain injury were referred to as "pump heads". The term "pump heads" is derived from the device, the cardiac bypass pump, which allows the patient's heart to be intentionally arrested or stopped to facilitate the precise surgery of bypassing coronary blood vessels that have "dangerous" blockage. While the patient's heart is stopped, the bypass pump artificially oxygenates the patient's blood and pushes blood through the patient's circulation. Unfortunately, this turns out to be a technology that created serious health risks. We only discovered the problem years after launching the new approach because the medical community was not scientific. It was not scientific because it was not held accountable for delivering the best health outcomes possible.

Remember, it's arrogant to think we know what is going to happen at the intersection of medical technology and human bodies. Only science will reveal the truth about these interactions. Does the medical technology provide a benefit after subtracting side effects and is the medical technology any better than existing, alternative approaches? The stakes are too high to take shortcuts. It turns out that the patients undergoing this coronary procedure were experiencing a blood reaction to the artificial surface within the bypass pump. This reaction included problems of too much clot formation with secondary strokes as well as a disruption of the clotting system. So, there was too much bleeding as well as a ramped up inflammation system which caused many problems.

Unfortunately just ONE of the problems of bypass surgery was becoming a "pump head", and this affected a <u>third</u> of the patients undergoing coronary artery bypass surgery! Of course if your husband, aunt, and grandfather have a bypass surgery, a one-third incidence of "pump-head" development means one of your loved ones is likely to suffer a brain injury! If they develop a stroke, they are no longer the same person; shouldn't we count this terrible outcome as a type of death?

It's not good enough to say that the patient is living longer when they're no longer the same person as a result of the brain injury that has significantly altered their personality. Similar to the hormone replacement fiasco Mom and many women experienced, the medical community accepted the results of observational studies, and then charged ahead with a new medical technology. Not until decades later was the new medical technology studied scientifically only to reveal it was more destructive and deadly than beneficial.

In particular, the medical community made two large scientific errors. First, the medical community did not establish that the new medical technology's benefits exceeded the side effects, what is referred to as NET benefit. Secondly, the medical community did not raise the bar and compare the new medical technology against the whole range of existing treatment options, what is referred to as RELATIVE benefit.

In the vast majority of healthcare decisions, we use medical technology without knowing the full implications, only to uncover many problems and often much less benefit than predicted. It just makes sense that we need to perform studies on new medical technology that clearly establish both net and relative benefit before we employ such deadly tools and unleash the "Dangers of Doing Too Much" (*Fig. 1.1*).

In contrast to the world of invasive coronary procedures, important studies were performed in the 1980s that demonstrated lifestyle interventions could reduce coronary artery related chest pain immediately. This is disturbing considering that the reduction of chest pain became the primary claim of value for invasive coronary procedures. Sadly, we've known about the benefits of <u>life style</u> interventions for 20 years but rarely acted on them. This falls under the category of not proving the <u>relative</u> benefit of the new coronary interventions compared to other available medical options.

Dr. Dean Ornish is famous for having been the first physician to demonstrate that coronary artery disease could be reversed through life style interventions based on scientific investigations including randomized controlled trials. According to studies performed by Dr. Ornish and his team, there was a 50% reduction in heart attack or near heart attack episodes and there was a <u>90%</u> reduction in chest pain as a result of the life style intervention he studied. The life style interventions employed in their study included group support, exercise, and a stricter diet. He also found that life style changes were maintained because patients enjoyed the reduction in symptoms. Finally, he estimated that some 80% of invasive coronary interventions were unnecessary.

So, if the relief of chest pain is the primary reason for coronary artery procedures to be performed, but there's something else that's cheaper and easier to do and better for your life overall, why aren't we taking advantage of the latter option? Why do we instead risk potentially devastating side effects from aggressive procedures? Again, this is allowed by there being virtually no healthcare system accountability for *overall* health outcomes. The situation is made even worse by the presence of the dangerous incentives in the form of fee-for-service reimbursement. Again, the latter means there is an incentive to perform medical interventions, *not* an incentive to produce the best health outcomes for the lowest cost. Besides lacking health outcomes accountability, there is also a gap in scientific accountability to ensure that the medical treatments *truly* produce net and relative benefit.

The coronary interventions example is a perfect reflection of modern medicine's collective failures as captured in the Three Root Causes of poor healthcare system performance. The healthcare system used medical technology unintelligently, medical technology is dwarfed by lifestyle factors' impact on most long-term health outcomes, and medical technology is fraught with problems due to the complex, error-prone systems within which it is delivered.

We *cannot* simply utilize new medical technology "just in case" it might help because it may cause much more harm, both directly and indirectly! WE MUST STOP THIS MADNESS! With your scientific thinking HQ boost, you can now insist on much greater scientific discipline for all the medical care you receive. As a result, you will automatically become healthier and wealthier.

This quote from a physician sums up the problem of poor scientific discipline in modern medicine, "Makes us yearn for much wider testing of one therapy against the other. It's ingrained in the American psyche that the worth of medical care is directly related to how aggressive it is." Another quote from a courageous cardiologist, "In your heart of hearts, you don't think it's right to do it but then you feel compelled to do something, otherwise what's your purpose of being there? They are not going to refer patients to you anymore if you're not going to do *something.*" Here's another courageous quote from a *cardiac surgeon*, Dr. Rose from Columbia Medical School in New York City, "This [coronary interventions] could be a lot like female hormones…we're famous for often being wrong but never uncertain…this is emblematic of modern medicine… [the new treatment or test] seemed reasonable and took hold before randomized controlled trials could verify their merits".

Let's recap the evidence against the overall value of most coronary interventions and why coronary interventions serve as a poster child for the Three Root Causes of modern medicine's failure. Coronary artery disease related death was already plunging well before aggressive coronary interventions were being employed on a large scale. Coronary interventions were never studied in an intelligent, scientifically disciplined manner. Our error of poor scientific discipline was exposed because we developed the wrong theory for the cause of heart attacks and proceeded to perform hundreds of thousands of procedures with no benefit and much harm. Furthermore and unfortunately, there is often no way to detect the development of harm unless we systematically track all outcomes. In the case of coronary interventions the medical community took *decades* to catch up to the harm it was causing in the context of much less benefit than imagined. Adding salt to the wounds, literally, many serious side effects from these coronary interventions were being "discovered" when we finally got around to looking. Sadly, we also knew about a more powerful treatment for chest pain, life style interventions. The incentives were just not in place to encourage this pathway. Amazingly, the medical community added ANOTHER coronary intervention to its holster, coronary artery stents. Not surprisingly, this medical technology also started to reveal problems well *after* its widespread use. What in the current fee-for-service healthcare payment model will encourage more intelligent use of medical technology in the absence of scientific evidence? Furthermore, how can we encourage more life style interventions, when these types of care aren't even on the fee-for-service list of procedures to be paid for? What will encourage us to simplify our systems and cause less errors, when our fee-for-service model encourages more doing?

What Will Cause Us to Correct Our Ways?

In the last decade we introduced yet another coronary intervention, coronary artery stents. At one point the healthcare system inserted approximately 1.5 million stents per year! Unfortunately, coronary stents suffer from the same problems as all the previously mentioned coronary interventions. They have not been proven to have net and relative benefit meaning the benefits outweighed the long-term side effects *in comparison to* alternative treatment programs *that were available* such as the Ornish lifestyle intervention. Given that the medical community had the wrong model for heart attacks, ANY coronary intervention would be ineffective on average. On top of the problem of questionable effectiveness of coronary artery stents, investigators started discovering that this new medical technology produced deadly clots *after* their wide-spread use. Here we go again!

Now, to completely cap off the coronary interventions saga, coronary interventions *were finally* studied scientifically! The study, called the Courage Trials, compared medical therapy vs. interventional coronary therapy with <u>randomized trials</u>. Amazingly, although not surprisingly given the evidence we have compiled, coronary interventions provided no greater reduction in coronary artery disease related death compared to just medication treatment. Why are we still performing millions of these procedures? It's a recurring theme: much incentive to do things and little accountability or scientific discipline to keep the system in check.

Does it mean that the surgery or procedure you underwent, including coronary intervention, was without value? If it didn't hurt you, meaning you got away with little or no harm, great, maybe it did directly benefit you. However, in the vast majority of instances, the surgery or intervention was not beneficial. If you got better, it was probably from one of several other confounding factors. Is it worth spending billions of dollars of society's income when the current state of healthcare means playing Russian roulette and there may be less costly and more effective alternative approaches to healing yourself? Of course not! We should KNOW that the treatment is better than placebo effect or existing treatment options.

The cardiac procedure and HRT examples provide definitive evidence that we must insist on strong scientific discipline before attempting a new therapy. We cannot simply trust the medical community's best guess. We must introduce scientific discipline, health outcomes accountability, and the right incentives for society to move in the best direction for health and healing.

Other Examples of Science Exposing Surgical Procedures

In the reference section, we will provide other examples of surgeries that achieved wide-spread use, only to be proven no more beneficial than basic medical measures! We can't resist mentioning a couple more here.

Arthroscopic knee surgery is frequently performed on patients who appear to have knee arthritis. Fortunately, the medical community eventually studied this type of knee surgery with a randomized trial comparing the procedure to a sham surgery. There was no long-term knee pain or function benefit from the surgery compared to a sham or pretend-surgery. A subsequent study also demonstrated no benefit compared to medical therapy combined with physical therapy. Yet, the number of these procedures does not appear to have diminished! Again, without the correct incentives...

Similarly, a randomized controlled trial was recently performed regarding the value of back surgery for chronic back pain. *Again*, the study revealed no benefit for chronic back pain on average. Considering 300,000 patients have these procedures *every year*, shouldn't we have studied this surgery scientifically in the first place? Interestingly, many surgeons protested the performance of this trial on ethical grounds because they were certain that their surgery was beneficial and thus must be used.

Recall Mom's tragic radical mastectomy? Thousands of heart-broken women received radical mastectomies only to realize 20 years later that they didn't need them. The medical community finally studied the matter scientifically only to demonstrate that a localized, limited mastectomy was just as good as the butchery of a radical mastectomy.

By now it should be clear that much of modern medicine is unintelligent.

Summary of the Poor State of Science for Accepting Medical Treatments

Time and time again, the "microscope" of scientific discipline demonstrates the poor NET and RELATIVE benefit of many of our interventions. These examples must inspire an insistence on greater scientific discipline on the part of society. Yet, in the vast majority of treatments and tests we do not learn their true benefit.

We hope that you agree with the following idea sequence because it will motivate a revolution in your own healthcare as well as a reworking of the healthcare system as a whole. You have now learned about many examples where the medical community's theory of health was wrong. Therefore, theory, including observational studies, is not good enough as a basis for healthcare decision making. Medical technology has certain cost and health risk. If we do not scientifically prove the benefit of any proposed healthcare intervention, we are truly playing a game of Russian roulette. You cannot simply take your healthcare provider's word. You must become an equal partner in your healthcare decision making and a rising HQ will provide you the skills and confidence to do so. We can and must do a better job at the individual and societal levels as we will describe in the concluding chapters.

Medical technology is not innocent until proven guilty. It needs to be guilty until proven innocent as a result of the "Dangers of Doing Too Much". Time to finally become smart about healthcare FIFTY years after we let the medical technology cat out of the bag! As we mentioned earlier, the fundamental problem has been the lack of accountability and incentives for the healthcare system to perform in the best manner possible. This has allowed the Three Root Causes to develop. Can you really <u>completely</u> leave it up to the "experts". As the saying goes, "Absolute power corrupts absolutely". We will continue to demonstrate that it is highly problematic to completely hand over medical decision-making power.

Screening Tests

Let's now explore another major category of healthcare, screening tests. Consider the following scenario. Your brother goes in for his annual physical exam. The doctor recommends that he receive a PSA (Prostate Specific Antigen) test to rule out prostate cancer since he is at risk based on his age. He had heard that many men have received this test and he is all for preventing cancer! It can never hurt to find cancer early and eliminate it. Right? Not so fast.

Unfortunately, his PSA test is "positive", meaning further testing is suggested. He then received the recommended scan and then rectal biopsy. The tissue they obtain from the biopsy is "suspicious" for early cancer. Thank goodness he caught it early! Your brother's urologist recommends a <u>radical</u> prostectomy. He's scared as hell, but this IS cancer we're talking about, so he agrees to the surgery.

The surgery goes through without any obvious complications and it's time for your brother and his wife to celebrate good health. Horror of horrors, his intimate moment reveals he is now impotent because of the surgery. Intimacy being a vital part of his marriage, things become tense between he and his wife as it is difficult to feel close. He understandably become depressed which creates even greater emotional distance. Sadly, your brother gets divorced a year later. He remarks to you, "Cancer would have been preferable to this sadness and destroyed quality of life". Heartbreakingly, you read in the newspaper that the PSA test was discovered to have NO EFFECT on prostate cancer survival rates if not *increase death* because of inappropriate risky interventions! Let's examine how this disastrous set of affairs is possible.

Well, surprise, surprise, screening tests fall on their face, scientifically, just like many medications and surgeries! The medical community, again, makes the mistake of not studying the tests for their actual impact on health outcomes, including mortality. Unfortunately, *again*, the horse gets out of the barn as the medical community starts performing millions of tests before scientific discipline is allowed to catch up and *prove* their net benefit. How can we allow all the cost, undue fear, physical harm from unnecessary follow up procedures, and profiteering without confirming an impact on mortality or disease? *Accountability and incentives...*

The medical community finally gets around to studying the test scientifically and discovers that many screening tests are not really doing anything to improve life expectancy. The tests are causing a lot of waste and harm because of all the follow-up procedures we "must" perform due to a "positive" or suspicious screening test result. This is like another blind leading the blind situation. Screening tests that have little or poor evidence which encourage more medical care which also has poor evidence!

Before we dive into more evidence of large-scale mistakes with screening tests because of poor scientific discipline, let's list the problems with performing screening tests "just in case".

The first problem is the "false positive" scenario. In this case, the test comes up positive as if there is a problem but, in fact, there isn't. People are unnecessarily scared into thinking they have cancer or some other disease. They unnecessarily endure many more tests, procedures, and treatments by error. Of course, these treatments and tests generate cost and health risks of their own.

A second problem with tests are "true positives" that don't matter. In other words, the disease exists but finding out earlier doesn't make a difference for overall outcomes. Finding out about the disease when the symptoms first show up still allows enough time to successfully treat the disease or the disease is so rapid that finding out early also doesn't make a difference.

Finally, another reason true positives would not matter is if the treatment creates more side effects than benefit and patients would generally reject this treatment option causing the test to be without value. It is not good enough to live longer if the quality of your life deteriorates like the above PSA story.

So one needs to get lucky and have the test's "discovery" be in that window where treatment will have a positive impact on outcomes. The window is made smaller due to a poor track record in treating most cancers and chronic disease. Do you realize that cancer death rates have remained unchanged for the past several decades? Therefore, be careful in placing all your hope/trust in screening and treatment.

Screening for cancer and other disease often is a crapshoot because of the poor state of scientific discipline for the tests and treatments. What good is a screening test if the medical community does not scientifically establish a real benefit? Such is the state of screening tests analogous to interventions and medications. There's plenty of theory but little scientific discipline to show us the real story. Again, it's playing Russian roulette to get a screening test "just in case".

It bears repeating that medical technology, including treatments and tests, *cannot be trusted without scientific discipline to support it*. No matter how intelligent and caring healthcare providers are, if they do not possess the tool of scientific thinking as well as the scientific evidence itself, their decisions are best guesses. Best guesses will not cut it when it comes to complex medical technology interacting with complex human beings. If there is a possibility of being worse off with unintelligent treatments and tests, what's the point of screening? Making matters worse, most of the treatment that screening leads to is unintelligent because of poor scientific evidence proving its value.

Do you think all these problems with screening tests are factored into the calculation for recommending a particular test? Of course not. There is also a financial cost for doing unnecessary tests which will increasingly be shouldered by the patient and their family. Recall one of the "Dangers of Doing Too Much" is wasted resources. This can hurt indirectly because of missed beneficial healthcare options as a result of depleted financial resources.

You cannot use screening loosely. It's just not that simple.

Back to your brother's prostate fiasco. How tragic that the PSA test ultimately proved to have *no* impact on life expectancy! Worse than no benefit is the addition of side effects. In the case of prostate surgery, side effects include a 9% incidence of bladder control problems and 58% incidence of problems with sexual functioning. In fact, in England only

5% of men get the PSA test vs. over 30% of American men. The British are thinking more carefully about their healthcare resources and how to use them. Again, it's not that a nationalized healthcare system is the answer, but Americans need to think intelligently about how they use their resources. The United States is currently nowhere close to doing that.

Similar to the PSA test receiving wide-spread application before it was proven to be of overall value, mammography testing for women between the ages 40-50 has recently been vigorously debated. Why was the medical community having this debate *20 years* after *millions* of mammograms were performed? That again, in a nutshell, is how the health care system operates when it doesn't have accountability.

The following is a quote from leading physicians in the field of mammography which puts things in perspective, "There are 1.5 million false positives out of 30 million mammographies in 2001, therefore 2 negative biopsies for *every* woman in the U.S. in her lifetime. It is misleading for survivors to claim victory because of discovering a tumor, most women with breast cancer survive without treatment. There was *no change* in breast cancer death rates between 1970 and 1997 (despite mammography)! Breast cancer screening *does not save lives* it creates patients with cancer".

The Sad State of Chemotherapy

Chemotherapy is another poster child for the healthcare system and its lack of accountability and resulting poor scientific discipline. Like most medications, chemotherapy is not compared to existing treatment options, including alternative medicine. Chemotherapy is not analyzed for its net benefit after subtracting the side effects. Death rates from cancer are basically unchanged over the past several decades! The hope projected onto chemotherapy distracts the medical community from the full range of healing options that are available as elaborated upon in Root Cause #2 (Chapter 4). Cancer patients can be made sicker by the chemotherapy and thus are more susceptible to the array of errors within the healthcare system that we will describe in Root Cause #3 (Chapter 5). As with aggressive interventions, there must be a powerful placebo effect that can only be accounted for by comparing new medications against existing medications or active agents as we discussed earlier.

The bias to do something is particularly strong in the realm of chemotherapy because of the great fear of cancer and the great hope projected onto modern medicine. This allows for significant inappropriate use of chemotherapy. Furthermore, oncologists and medication manufacturers make a tremendous amount of money by selling these products. By some estimates, two-thirds of oncologist's salaries are derived from the chemotherapy agents they sell! Can you imagine a more disturbing conflict of interest? You have patients who are desperate for any basis of hope with the specter of cancer hanging over them. Patients are subjected to dangerous medications that have an incredible ability to generate profit, and there is little science and health outcomes transparency to validate these treatments! This is a completely intolerable conflict of interest in the setting of poor scientific discipline.

The explosion of chemotherapy being delivered to patients considered "terminal" is further evidence of this disturbing conflict of interest. Terminal cancer patients are those with no evidence of cure from any current chemotherapy options. At this point, when there is little other hope, you might say, "Do everything possible, doc", but this is tricky. If a patient is paying for the unproven treatment themselves then that is their right. If they are not, it is the right of the community to use the funds in the best manner possible to produce the best overall health outcomes. As described in the "Dangers of Doing Too Much" *there is a health cost for wasting resources.* At some point we must use resources in a manner that helps the most people. If we spend thousands of dollars on one patient based on wishful thinking and then harm 50 other people due to missed healthcare opportunities as a result of inadequate resources, does this make sense? We'll address this further in the conclusion chapter.

Why are the medical community taking shots in the dark? Why is it using treatments without ANY scientific evidence of their benefit? We do this because we haven't made the investment in scientific discipline as a society. There is no need to guess, we can know the truth about a particular treatment's value with well designed clinical trials looking at NET and RELATIVE benefit. You now know that treatments and tests can harm individuals just as well as they can help; we cannot intervene "just in case" as this could easily backfire, and often does as illustrated by the numerous examples in this book.

Again, as with the coronary interventions example, you undoubtedly have friends or family members who swear they were saved by their chemotherapy. Again, without comparison to existing treatment options, there is no way to prove that it was the chemotherapy directly healing patients vs. the placebo effect. In the latter case, again, the patient's sense of hope fueled by belief in the power of chemotherapy allowed their self healing power to suppress the cancer or the patient might have self healed regardless, and the chemotherapy was simply going along for the ride.

Cancer cells are present in everyone but we usually keep them at bay with our immune system. On occasion the cancer cells expand more rapidly than the immune system can handle. The immune system can be overwhelmed either because it has become weaker and/or because some toxin is stimulating the cancer cells to grow at a rate that's faster than their immune system can handle. Shouldn't it be possible to increase your immune system's strength? Of course it should be and this is where self healing through the placebo effect comes in. You may say, "Who cares if it's the chemotherapy or the placebo effect?" It is more critical to know that the treatment is directly causing health improvement when there is greater cost and more uncertain side effects. In other words, the newer and more expensive an agent, the more critical it is to establish NET and RELATIVE benefit of the new treatment against existing treatments through double blind randomized controlled trials. The new treatment might make things worse or do no better. We should not be gambling with our health.

Thinking Tool—Technological Advancement is Different than Scientific Advancement

Most of our medical decisions, including the use of expensive and dangerous tests, medications, surgeries, and other interventions, are based on false, weak, or no science.

The problem with poor scientific discipline is that confounding factors and bias have not been controlled. We often mistakenly attribute the positive change in health (B) to treatment (A) when in fact there is a factor (C) and/or bias creating an illusion. In summary, we might be advanced in the technology we use for health but we are unintelligent in determining whether this technology is *actually* providing net benefit compared to existing therapy. This is an intolerable situation causing the United States to waste TRILLIONS of dollars and produce some of the worst health outcomes of any of the richest nations.

The implications of this lack of scientific discipline are nothing short of the need to completely restructure modern and especially American medicine.

My acquisition of a master's degree in clinical research and subsequently designing and running medical research trials has helped to identify our Root Cause #1; The medical establishment uses technology very UN-intelligently. The medical community is not good enough at accounting for or removing confounding factors and bias. The result is frequent causal confusion. Causal confusion means wasted resources and worsened health.

The following quote sums up the situation differently: "The widespread gaps in evidence-based knowledge suggest that systematic flaws exist in the production of scientific evidence, in part because there is no consistent effort to conduct clinical trials designed to meet the needs of decision-makers. Clinical trials for which the hypothesis and study design are specifically designed to answer the questions faced by decision-makers are called pragmatic or practical clinical trials (PCTs). The characteristic features of PCTs are that they 1) select clinically relevant alternative interventions to compare, 2) include a diverse population of study participants, 3) recruit participants from heterogeneous practice settings, and 4) collect data on a broad range of health outcomes. The supply of PCTs is limited because the major funders of clinical research, the National Institutes of Health and the medical industry do not focus on supporting such trials".

Comparing alternative therapies, as described above, is a different method of taking bias out of the equation. It is often difficult to perform a blinded examination of interventions. If we simply *allow* bias to exist in all the study groups, then the bias and placebo effect will likely be equivalent between treatment groups. We can still randomly assign a large number of patients to the various treatment groups and thus take confounding factors out of the picture.

Of course technology can be helpful but we must not use technology blindly. Large agencies (governments, corporations, consumer advocates, healthcare systems, and insurance companies) must step in. Individual healthcare providers cannot *practice* intelligently no matter how intelligent and caring they themselves are IF they possess little guiding science, an overwhelming amount of information, a bias to do things, and much expensive and dangerous medical technology at their disposal. We need to have decision-making systems to help make decisions intelligently. More importantly, we need the evidence to empower these decision-making systems.

A Review of the Steps Towards Scientific Discipline

Scientific discipline is like a series of **progressively taller hurdles** (*Fig. 2.19*) that must be cleared in order for our causal connection (A causes B) of treatment or test causing improved health outcomes to be verified.

1. **The anecdote or case report hurdle**—This is the first and typically the only hurdle that is cleared by the medical community before proceeding with a new medical technology. Someone reports that a patient's health improves and

everyone presumes it was the treatment or test that caused the benefit, and then the medical community is off to the races in utilizing the technology! Only much later does the medical community realize that it made a mistake as costs and harm start to accumulate and worse, it realizes that the treatment was no better or even less effective than existing options. Unfortunately, *this low hurdle of scientific discipline (anecdote or case report) is the only one cleared by the vast majority of surgeries, interventions, and tests!*

2. **The dummy pill comparison hurdle**—The next hurdle is for a treatment to be compared to a so-called dummy pill. As we discussed this is a weak comparison or low bar. It's very easy to beat nothing! We certainly need a higher standard of excellence. *Unfortunately, this is the hurdle that most medication investigations clear. This is not much better than surgeries, interventions, and tests and can actually be worse if there is bias or manipulation.*

3. **The NET benefit hurdle**—It's even more sophisticated to compare the benefits and the side effects. Why? Because if you have some benefit but a lot more side effects, you might have less disease or even live a little longer but be miserable along the way. What's the point of undergoing the treatment if your quality of life is worse? Remember your brother's prostate surgery and Mom's radical mastectomy? That's why a better measure of a new treatment's usefulness would be the number of quality days of life gained. *This hurdle is basically never cleared for any of our medical technology or treatments.*

4. **The RELATIVE benefit hurdle**—The next taller hurdle is called relative benefit and involves a comparison of the new treatment to existing therapy. This is rare, but the ALLHAT trials illustrate the surprising results when comparison is made to existing therapies. Surmounting this hurdle is an important act of scientific discipline, but a lack of account-

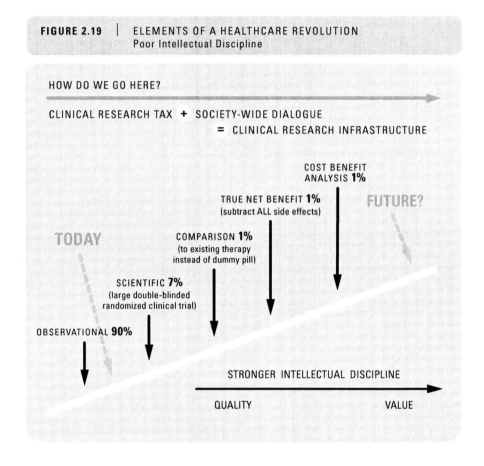

FIGURE 2.19 | ELEMENTS OF A HEALTHCARE REVOLUTION
Poor Intellectual Discipline

HOW DO WE GO HERE?

CLINICAL RESEARCH TAX + SOCIETY-WIDE DIALOGUE
= CLINICAL RESEARCH INFRASTRUCTURE

COST BENEFIT
ANALYSIS **1%**

TRUE NET BENEFIT **1%**
(subtract ALL side effects)

FUTURE?

TODAY

COMPARISON **1%**
(to existing therapy
instead of dummy pill)

SCIENTIFIC **7%**
(large double-blinded
randomized clinical trial)

OBSERVATIONAL **90%**

STRONGER INTELLECTUAL DISCIPLINE

QUALITY   VALUE

ability for health outcomes by the medical community has caused this hurdle to also virtually never be cleared.

5. The cost/benefit hurdle—There is even one more hurdle called "cost effectiveness". Is there net relative benefit at a reasonable price? You may say, "I don't care about cost", but we simply refer you to the "Dangers of Doing Too Much" and understand that you may be worsening your health by reducing your ability to afford treatments that work better. It's time for us to come to grips with our limited resources. Cost benefit analysis is a powerful tool to help society decide where it can get the best bang for the buck.

Some analysts will try and scare you away from cost benefit analysis discussions because it means "rationing". Ignore all the people who use that word as if it is evil. Rationing is smart. It means deciphering where society and individuals can get the most health improvement for the lowest cost.

Whether you are paying for healthcare costs directly from your wallet or through insurance, we all operate with limited resources. Insurance represents the resources of the community pooled together. The community *should* decide how to help the most people with limited resources. Yes, at an individual level, you will try and advocate for the most care possible but we hope you are now more at peace with not getting everything. The examples we have provided you thus far should have convinced you of the "Dangers of Doing Too Much". Getting as much care as possible is not intelligent and just as likely harmful. Furthermore, if you choose to be part of the community, then you need to obey the communities rules including producing the most benefit possible with limited resources. You would be at great financial risk to not be part of some resource-pooling community. *The only sensible option is to ration!*

People will try and scare you into thinking rationing means limiting your options. Yet, options that are of uncertain value *SHOULD* be limited until our scientific discipline catches up. Medical technology should be approached with caution and not accepted unless scientifically supported. What those fear-mongering analysts don't know, or aren't telling you, is that much of the medical community's recommended medical care is of unproven value. The alternative to rationing is the disaster the American healthcare system has produced including trillions of dollars wasted AND *worse* outcomes. We need to keep pushing towards widespread cost benefit analysis as a guide for our healthcare decision making because it's the most intelligent, most scientific tool we have for assessing the value of the medical community's treatments and tests.

Critics will occasionally refer to rationing as "death panels" because a group of experts might decide that you cannot receive certain care. There are several issues being left out by the critics. First, to *not* have an intelligent basis for using our limited resources causes *more* death than not having a death panel! Second, getting all the therapy possible no longer makes sense and could likely *accelerate* your illness! By the end of this book you should be at a point where you are comfortable with not having every therapy possible *unless it is of proven value.* If a treatment or test is of proven value it will, by definition, be included in your insurance coverage. If it is not of proven value, don't play Russian roulette.

Conclusion

Chapter 1 and 2 were intended to teach you the tool of scientific thinking which, in turn, boosts your HQ. Then, we applied the HQ tool to analyze current healthcare decision-making. The result of this analysis is the awareness that modern medicine is remarkably unscientific and therefore unintelligent. The tool of scientific thinking *is almost never applied due to the healthcare system's lack of accountability and incentives for efficiently delivering excellent and improving health outcomes.* We explored many examples of health outcomes *worsening* as a result of the proposed treatment or test which validates the need for scientific discipline in applying new medical technology. **So the bottom line is this: it doesn't make sense to assume that modern medical tools are good until proven otherwise; quite the opposite is true. Say NO to modern medicine unless it is scientifically proven. This has profound implications for your health insurance coverage as well as your personal health and healing approach.**

Your rising HQ will now allow you ask the following key questions in deciding on proposed medical approaches:

- Has this treatment or test been scientifically proven with a randomized double blind controlled trial?

- Has this treatment been compared to existing treatment options (relative benefit)?

- Have the benefits of the treatment been compared to a broad and long-term assessment of side effects (net benefit)

- What are true costs of this treatment or test (cost-benefit analysis)?

- If scientific assessments of the proposed treatment or test do not exist, have there been collections of patient outcomes after undergoing similar healthcare experiences?

It's obvious that the medical community is flying blind *much* of the time and the "Dangers of Doing Too Much" should make it clear that flying blind will make you sicker and poorer. The next chapter will seal the deal on the idea that modern medicine is unintelligent when we provide the big-picture evidence of a failing American system stemming from many blind decisions. Poor accountability, poor incentives, poor scientific discipline, a bias to just do something, and expensive/dangerous medical technology all create a poisonous brew. Let's now see the side effects of this deadly mix.

Chapter Three

Haunted by Unintelligence

Evidence for a Broken American Healthcare System,
The Culmination of Root Cause #1

So far you've learned the powerful tool of scientific thinking. Hopefully you have realized that modern medicine is highly <u>un</u>scientific and, thus, unintelligent. Modern medicine is highly *technologically* advanced but poorly developed in proving that this technology is *actually* improving health outcomes.

Recall that we are advocating a much stricter and therefore more intelligent definition of "improving health outcomes". Health outcomes must include an accurate assessment of benefits minus a full accounting for side effects over time. An even more powerful scientific appraisal of a treatment's value is to compare it to existing treatment options including an assessment of cost effectiveness. We are nowhere near this standard, which explains the evidence you are about to learn in this chapter. Without an intelligent approach to medical technology, you are constantly being exposed to the "Dangers of Doing Too Much" *(Fig. 1.1)*.

Sadly, it's even worse than you probably imagine. You've clearly seen how large-scale errors happen all the time on a micro level. What we mean by micro is specific healthcare decisions made for specific healthcare problems; for example, Dad receiving coronary artery bypass surgery for coronary artery disease. But what happens when there are problems of poor scientific discipline throughout the healthcare system? How do many failures at the micro level add up?

In this chapter we are going to look at the performance of the

American healthcare system at a national or macro level. In fact, you will soon see that the American health system is one of the worst in the world. We have been exploring ways in which modern medicine is unintelligent, but in this chapter we will drive this point home through the American example. By the end of the chapter you will wonder how we ever began believing that the American health care system was advanced at all. Let's explore some of the key "problems" of an American health care system that is severely underperforming.

Problem #1: The American Healthcare System is Too Expensive

Where do you think the American healthcare system ranks relative to the other developed nations of the world for cost of healthcare per person, per year? The United States is typically compared to the 30 richest countries in the world in a group called the Organization for Economic Cooperation and Development or OECD. Within this collection of developed nations, the United States is by FAR the most expensive. The United States spends approximately $7,600 per person per year or 16% of our total economy! Just to clarify figures, earlier, we mentioned a figure of $8,000 *per family* per year of *waste*. This $8,000 waste figure is derived from an assumption of 25% waste, multiplied by nearly $8,000 healthcare spending per person per year (rounding off the above $7,600 figure), and assuming four people per family. As you will see, this is likely an *underestimate* of the actual waste figure!

Let's put things in perspective with some numbers. The total economy (also referred to as the "Gross Domestic Product" or GDP) of the United States is approximately $14 trillion. If the American healthcare system represents approximately 16% of the GDP, this equals almost $2.3 trillion. Only England, France, Japan, China, and Germany have larger *total* economies than our *healthcare* economy! With this kind of scale, mistakes in scientific thinking can be greatly amplified. Just to close the loop on the numbers, the United States spends approximately

$2.3 trillion on healthcare for approximately 300 million people. When we divide $2.3 trillion by 300 million, that results in approximately $7,600 spent on healthcare per person per year in the United States.

No country is even close to the United States with regard to healthcare spending *per person*. The average wealthy nation spends HALF as much as we do! Now, just because the Americans spend more does NOT automatically mean they receive worse healthcare value. If the health outcomes are better than the other developed nations, then the United States experiences potentially equal or better value. Common sense would say, "We better be producing *much* better outcomes to justify the cost." Most Americans know they have an expensive system but tolerate this situation because they presume that their healthcare outcomes are better than other nations.

Problem #2: The American Healthcare System is Not Helping Americans Live Longer

What are some measures of how the American healthcare system is performing relative to healthcare outcomes or benefits? Again, common sense says that important measures of healthcare system performance should include how long people are living, the quality of people's lives after they suffer illness, and the likelihood of developing illness in the first place.

Where do you think Americans rank relative to the 30 richest nations with regard to how long they live? Ponder whether they are in the top, second, third, or last quarter of the international rankings.

Most Americans assume they are in the top or second quarter. Frankly, the reason most people answer anything lower than the top half is because the question is being asked.

Americans actually sit at the *very* bottom. Americans are *not simply in the lowest 25% but actually the <u>lowest</u> of ALL* the wealthy nations with regard to life expectancy AND infant mortality performance! In fact, there are a significant number of third world countries that have now equaled or surpassed the United States in life expectancy! This fact is easy to verify with an online search of international life expectancy rankings. Thus, one cannot make the argument that the United States' poor healthcare system performance is caused by its immigrants and poorer families since entire *nations* of impoverished individuals are rivaling the United States for life expectancy and infant mortality performance!

The U.S. is all the way down to 48th in the world for life expectancy. Equally amazing is that Cuba and other so-called "developing" nations are nearly equal to or have passed the United States with regard to life expectancy!

Thus far in this book, we have demonstrated that poor healthcare decision-making especially on the part of the American healthcare system; tremendous healthcare system expense relative to the developed world; poor life expectancy results relative to the developed world; and poor infant mortality results relative to the developed world. So far, so bad. So again, ask yourself, "What are Americans receiving from their healthcare system for all the money they're spending?"

Let's go one better: the American healthcare system is clearly the most expensive in the world. Yet not only are there no clear benefits to show for this expense, the evidence is mounting that the American healthcare system produces some of the *worst healthcare quality* in the developed world!

Problem #3: Where's the Improved Quality of Life Delivered by the American Healthcare System

What about the quality of people's lives after they suffer illness? We challenge you to provide ANY evidence that the American healthcare system produces a better quality of life for its patients whether it be superior recovery after illness or prevention of illness in the first place. Given the evidence for poor scientific discipline, expense, and poor overall outcomes, the burden of proof must be on the healthcare system's shoulders.

Problem #4: The Argument that Americans Wait Less to Receive Healthcare is FALSE

Americans tend to reach into their grab bag of excuses for their healthcare system, and say, "Oh yeah, but we don't have to wait in line for getting healthcare like people in those other socialist countries". In other words, at least Americans have better access to healthcare compared to other developed nations. You're not going to believe it but that is also WRONG, contrary to what many media pundits would have you believe!

Let's define what waiting in line or access to healthcare means. Does it mean being able to get that fancy medical procedure? Don't get us started! Does access to better healthcare mean more days in the hospital when you have illness? Does it mean getting in to your primary care doctor more often and for longer? Does it mean access to the emergency room?

It would seem that "waiting in line" should be defined as the ability to receive the best access to TOTAL care. We already demonstrated that most of those fancy procedures offered to Americans are based on "smart" theories which are often wrong and can hurt patients in the process.

If we look at all the categories of access to healthcare, the U.S. is towards the bottom of the pack of ALL developed nations! It provides less access to hospital AND primary care than the Canadians! As far as total access to healthcare is concerned, believe it or not, Canadian citizens receive more physician visits per person per year, more days in the hospital per person per year, and more days per year for emergency care! This type of access is what matters, *NOT access to surgeries that may do nothing or may be more harmful than beneficial due to the lack the scientific evidence. Don't be fooled by the scare tactic of other nations' citizens get less or inferior care. That is wrong!*

One critical aspect of access is primary care. Primary care means basic and preventative medical care that can keep you well and prevent you from virtually ever getting sick. This type of care is in contrast to tertiary care which is directed at more immediate medical problems. Importantly, primary care availability predicts the life expectancy within a community whereas access to specialists does NOT! This fits with Root Cause #1, as the specialists blindly apply one piece of medical technology after another. In contrast, primary care tends to focus on the whole picture including self healing (Root Cause #2, Chapter 4) which we will discuss in the next chapter.

With regard to primary care access Americans receive only 1/3 the amount of annual time with their doctor compared to other developed nations such as New Zealand and Australia.

Then you may say, "Yeah, but if you need that cardiac or knee surgery, those "unfortunate" Canadians have to come across the border." We argue that this is a highly overstated argument. Recall that *scientific evidence* proved that many of these surgeries or procedures end up being useless and sometimes harmful. Get ready for a unique collection of arguments for saying "Who cares about waiting for surgery".

Is there any real proof, (other than a few stories), about Canadians suffering longer or dying sooner because of waiting in line? Actually, Canadians live longer than Americans do! It can't be because they're dying waiting in line. Equally surprising is that Canadians are more satisfied with their healthcare than Americans and they rate healthcare as one of their best government services. Critics picked on the wrong country! Frankly, any developed nation can beat the United States for cost AND broad quality combined!

For most of the chronic health problems we suffer from, whether they're related to the knee, back, heart, cancer, or you name it, fancy procedures and medications are usually NOT proven to work. Recall that proof, when it comes to healthcare choices, means randomized controlled trials which include analyses of net, relative, and cost benefits. The medical community uses the vast majority of its tools without proof of their positive impact on patients. Furthermore, chronic or long-term healthcare problems are the VAST majority of our patient's problems. But wait, there's more!

It turns out that there is a reason that these procedures do NOT work! The medical community have the wrong overall model for health and healing. This is the basis for Root Cause #2, "Modern Medicine is Overrated" (Chapter 4). There is a much more powerful method of enhancing your healing and we are distracted from this by the false hope attached to medical technology.

There's one more reason to discourage the Canadians from running across the border for that precious American intervention. The American healthcare system has become a game of Russian roulette. It is so complicated and prone to error that you have a good chance of being injured or killed by it. We call this Root Cause #3, "Modern Medicine Is Harmful" (Chapter 5).

If the Canadians knew the truth about the Three Root Causes of poor American healthcare system performance, they would start running back across the border. That is, if they've ever crossed over in the first place! Ok, so those were negative reasons for the Canadians to run back across the border. Negative meaning problems with the American system. In reality there are also positive reasons for the Canadians to stay put in the first place.

Logically, total healthcare access is what truly impacts overall health outcomes and the American healthcare system is at the bottom of the pack for this category! There is one area of healthcare delivery where the U.S. might be superior to the other developed nations, the delivery of medical technology. Yet, the healthcare system's use of medical technology is so unscientific, overrated, and harmful that it is not something to be excited about in its current form!

You see, the waiting line argument is a complete distraction from the real evidence. The reality is that Canadians have better total access to health care than Americans do per person, per year, and especially regarding healthcare that matters.

Furthermore, how are the waiting lines for the 50-80 million uninsured in the U.S.? That's an astonishing figure *since __none__ of the other 30 or so developed nations have ANY uninsured.* Again, the real issue is *overall* access, not just access to one or two questionable procedures that can, for example, leave you with "pump head".

Let's summarize the American's access to healthcare which is what we feel is the real "waiting line" picture. American access to primary care is towards the bottom of the developed nations. Americans receive less total physician visits per year than the Canadians. Actual hospital access for Americans is also towards the bottom of the developed nations. Of course, you can no longer be fooled by the access to surgery argument. We need to care about waiting longer for what matters (primary care), and be less concerned about waiting for what is not scientifically proven. The Americans can't even win the access game!

Highest Expense and Worst Quality!

This quote from the Commonwealth Fund's Karen Davis sums it up: "Despite having the costliest system in the world, the United States ranks last compared to five other affluent countries in measures of quality, access, efficiency, equity, and outcomes." What's left! The study that generated these findings was performed by a non-profit foundation called The Commonwealth Fund which has extensively studied the American healthcare system.

So let's be clear, it is totally inappropriate to describe an isolated story of someone in another nation waiting for a particular procedure and then being "saved" by the American healthcare system as if this is a reflection of the quality and efficiency of care that Americans experience. No way! What matters is TOTAL care, TOTAL access, and TOTAL outcomes. It's the whole truth that matters.

Those isolated examples of a sophisticated surgery or technology confuse the real picture of an American healthcare system that is failing you. However, as you will see, we are optimistic about the kind of wonderful healthcare system Americans can produce once the healthcare system is held accountable and rewarded for TOTAL healthcare outcomes performance. We want the American healthcare *system's* success; we don't want to cling to isolated victories that may be the exception rather than the rule.

The American healthcare system needs to demonstrate how it is "the best". The ball is now in the American healthcare system's court. We can easily demonstrate that the American healthcare system has by far the highest cost of any system in the world and the worst performance in multiple healthcare categories.

Recall that Cuba, a relatively impoverished nation, has basically the same life expectancy as the United States. In contrast, how much do you think Cuba spends on healthcare per person per year?

Less than $200 per person per year!

It fits that if the United States performs poorly in the category of life expectancy, especially relative to the money it spends, that it may perform poorly in a category such as infant mortality. To borrow from a New York Times article, it's ironic that we criticize the Chinese for having human rights violations, but Beijing's infant mortality rate is better than New York City's – so, where are the human rights here? In our mind, it is a human rights violation to produce healthcare outcomes so far below what our resources can afford.

In summary, an international comparison of the American healthcare system reveals a poor ranking in almost all the important categories of healthcare system performance including life expectancy, infant mortality, access to care, and quality of care. Thus the American healthcare system delivers the highest expense and some of the worst outcomes; this makes it the worst overall healthcare system in the developed world!

Regional Evidence of Waste and Poor Performance

We can provide even more evidence of American healthcare system ineffectiveness beyond the international comparison. A group led by Dr. John Wennenberg from Dartmouth Medical School (Dartmouth Atlas of Healthcare) started demonstrating, 30 years ago, great variability in the rate of healthcare interventions or surgeries performed around the country. Examples of interventions analyzed included hysterectomies, gall bladder removal, and many others. The logical question would be, with so much variability in intervention rates, was there an intelligent basis for performing these procedures?

Experts offered many excuses for this variability until Dr. Elliot Fisher, also from Dartmouth Medical School, published an important study in 2003. He took the analysis of variability in medical practice to a higher level. He asked the next logical question, "Was there a correlation between higher spending and better health outcomes?" Yes there was but inverse: the higher the spending, the _worse_ the outcomes!

Being a budding HQ expert, you may wonder about confounding factors and ask yourself, "Did the higher spending regions simply have to pay more to care for the sicker patients, or perhaps the higher spending regions simply had a higher cost of living which has nothing to do with how much care was being delivered?" Fortunately, Dr. Fisher and his colleagues accounted for and subtracted the variables of patient illness levels and regional costs from the final outcomes.

Recently, Dr. Fisher and his group performed another analysis that went even further than the first analysis. The initial analysis was at the regional level, but the more recent analysis examined data from individual hospitals and compared their results. The numbers came to the same conclusion. Dr. Fisher summarized the first set of results in a New York Times editorial entitled _More Medicine is Not Better Medicine_ in Dec. 1, 2003 and also estimated that <u>one-third</u> of American healthcare spending is unnecessary.

Summary of Root Cause #1

There you have it, Root Cause #1! You cannot pretend that the American healthcare debate should be about insurance coverage for all and who will be stuck with the bill. The debate MUST go MUCH deeper since all Americans are constantly at financial and physical risk under the current system. Unintelligent care stemming from poor scientific discipline launches the "Dangers of Doing Too Much" which can easily explain the American combination of high spending and poor outcomes. This poor performance is in great part caused by Root Cause #1 as explained in Chapters 2 and 3. Poor scientific discipline causes us to squander hundreds of billions of dollars and make mistakes that actually worsen health.

It's just incredible given the American history of pragmatism and frugality that the United States allowed its healthcare system to waste resources at such an incredible rate while not producing results commensurate with the spending! Certainly the United States will by nature spend more than other nations because of its resources; entrepreneurial and therefore innovative nature; and higher cost of living. Yet, if Americans spend more than the other wealthy nations, it should demonstrate some improvement in longevity or other quality of health outcomes for the investment.

The United States must make the investment in a clinical research and health outcomes tracking infrastructure to prove that the various technologies it employs are truly beneficial.

Our point is this: we need to face ALL the facts of poor American healthcare system performance in order to motivate comprehensive reform. We're not advocating a nationalized system but the United States certainly has a long way to go in even *matching* the performance of healthcare systems within nations with government based healthcare. You can't both attack the socialist systems with incomplete or inaccurate evidence and also continue to do little to make our market place for healthcare work better.

We believe that once the average American realizes the truth about the unintelligence, wastefulness and harmfulness of modern and especially American medicine, they will push for real healthcare reform. Change will require the correct set of accountability and incentives to motivate excellent and improving healthcare system performance. The current healthcare reform debate addresses neither of these issues causing current proposals to be virtually useless in achieving better health outcomes. The purpose of this book, therefore, is to motivate both change at the individual and national level.

Recall we stated that modern medicine is unintelligent, overrated, and harmful. Amazingly, we have thus far only described the unintelligence of the system. We have yet to describe the other two problems which will further increase your HQ. A higher HQ will cause you to be even more demanding of improving healthcare system performance as well as control of your health and healing program.

Let's go back to the health and healing wall we are trying to climb hoping to reach the paradise of great health. Unintelligent medical technology is like a broken ladder that causes us to keep falling down in our journey up the wall. There may even be points we can't move past. Even more unfortunate would be if we mistakenly placed the ladder against the wrong wall. That is the point of Root Cause #2, modern medicine is overrated. As compelling and maddening as Root Cause #1 is, it is nothing compared to Root Cause #2! Root Cause #2 will demonstrate that the western medical community is misguided in its structuring of healthcare delivery. We're up against the wrong wall and on the other side of THIS wall is not the paradise of wonderful health but rather the desert of chronic disease. Time to receive another very large HQ boost by learning about Root Cause #2, your remarkable and incomparable ability to self heal.

Part II

ROOT CAUSE #2 :
MODERN MEDICINE IS OVERRATED

Chapter Four

The Power of Self-Healing and Life Ecology Factors

The first HQ boost you received was learning about scientific thinking as applied to healthcare so that you can counter Root Cause #1. Going back to our ladder and wall analogy, having a good ladder is useless if it is up against the wrong wall! So, what is the right wall to climb so that we may enjoy the paradise of wonderful health and healing? In Chapter 3 we will add a significant boost to your HQ, ensuring that you are climbing the correct wall. Learning the correct healthcare wall to climb is clearly the most powerful HQ boost one can experience. Now you will take the second big step in HQ building: unleashing your self healing power through Life Ecology Factors.

First, a little story of how I happened upon an important collection of health and healing evidence. In the middle of medical school, I was inspired by a good friend to explore other areas of learning besides medicine. On his bookshelf were several classic self-help books that I became consumed by such as *How to Win Friends and Influence People* and *The Road Less Traveled*. I became hooked on the genres of psychology and spirituality.

It was a natural progression for me to also become interested in studying various life factors and their impact on health outcomes. I started with a study of the impact of happiness on health outcomes. Soon thereafter, I was stunned to discover how much science there was to prove that *many* life factors powerfully influenced the development of disease as well as how long people lived! Before we explore this body of evidence, let's step back for some perspective on life expectancy gains that society has experience over the past couple hundred years, before we explore the exciting evidence supporting life factors' impact on health outcomes.

Think about this question: how much has our life expectancy as a society increased over the last 150 years? Currently, our average life expectancy is now approximately 80 years of age, but what do you think it was 150 years ago? Believe it or not, just 40 years. That means we've experienced a 40 year explosion in how long we live in just the past 150 years.

What percentage of this 40 year increase in life expectancy is attributable to "modern" medicine? We are defining modern medicine as the period after the 1960s when the medical community used progressively more technology in the care it delivered. Amazingly, only 7%, (approximately 3 years), of this 40 year gain in life expectancy is attributable to modern medicine!

Most of the 40 year gain in life expectancy is due to knowledge gained about the interaction between the environment, health behavior, and our bodies. Examples of these gains include the positive impact of clean water, better sanitation systems, improved nutrition, isolation of the infected individual, as well as other valuable discoveries about the world we live in. These have nothing to do with advanced medical technology but rather the science of our environment and how to navigate it from a health perspective. I didn't learn these concepts in medical school itself but rather because of happenstance and a discovery of other large collections of science that we will introduce you to. The message of this evidence is virtually ignored by the medical community.

In Figure 4.1, the "Modern Medicine is Overrated" idea becomes obvious. If you look at any graph of changes in life expectancy over the past couple hundred years, it is apparent that most of the gains occurred before the 1960s *(Fig. 4.1)*. For example, the left side of the upper graph represents 1850 and the far right time point is 1990. Notice a significant rise in life expectancy starting from the 1850s onward. As you follow

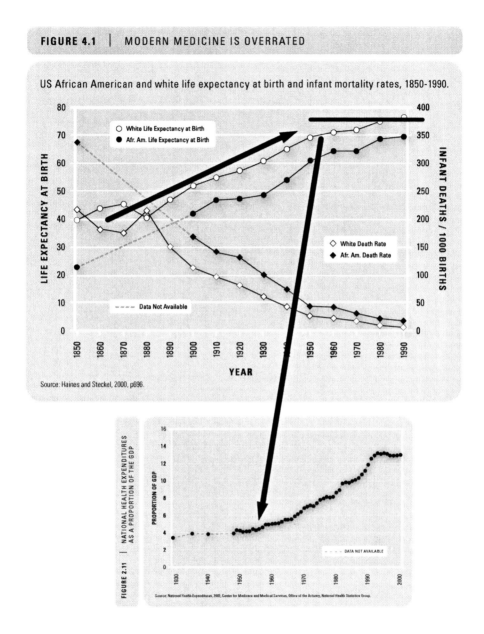

FIGURE 4.1 | MODERN MEDICINE IS OVERRATED

US African American and white life expectancy at birth and infant mortality rates, 1850-1990.

Source: Haines and Steckel, 2000, p696.

the life expectancy line from left to right, notice there is a plateau or leveling of life expectancy after the 1960s. Guess when healthcare spending (as a percentage of the total US economy) really takes off?

The lower graph represents American spending on healthcare as a percentage of the total economy or GDP. The United States was spending approximately 3% of GDP on healthcare until 1960 whereupon it steadily rose to its current level with healthcare spending representing some 18% of the total American economy! Notice that spending on healthcare takes off *after* most of the gains in life expectancy have already been obtained!

Contrary to what most people believe, modern medicine is *not* the primary reason for our longer lives! This is why we titled Part II "Modern medicine is *overrated"* which represents Root Cause #2. Yet, the belief that modern medicine is the primary cause of our longevity is a major reason society has held back from demanding greater accountability in the healthcare systems' performance.

Now ponder the following question. What is the most important specific, *controllable* predictor of how long you will live? For the purpose of this question you can't say lifestyle, that's too broad. You also are not allowed to choose genetics because that's not controllable.

The answer is *relationships.* More specifically, one's strength of relationships or sense of connection correlates with the avoidance or delay of major medical illnesses and thus predicts one's length of life. *This factor is the number one predictor of how long an individual will live and almost no one within the healthcare system realizes it!* We will soon describe the *science* behind the relationship factor but first let's describe an important thinking tool that captures this entire chapter including the relationship factor. Relationships are one of the variables we call Life Ecology Factors. These are collectively the most powerful predictors of health outcomes including length of life, yet surprisingly, they get little attention from the healthcare system.

Thinking Tool—The Life Ecology Factors Concept

The term "ecology" refers to a system with one central variable or factor interacting with other elements in its environment. In the case of Life Ecology Factors (as defined in this book) the central variable is our body

FIGURE 4.2 | THE POWER OF SELF-HEALING & LIFE ECOLOGY

MAJOR PREDICTORS OF LONGEVITY

INNER ECOLOGY	OUTER ECOLOGY
• Religiosity or Spirituality	• Strength of Relationships
• State of Mind (SOM)	• Diet
• Sleep	• Infections
• Exercise	• Accidents

which is interacting with the various aspects of our life. Our body and the various factors interacting with it make up our life ecosystem or life ecology. This book uses the term "Life Ecology Factors" to indicate the many components of life that can interact with an individual's health.

We can subdivide the Life Ecology Factors into inner and outer ecologies *(Fig. 4.2)*. Inner ecology factors include health influences from within our body such as being religious or spiritual, one's state of mind, sleep behaviors, and exercise habits. Outer ecology factors include influences such as relationships, diet, and infectious disease.

These Life Ecology Factors together can predict between *15 to 20 years impact on how long you will live*. This is particularly highlighted by long-living communities where some of their members adopt more Western lifestyles, only to see their life expectancies plunging by nearly 20 years. Similarly, extremely obese individuals experience an approximately 20 year drop in life expectancy which is probably explained by a combination of interconnected Life Ecology Factors. In stark contrast, modern medicine, as we pointed out earlier, has had *only a three year impact on life expectancy*. This is what we mean when we say the healthcare ladder is up against the wrong wall by focusing on technology-oriented healthcare. This is why we will continue to refer to modern medicine as overrated until it adopts practices that facilitate patients' self healing through Life Ecology Factors.

In fact, three years may actually be an overestimate of the impact of the technology-centered healthcare care. After the 1960's, major public health care gains were also being accrued as a result of changes including the reduction of smoking and high blood pressure. To reinforce the point, recall the graph in Chapter 2 illustrating a plunging heart disease related death and how well it correlated with the drops on smoking rates. Thus, even the *relatively* minor improvements in life expectancy we have experienced over the past 40 years have been highly influenced by environmental factors such as reduced smoking. This even further reduces the contribution of modern medicine to people's longevity.

Medical technology oriented healthcare is plagued by at least three problems:

1. It wastes precious resources that could be used for better healthcare options thus causing indirect harm.

2. Medical technology can directly worsen patients' health.

3. False hope that is pinned to medical technology distracts us from the power of self healing through Life Ecology Factors.

Let's paint an image to help explain why medical technology has a smaller impact than most people think and why self healing fueled by Life Ecology Factors is so critical. Think of the body as a dam holding back the waters of disease. The dam is made up of bricks and mortar. Time passes and one of your bricks pops out and you start leaking. The leaking represents the symptoms of disease starting to flow. The health care system comes along and says, "We have a gold brick and gold mortar to fix that leak so it will never come back". We know how expensive gold is and the gold repair even proven to work better than other material?

The gold brick works initially. Pop! Pop! Pop! The *other* bricks of your dam start popping out over time. Unfortunately, your body was not doing such a good job of building, maintaining, or repairing the other bricks and mortar of your dam. No one *taught* you how to heal yourself with lifestyle changes that can prevent and reverse major disease. Despite modern medicine's gold repair job, the symptoms come back even stronger. In response, the healthcare system desperately and ineffectively runs from one brick to the other slapping in expensive gold bricks. The healthcare system tries to slow down the symptoms but, eventually, the disease becomes overwhelming. Unfortunately, in the process, the healthcare system also damages the other bricks and mortar causing your body to be worse off.

Then it turns out that there were knowledge and tools to help you build/repair your own bricks and mortar. You were too distracted by the flashy gold bricks and mortar and you ran out of resources to take advantage of the more basic and powerful dam repair building tools and techniques available. It is much more powerful to have an entire functioning *system* of brick and mortar production rather than running after one failing brick after another hoping to stem the flood of water. The latter will not work in the long run.

In the meantime, while you were not properly maintaining your dam, you also started to generate an "acid" that actually eats away at your bricks and mortar. In the coronary artery disease version of the analogy, the acid is represented by various forces that are destructive to the coronary artery blood vessels. Specifically, these acidic forces include inflammation, high blood sugar levels, high blood pressure, high cholesterol, high adrenaline, and environmental toxins such as smoking.

The result of the acid's erosion is a jagged lining of the heart vessels where clots can develop. The gold brick and mortar that the healthcare system had to offer was "Hey, there's a blockage in your coronary artery. That's bad, and we can tunnel through or bypass the scoundrel". In the meantime, the flood of inner destruction continues and overwhelms whatever targeted interventions could be performed such as balloon or stent opening of the blockage or surgery to bypass the blockage. Due to the destructive inner-body elements building up in your system (the "acids") other blockages develop and coronary artery disease continues causing problems.

Again, (as discussed in Chapters 2 and 3), shouldn't we know the truth about the net and relative benefit as well as cost effectiveness of our proposed treatment? What if there are disease reversal techniques that you can drive? How can we know the whole truth without comparing all possible approaches to a health concern? In the absence of the truth, we have seen plenty of examples of problems created by medical treatments. Remember, it cannot be innocent until proven guilty with medical technology; given the "Dangers of Doing Too Much" it is guilty until innocence is validated. The evidence in this chapter should further amplify the argument against medical technology's assumption of innocence. The power of life ecology factors and the less than expected impact of technology should further force scientific discipline for all of our healthcare decisions. A perfect example of the evidence encouraging a tilt towards life ecology factors and away from technology is the coronary interventions saga. When it comes to coronary artery disease, lifestyle interventions turned out to be just as effective as the cardiac procedures and likely much less expensive.

The reality is that coronary artery disease is throughout the heart's blood vessel system. It's not just in one artery; it's a systemic disease. That's why cholesterol reduction works while coronary interventions such as bypass surgery, angioplasty, and stents often do not. The "disease" of coronary artery disease is not just in one or two locations but potentially in many locations because the "acid" can go anywhere. Once the conditions are in place for internal injury we are MUCH better off reducing the acid rather than trying to fix one "leak" or one site of corrosion at a time. The key to reducing the acid is Life Ecology Factors!

The Dam analogy and coronary interventions saga encapsulate Root Cause #2: modern medicine is overrated. Not only does medical technology have a much weaker impact on health outcomes than we realize, it also pales by comparison to self healing and Life Ecology Factors. The latter actually addresses the cause of the problem rather than trying to put together the pieces after destruction has already set in. It is much more difficult to put the pieces back together compared to keeping things whole. Our own self-healing ability MUST be the foundation of an intelligent healthcare program because nothing compares to its sophistication and power.

The vital need to place Life Ecology Factors at the center of care is reinforced by the fact that 90% of our healthcare needs as a society are related to chronic disease. Chronic disease is **BOTH** the dam in a state of deterioration as a result of an excess of various inner-body acids AND a poor repair system. In the body, a malfunctioning repair system means a depressed immune system. We have to fix our own dam by both reducing the inner acid and optimizing our own healing ability before the widespread leaks overwhelm the healthcare system. It is madness for you to not take control of your own health. You must also insist on the health care system becoming more focused on facilitating your self healing, not to mention being more scientifically disciplined when it attempts to fix the leaks directly!

The dam analogy explains why Life Ecology Factors can so significantly impact life expectancy. Life Ecology Factors reduce the amount of acid and cause the repair system to function better. Let's look at the individual and collective Life Ecology Factors *evidence* to make you real believers.

The Relationship Factor

Earlier, we described relationships as the most powerful, controllable predictor of how long you will live. We also criticized the Harvard Nurse's Health Study because it incorrectly concluded that hormone replacement therapy improved health let alone harmed some people. Let's give Harvard College another chance.

The Harvard Stress Mastery Study (HSMS) followed a random collection of college students from the classes of 1952, 1953, and 1954. The goal of this study was to determine the students' sense of connection to both of their parents and the effect of this sense of connection on their health. The investigators asked a very simple question: "Is your relationship with your mother and father warm or cold?" The study revealed some interesting results. The participants who reported a warm connection with Mom and Dad averaged a 25% incidence of major mid-life illness in their 50s. Illness was defined as alcoholism, depression, cancer, and/or heart disease. The participants who rated their relationships as "cold/cold" had an almost 90% likelihood of having a major mid-life illness! The students who rated their relationships as cold/warm or warm/cold were right in between with mid-life illness rates in 60-70% range.

Given your expertise in scientific thinking, you might ask "Wait a minute, isn't this an observational study?" You're right! Recall the NHS observational study analyzed participants at *one point in time*. The HSMS was much more powerful because it tracked people over a long period of time and well before the illnesses developed. This is referred to as a "prospective cohort study".

The term "prospective" means the study participants are followed forward in time as opposed to retrospective, and "cohort" because the investigators are following a group or cohort with similar characteristics. If this study were performed as an analysis at *one point of time*, like the NHS hormone therapy study, we could not be certain whether the poor relationships were causing the illness or the illness was placing patients in a bad mood so they were interpreting their relationships more negatively. With a long-term prospective cohort study like the HSMS, that type of healthcare causal confusion is much less likely to occur as we will explain next.

A long-term prospective cohort study is the most powerful scientific tool next to a randomized controlled trial. Obviously, investigators cannot randomly assign participants to warm or cold relationships! In a prospective cohort study, the causative factor (A) is occurring well before the illness (B). If A increases and THEN B increases, we can be more confident that A is truly causing B.

Now let's think through the potential bias and confounding factors in the HSMS. There was no interventional bias because there was no intervention! There was no patient selection bias because they randomly selected study participants. There does not appear to be assessment bias since there do not appear to be any relationship studies showing *no* impact of perceived relationships strength. Furthermore, the outcome of the HSMS was precisely defined well ahead of time as opposed to tracking multiple outcomes and then conveniently pointing to the measurement that has changed significantly as if there is a causal connection. Given your emerging HQ, you can no longer be fooled by that kind of assessment bias. But what about confounding factors?

As you know, it is critical to account for confounding factors lest we inappropriately credit the wrong thing for improving or worsening health. Confounding factors for health outcomes include common sense items such as access to healthcare, health behavior (exercise, smoking, weight, and diet), and income/education levels. Income and education levels likely improve access and health behaviors themselves. Of course we should consider other Life Ecology Factors besides relationships as confounding factors.

In the HSMS, the socioeconomic and education confounding factors were already taken care of because the study participants were graduates of Harvard. The access to healthcare and health behavior confounding factors were easy to account for by surveying patients. These confounding factors were <u>not different</u> between any of the groups. That brings us to Life Ecology Factors as potential confounding factors.

One of the major points of this chapter is that it doesn't matter if there is some overlap between Life Ecology Factors. We do not need to know exactly which life ecology factor is causing what part of the health outcomes improvement or deterioration. Life Ecology Factors will naturally improve or worsen together. Unless we are able to perform a randomized controlled trial on an individual life ecology factor (if that is even feasible), it would be difficult to separate which life ecology factor is producing which health outcomes improvement. For example, if a study indicates a correlation between sleep duration and the development of coronary artery disease, is it the better sleep that caused lower coronary artery disease or did sleep duration act as a marker of better state of mind. In this case, better state of mind was the actual cause of reduced coronary artery disease and the sleep factor was "going along for the ride". Similarly, one could be sleeping better if one's relationships were healthy and satisfying or one was getting good exercise. To be safe, improve them all! *Now* it's OK to say "Let's do them all, doc"!

Interestingly, the studies that analyze Life Ecology Factors are *scientifically stronger than medical technology science*. Medical technology has weak science making its use quite blind as described in earlier chapters. There are virtually no double blind randomized controlled trials or prospective cohort studies for medical technology. We must prove the net and relative benefit of proposed interventions or suffer from the "Dangers of Doing Too Much" *(Fig. 1.1)*. The Chapter 3 evidence for the overall failure of the American healthcare system indicates that modern medicine is indeed being collectively ineffective in producing the best possible health and healing for society.

Therefore, the HSMS uses a stronger scientific tool than modern medicine AND accounts for all the major confounding factors making the connection between A and B quite strong. The connection between strong relationships and positive health outcomes is further confirmed by a so-called "dose-response relationship". A dose-response relationship means that the stronger or in this case the warmer a relationship is, the less illness develops. Finally, there are MANY other studies to validate that relationships have a profound effect upon death and disease. Let's look at a couple more.

The Alameda County Study is one of several large studies that analyzed whole communities. According to this study and other similar studies, the effect of relationships on various health outcomes is so powerful that *even if you have poor health behavior* (including not exercising, not eating well, smoking and drinking alcohol) *you're better off* as long as you have strong social ties! You are actually worse off if you possess weak social ties and all the healthy behavior you can muster. Can you imagine how powerful that is? So it is not surprising that some experts estimate that the relationship factor can impact as much as 8 years of life expectancy! The ability of the relationship factor to over-come multiple health risk factors is *a recurrent theme in many scientific relationship studies.* There cannot be any denial of the power of relation-ship strength in improving one's health. Is there anything in the current healthcare financing model or healthcare delivery thinking to tap in to this power? No! We must change our health outcomes accountability and incentives so that the medical community innovatively taps into this and other Life Ecology Factors.

A study of post-World War II Japanese immigrants to the United States provides another powerful testimony to the importance of rela-tionships in promoting health outcomes. This study demonstrated that the Japanese individuals who stayed connected to their communities after they immigrated to the United States had *3 to 5 times* less heart disease than the individuals who were more integrated into American society. Again, the individuals who smoked but were still tied to their Japanese community *were better off* than those who were assimilated into the American society and *didn't smoke.* Of course we know how power-fully smoking increases heart disease! So again, relationships or con-nection have a profound impact on health outcomes that is even greater than health behavior risk factors most people are well aware of.

Other experimental studies have also been performed with fascinat-ing confirmation of the power of connection. In one study, rabbits with identical genetics were raised with identical diets. This caused the ma-jor confounding factors to be equal between the study groups. The fac-tor (A) that was different between the "treatment" and non-treatment groups was the ability to interact with other rabbits. Remarkably, the experimental group with rabbits that were allowed to interact had *60% less heart vessel blockage!* This is a completely scientific study which is easier to accomplish in a lab. Of course, we feel badly for the poor bun-nies that developed coronary artery disease, but we can thank them for the scientific illumination they provided on an important issue.

Human experiments have also illustrated the profound impact of social connection. Dr. Spiegel showed a doubling of advanced breast cancer survival from 18 months to 36 months in patients who were randomly assigned to a group receiving psychotherapy compared to a group receiving nothing similar. The same positive effect of group therapy was produced in a study of patients with another type of advanced cancer called metastatic melanoma. To be fair, Dr. Spiegel was not able to reproduce his results in a follow-up study. One can speculate that standard of care had improved to include group therapy and thus, it would be difficult to create enough of a separation between the "treatment" and comparison group to show the real benefit of therapy. Also, was it possible that the new treatment group didn't develop the kind of connections that would lead to self healing? Certainly the Relationship Factor is undeniable but the next challenge will be how do we enhance this factor and *then* what is the health impact? This is the kind of exciting healthcare science we can look forward to! Life Ecology Factors are the types of medical technology to really focus on and develop.

Another amazing study of social connection was published in the *American Journal of Cardiology*. Investigators were studying new medications to treat dangerous heart rhythms in patients with severe coronary artery disease. The study was interrupted because the medications were killing people faster than the placebo group. A fascinating finding was discovered after the study was ended: the dog owners within this high-risk group had much less heart disease-related *death* than the non-dog-owners. In the non-dog cohort there were 19 deaths out of approximately 282 patients compared to only *one* death out of approximately 87 dog owners!

As an interesting side note, if the medications that were being studied in the first place caused the kind of benefit provided by being pet owners, the investigators who discovered the medication would probably win Nobel Prizes and the pharmaceutical company with the patent would earn billions of dollars! This is powerful stuff. Just having a loving animal companion can have a profound impact on your state of mind and your health.

One of my inspirations for developing the Life Ecology Factors concept was Dr. Dean Ornish. Dr. Ornish and his group at the University of California, San Francisco were the first to demonstrate that it was possible to reverse coronary artery disease with lifestyle interventions. Most importantly, these results were derived from a well designed scientific trial. Furthermore, Dr. Ornish wrote a wonderful book called *Love and Survival*, which is an excellent description of many relationship factor studies.

The State of Mind Factor

Another powerful Life Ecology Factor is state of mind. In one study, they followed a group of middle-aged individuals over a 25 year period. This analysis is equally as powerful as the HSMS since it was also a long-term prospective cohort study. The study revealed that the individuals who had a positive view of aging lived 7.5 years longer! Again, one cannot make the argument that the patients were healthier and *that's* the reason for their better state of mind. In this case, the better state of mind was already in place and therefore strengthens the argument that it caused those individuals to live longer.

Other investigations have clarified what aspect of state of mind causes better health outcomes. It is not whether you put a smile on your face that predicts a longer life but rather your resiliency or ability to adapt. So, when we say "positive" state of mind, it's the ability to deal with the "ups and downs", not an overly sunny disposition *per say*.

Another way to demonstrate the power of state of mind is to analyze the impact of *negative* states of mind on health outcomes. Studies about negative states of mind have been conducted for more than 20 years. This body of work uncovered that negative states of mind such as Type-A personality (meaning highly and even angrily driven), anxiety, time urgency, and hostility produced greater hypertension and coronary artery disease related death.

Studies of the health benefits of meditation also support the importance of state of mind. Investigators employed <u>randomized controlled</u>

trials to explore the health benefits of meditation, which you now know is a scientific approach! Approximately 200 patients were randomly assigned to either a transcendental mediation group (TM), a stress-reduction program group, or a mindfulness meditation group. In other words, this was not simply a randomized controlled trial with a "dummy pill" comparison but rather, a much tougher comparison to other treatments of a similar nature. The only thing lacking from a scientific perspective was blinding, but there was randomization, relative benefit analysis, and the participants were followed over a 20 year period. These are all strong elements of scientific discipline which is more than almost any introduction of new medical technology!

So what were the results? For the TM group there was a 23% lower incidence of death compared to the other study groups over a twenty year period! We challenge you to find any recent medical intervention that can come close to this effect. The investigators were quite thorough and even measured the effect TM had on the inner-body elements that predict disease including: blood pressure, cholesterol, stress hormone levels, and inflammation. ALL these factors improved in the TM group relative to the other two study groups. If any medication or surgery were discovered to yield this degree of health benefits, the investigators would *also* share the Nobel Prize that went to the pet-companion study investigators!

Now would be a good time to discuss (if there ever is a good time) the various inner-body elements that predict chronic disease and premature death. Earlier we referred to these inner-body elements as a kind of acid eating away at your dam's bricks and mortar. High blood pressure, high cholesterol, high glucose (sugar), and high inflammation levels cause damage to the lining of blood vessels. Damaged blood vessels serve as a landing zone for clots which, in turn, block off blood vessels. Blood vessel blockages reduce the amount of blood and oxygen delivered to the vital organs. Vital organs include the brain, heart, liver, kidneys, and so on which are damaged because of poor oxygen supplies.

High stress hormones such as cortisol and adrenaline also create problems such as elevating blood pressure, depressing the immune system, and increasing clot formation. Clot formation occurs because the blood becomes more "sticky" as clot-forming factors in the blood become activated. Stress hormones and glucose can directly depress various components of the immune system. A depressed immune system can allow for such problems as infections, cancer, and overall poor injury healing.

Inflammation can cause a destruction of any tissue besides blood vessels. For example, the toxic chemicals generated by the inflammation reaction can launch the development of cancer. There is a powerful correlation between these various inner-body elements and almost all of the chronic diseases that people suffer from and ultimately succumb to. It is vital for people and their healthcare system to learn how to "cool" those factors down. This will represent a large part of future medical delivery models and will not come about with the limited fee-for-service reimbursement structure Americans currently possess. Fixed budgets will force healthcare systems to be as innovative as possible in tackling patient's inner-body elements when they are excessive.

Please think back to our analogy of the dam as a representation of the body holding back the waters of disease. The various inner-body elements in excess such as glucose, cholesterol, stress hormones, as well as high blood pressure represent an acid eating away at the bricks and mortar. No matter how effective our medical technology is at replacing individual bricks, it cannot overcome a system-wide problem eating away at ALL of the bricks and mortar simultaneously. The medical community's lack of scientific discipline makes the case for the value of gold bricks and mortar even more troubling. The medical community is likely squandering resources on the expense of gold which prevents the pursuit of other effective approaches to sealing the dam. The medical community also didn't realize that its gold repair was itself acting like an acid and causing collateral damage resulting in other leaks.

In real life, our immune system represents a body-wide repair shop that helps to maintain the dam. Any system-wide phenomena, whether it is a positive, creative force like the immune system or negative forces such as the acid-like inner-body elements in excess, *must be more powerful* than treatment focusing on an isolated part of the body such as a vital organ that is "falling apart". Medical technology generally focuses on one brick whereas Life Ecology Factors focus on the entire dam. This does not mean temporary assistance with leaking bricks is of no value. The leak itself causes damage. The medical community provides a service by slowing or stopping the leak but it is still essential to keep the dam in good repair before bigger and more numerous leaks appear.

The image of dam repair represents the essence of Root Cause #2, Modern Medicine is Overrated. The medical community focuses excessively on individual bricks and pays virtually no attention to helping patients build and maintain their dam. The dam analogy also explains the vast difference in life expectancy impact between modern medicine, at only a few years, versus the double digit impact of Life Ecology Factors.

The Inflammation Factor

Let's discuss one of the specific inner-body elements, inflammation. Inflammation literally means "to be on fire". Dr. Bruce McEwen's book *The End of Stress as We Know It* nicely describes the phenomena of inflammation and our ability to measure the long-term accumulation of stress in the body. We can measure the buildup of stress and inflammation with specific hormone and protein tests. This is helping scientists to learn what worsens or improves our accumulated stress.

Inflammation is a key predictor for the development of major illness because it can cause the breakdown of the body. Breakdown can occur in the blood vessel system, leading to heart disease, renal disease, and stroke depending on which vessels are effected. Tissue breakdown can also cause damage to one's genes that can, in turn, trigger cancerous tissue growth. The nervous system can break down producing problems such as Alzheimer's and Parkinson's disease.

Dr. McEwen's book concludes with a nice summary of the types of studies exploring methods for reducing the long-term accumulation of body stress and resulting disease. Virtually every factor that contributes to a reduction in the stress load of the body is a Life Ecology Factor!

Before we go on to more Life Ecology Factors evidence, ask yourself, "How will fee-for-service reimbursement encourage a development of the most powerful forces in health and healing including positive health behavior and especially Life Ecology Factors improvement?" Currently, fee-for-service menus do not even include Life Ecology Factors enhancement programs. Yet these same menus are loaded with medical technology that has virtually no real science to validate their net and relative health benefits! Time and time again, studies of Life Ecology Factors reveal an ability to "cool down" the system by improving virtually every inner-body element that causes problems. The meditation studies cited above were a perfect example of this across-the-board reduction in excess inner-body elements. The evidence is just staring the medical community in the face! Reduction of excess inner-body elements causes less damage and disease, and Life Ecology Factors cool down excess inner-body elements. It just makes sense to tap into this power!

The Diet Factor

Investigators have analyzed the impact of nutrition on chronic disease and life expectancy. There are several categories of diet investigations. One group of studies has analyzed communities with an above average life expectancy and collected their dietary patterns. Another type of study has measured the correlation between various food categories such as fruits and vegetable consumption and cancer and heart disease rates. Finally, there have been interesting explorations of the impact of low calorie diets on a whole range of inner-body elements. The common theme, though, is that positive health outcomes seem to derive from a diverse diet including significant amounts and types of fruits and vegetables as well as a low to moderate calorie intake.

Fruits and vegetables seem to possess a very strong chemical basis for health promotion. As many are now aware of, fruits and vegetables deliver a host of antioxidants which reduce the damage of inflammation! Studies have revealed *half* the rate of cardiovascular death for patients with a significantly higher consumption of cereal fiber, fruits, and vegetables. Studies have also revealed a profound negative impact of simple sugars, highly processed foods, trans fats, saturated fat, and high fructose corn syrup.

In Chapter 1 we presented several examples of vitamins producing *worse* health outcomes when analyzed scientifically. Supplements, in general, are an attempt to harness the power of nature's healing chemicals. They often fall short, as they are relatively unnatural. Why not go to the original source; natural, whole food? There are certainly specific instances where supplements have been scientifically proven to be beneficial for health but short of scientific proof, be very careful about supplements. It makes much more sense to go the whole foods route based on the evidence.

Let's be scientifically disciplined with these studies just as we challenged medical technology in the previous chapters. In fairness, the studies of fruits and vegetables were observational. You could ask, "Was it the fruits and vegetables causing the improved health outcomes or were fruits and vegetables a marker of other confounding factors that were actually causing the reduced heart disease or cancer?" This would be analogous to the mistaken understanding that hormone replacement therapy was decreasing heart disease related death. As we theorized in Chapter 1, the medication was a marker of a confounding factor that truly explained a reduction in coronary artery disease. The most likely candidate for a confounding factor was a combination of multiple Life Ecology Factors. Participants who were already optimizing various aspects of their health were also optimizing their Life Ecology Factors in the process. The patients with higher Life Ecology Factors were more likely to select hormone replacement therapy as part of their health and wellness program. Hormone replacement therapy was going along for the ride and only looked to be correlated with lower coronary artery disease. Of course, we know that it not only did not cause lower coronary artery disease, but it actually increased.

So, what could be the confounding factors with regard to the benefits of fruits and vegetables? The list of confounding factors is logically the same as with the relationship studies. The general categories of confounding factors include other Life Ecology Factors, access to healthcare, and health behaviors or risk factors. Again, the large fruits and vegetables studies were quite scientific as they accounted for all the major confounding factors by demonstrating that key confounding factors were equivalent between the groups. Interestingly, as with most of the large Life Ecology Factors studies, the healthcare access and healthcare behaviors confounding factors are relatively easy to account for. Once again, though, there remains the possibility of *other* Life Ecology Factors as confounding factors. We cannot *know* whether fruits and vegetables are the *primary* cause of improved health or simply a marker of other Life Ecology Factors being optimized, again analogous to the hormone replacement therapy confusion. Bear in mind, fruits and vegetables can also act through the placebo effect but this would also be working through a Life Ecology Factor, state of mind! Once again, we must hedge our bets by optimizing ALL the Life Ecology Factors.

Speaking of optimizing all our Life Ecology Factors and health behaviors, an interesting question is, "Is there a limit to how much we can "cool" the excess inner-body elements?" Of course, at some point, our inner-body elements will no longer be at excessive levels and our immune system will be functioning optimally. An exciting area of new research will be how to improve Life Ecology Factors and health behavior and at what point do we achieve a maximum benefit. We have all the necessary tools to perform such investigations! Certainly we can focus on the most powerful Life Ecology Factors and work down from there.

In addition to the diet category of types of calories consumed whether fruits, vegetables, nutrients, or harmful items, there is the matter of *total* calories consumed. For some time scientists have discovered through animal studies that the only diet factor affecting length of life is the amount of calories consumed. The lower the calorie content of an animal's diet, the longer they live. Now, for the first time, the same phenomenon has been demonstrated in human beings.

We've recently acquired important evidence of the health benefits of calorie restriction in *humans*. Two specific groups that have been studied for the effect of caloric restriction are the participants in the Biosphere studies and a Seventh Day Adventist group. The former occurred by accident because of a short supply in food but the latter restricts caloric intake based on religious recommendations for a stricter diet. In both groups, biophysical measurements demonstrated an improvement in almost all important excess inner-body elements including cholesterol, blood pressure, blood sugar, and inflammation levels compared to average people not in these groups. In the Seventh Day Adventist group, the participants possessed arteries as clean as average individuals who were years younger!

It seems that the less you eat, the longer you live because of a cooling down of many of the destructive factors within the body. The opposite is also true; the greater one's weight is above their ideal body weight, the greater the risk of a multitude of chronic disease as the dam is being eaten away by various excess inner-body elements. Remarkably, highly obese individuals have as much as a <u>twenty</u> year shortening of their life span. This makes sense since highly obese individuals may be caught in a vicious cycle of Life Ecology Factors deteriorating including state of mind, relationships, sleep, exercise, and diet.

The Exercise Factor

As opposed to diet and relationships, exercise has been studied with the most powerful scientific technique available to us, the randomized controlled trial. Of course one cannot blind the participants from whether they are exercising or not! In one particular study of exercise, 160 individuals were randomly assigned to exercise or no exercise. Within only a few months, the group assigned to exercise developed substantially less respiratory colds and respiratory illness in general.

The Framingham study, (discussed in Chapter 1 with regard to fat consumption and its impact of coronary artery disease), produced data that has been analyzed to estimate the impact of exercise upon longevity. The group labeled as the "higher exercise group" lived three and a half years longer than the lowest exercise group and the moderate exercise group added one and a half years. Again, one could surmise the possibility of confounding factors in these studies because they are observational in nature. Exercise could simply be a marker of someone who has many aspects of their lives working well and they simply want to add exercise to make their health even better. Doesn't this sound familiar? This could be analogous to the Nurses Health Study and the confusion regarding the benefits of hormone replacement therapy. Or perhaps exercise is functioning like meditation. We have already witnessed the scientifically validated power of meditation. Finally, based on the randomized controlled trials of exercise and its lowering of infections, there is clearly some impact on the immune system which in turn will improve life expectancy and quality of life to some extent.

Our conclusion from the exercise data is that it *is* a factor in health and healing but its benefit is minor compared to state of mind, spirituality, and relationships factors. In particular, there is no evidence for the benefits of exercise beyond simply walking on a regular basis. Can you picture any of the famous groups of long-lived people, such as the Okinawans, participating in western examples of high-intensity exercise? It's back to nature as these groups derive the benefit of exercise from walking, gardening, tai-chi, and other moderate but natural activities. Are they engaging in high-impact aerobics or running for miles? No!

Our point is, don't obsess about exercise for the sake of extending your life or improving your health. The problem with anxiety or fear-based exercise is that it might represent one step forward and one or more steps backwards. In other words there is some increased healing power from exercise, but when the motivation to exercise arises from a fearful or negative state of mind, there may be a greater net rise of destructive inner-body elements. The net effect could be greater damage. However, the combination of exercise, positive state of mind, and other Life Ecology Factors can be a powerful health and healing tool that is available to you at all times.

When Life Ecology Factors Work Together…

Thus far we have looked at individual Life Ecology Factors, including: state of mind, strength of relationships, diet, and exercise. If you look at the Life Ecology Factors working together, however, the Life Ecology Factors model is even more compelling. Studies of religion and its impact on health outcomes likely represent a combined effect of multiple Life Ecology Factors.

Religious people, on average, live ten years longer than nonreligious people. Jeff Levin has written a wonderful summary regarding the religion effect on health outcomes in a book called *God, Faith and Health*. There are several *hundred* studies to validate the powerful health impact of being religious including an improvement in cancer, heart disease, and hypertension rates.

Again, as with the relationship studies, it is impossible to perform randomized controlled trials of religious activity. The next most powerful scientific analysis tool the medical community possesses is the prospective cohort study. This powerful scientific tool has been the basis for understanding the religion effect on health outcomes.

The positive health power of being religious is validated for multiple reasons. The connection between religiosity and positive health outcomes has been confirmed in multiple studies. Multiple disease categories are improved including cancer and heart disease which fits with the dam analogy. There is a dose-response relationship, meaning the more religious a person is, the bigger the health effect. All major medical confounding factors including access to healthcare and health behaviors are measured and equivalent between the religious and nonreligious. The Life Ecology confounding factors are not relevant because the recommendation of this book is to enhance the Life Ecology Factors collectively. Assessment bias is countered by the fact that the same results have been produced in numerous studies. Finally, selection bias is a non-factor since these studies analyze large population groups rather than subjects individually chosen.

The religion factor is likely a collection of multiple Life Ecology Factors working together including positive state of mind, stronger relationships, and an encouragement of healthy behavior. Regardless, there is no factor as powerful as religiousness in impacting life expectancy. Earlier, we described strength of relationships as the top predictor of longevity. To be clear, relationships are the most powerful *individual* life ecology factor. Being religious undoubtedly includes the relationship factor as well as other Life Ecology Factors. Thus, religiousness is the most powerful example of *multiple or combined* Life Ecology Factors in action.

Another important collection of evidence of Life Ecology Factors working together are long-living communities. The Okinawan experience is particularly illuminating as this is the largest group of centenarians (those living to one hundred years of age) in the world. Okinawa is a collection of Japanese islands whose inhabitants have been extensively studied to understand why they have such unusually long lives. What are the factors that cause this group to live longer?

This group of individuals has several lifestyles that are different from other shorter lifespan communities. Among the differences are spiritual practices, low calorie/high vegetable diets, community-support institutions, regular exercise including tai-chi and gardening, outdoor lifestyles, and resilient attitudes. In fact, when their next generation assimilates a western-style lifestyle, their life expectancy plunges by 18 years on average! Again, there is that double digit impact on life expectancy as a result of Life Ecology Factors!

The Okinawans represent the perfect natural experiment proving that life ecology variables are the force behind health and healing. First, they possess multiple individual Life Ecology Factors that have been demonstrated to be powerful predictors of reduced disease and increased longevity. Second, they have unusually greater average life expectancy. When their members reduce their Life Ecology Factors by becoming more westernized, their life expectancy drops significantly. Finally, when outside populations, such as the Japanese, have adopted the Okinawan lifestyle, their life expectancy has improved!

Let's look at another study of the aging. This will provide more evidence of the power of Life Ecology Factors. The Harvard Study of Adult Development is the longest study of aging in the United States and the results were recently published. Again, it showed that state of mind and other Life Ecology Factors predict not only how long you live but how well people aged. "How well people aged" includes happiness and level of functioning. This highlights another vital concept about Life Ecology Factors.

One can easily argue that quality of life is much more important than how long one lives. Life Ecology Factors are even *more* powerful than medical technology in impacting quality of life. Unfortunately, the medical community rarely measures its patients' quality of life and whether this is improving as a result of its treatments and tests. Life Ecology Factors would "blow away" medical technology based on its impact on health outcomes and quality of life combined!

Another important finding of the aforementioned Harvard study is that genetics were NOT the dominant factor in predicting length of life. In fact, genetic factors only represented 20% of the explanation of why people lived to a certain age. The power for health and healing is primarily in your hands not in your genes or in the hands of the healthcare system!

Now let's jump to another collection of evidence to indirectly validate the power of self healing. The phenomenon of so-called "miraculous" recovery from widespread or metastatic cancer is actually well documented. Another interesting book called *Spontaneous Remission* contains hundreds of examples of such cancer recoveries as documented in major medical journals. These are often cases that have been unresponsive to traditional medical treatment (such as chemotherapy), and then suddenly undergo remission. In these instances, there is no explanation for the recovery other than self healing and/or alternative medical approaches. Again, this makes the point that nothing compares to our own self-healing ability. To tie this phenomenon to our dam analogy, modern medicine cannot overcome multiple bricks coming out at the same but the body DOES have the ability to fix many aspects of the dam simultaneously and with great effectiveness.

Interestingly, whereas Life Ecology Factors such as state of mind, strength of relationships, and religiosity individually predict 7-10 years difference in length of life, traditional health behaviors or risk factors such as smoking and exercise have a surprisingly smaller impact on life expectancy. For example, experts estimate that cholesterol and blood pressure control have a 4 year impact on longevity. Smoking and exercise each appear to have a 3-year impact on life expectancy, which surprisingly pales by comparison to other Life Ecology Factors.

The <u>Scientific</u> Evidence Supporting Life Ecology Factors

Just to review, the science supporting the power of ecological factors is actually very strong. Large studies have been conducted over 30, 40, and even 50 year periods. Furthermore, these studies account for all the healthcare access and health behavior confounding factors we can anticipate. These Life Ecology Factors studies have been performed in diverse settings. The results affirming the impact of Life Ecology Factors have been reproduced in multiple separately performed studies. Whereas we criticized the Nurses' Health Study for being observational, there is a critical distinction between that observational study compared to many of the observational studies validating Life Ecology Factors.

The observational studies like the Nurse's Health Study were retrospective in nature. Retrospective means the investigators look backwards. This creates a few problems. First, the investigators depend on the patient's recall of whether and when they were receiving the factor (A), for example hormone replacement therapy or fruits and vegetables.

Secondly, the patient's current health status can color their answers. For example, the study participants might know that fruits and vegetables are good for them and if their health is good, they might report a higher intake than actually occurred. Further, the behavior or risk factor (A), is occurring at the same time as the health outcomes (B), so we are less certain that one caused the other.

In contrast, many of the Life Ecology Factors studies are prospective observations. This means the factor A was identified well ahead of time before any health outcomes (B) even developed. This type of study is more powerful at making accurate A causes B statements since it is easy to identify which element came first and therefore more likely to have been the true causative factor of the other. For example, if strength of relationships (A) went up first and mid-life illnesses (B) develop later on, it's easier to be correct about the statement, "A is causing B". Of course, we need to account for confounding factors by measuring as many patients as possible. We also should account for bias by confirming the results with similar studies.

Thinking back to the science triangle (and especially confounding factors), it's easier for Life Ecology Factors studies to account for confounding factors of health care behavior such as exercise, diet, socioeconomic level, and access to medical care. In contrast, medical technology studies do not account for the Life Ecology Factors confounding factors. This is in part because the medical community has not been held accountable to a high scientific discipline standard and it has only recently started to acknowledge the influence of these factors, let alone measure them.

Let's review several problems with the state of medical technology *science*. If the science is poor we do not truly know whether the medical technology is providing any benefit. Not proving true benefit is unacceptable given the risk of unleashing the "Dangers of Doing Too Much" *(Fig. 1.1)*. The first problem with the state of medical technology science is the lack of randomized controlled trials. A second problem is the lack of comparison to existing treatment options, which means medical technology is overvalued since it often does not prove relative benefit. A third problem is that medical technology does not prove net benefit because side effects are not adequately accounted for. A fourth problem is the lack of cost effectiveness analysis. This *is* especially important because wasted resources leads to worsened health. A fifth problem is a particular susceptibility of medical technology to the placebo effect and thus, medical technology is prone to receive too much credit. Ironically, the placebo effect is being caused by a Life Ecology Factor, state of mind! Speaking of the power of Life Ecology Factors, a sixth scientific problem with medical technology studies to this point is a lack of accounting for Life Ecology Factors as the real cause of better health outcomes in many instances.

People with strong Life Ecology Factors and better health behavior are also more likely to pursue more technological approaches to improve their health odds. This is the problem that occurred with the hormone (HRT) study confusion. Recall that, within the HRT confusion, high Life Ecology Factors patients likely caused decreased heart disease related death and took the medication making it look like the medication was reducing heart disease. It was not the medication that was reducing coronary artery disease death *as scientific discipline proved* but rather the patients themselves.

Thus, from a scientific perspective, medical technology studies are often highly confounded and therefore unscientific. In contrast, LEF studies are impressively scientific! They utilize prospective cohort studies, contain large sample sizes, avoid selection bias, account for key confounding factors, and conduct multiple similar studies to confirm their results. Furthermore, there is extensive evidence that Life Ecology Factors improve multiple inner-body elements that, in turn, predict a reduction of both disease and premature death.

How ironic that the so-called "soft sciences" of psychology and spirituality have better health outcomes science than the "sophisticated" arena of medical technology! As we have stated, there is a big difference between technologic and scientific advancement. Furthermore, technologic advancement without scientific discipline in respect to health outcomes has contributed to the highly ineffective American healthcare system we see today.

With a grasp of scientific thinking, an understanding of how scientifically undisciplined modern medicine is, and an understanding of how under utilized Life Ecology Factors are, it should make sense that coronary interventions could have easily been a net *negative* in the case of Dad's story. Don't you feel your HQ rising?

Now, it should be more clear how lifestyle interventions such as Dr. Ornish's could produce such positive coronary artery disease results. To further reinforce the power of Life Ecology Factors in the cardiac arena, investigators recently demonstrated an ability to reduce cholesterol levels through dietary modifications just as well as anti-cholesterol medications.

As we have asked before, what in the current healthcare fee-for-service model would encourage the adoption of lifestyle interventions as well as a more scientifically disciplined approach to medical technology? The excitement for and financial reward of medical technology makes it even more difficult to shift to ecology centered care with medical technology applied in an *intelligent* manner. Now you, with a rising HQ, can challenge the healthcare system to function with a higher HQ.

Thinking Tool—Primary Care and Alternative Medicine as Vehicles for Life Ecology Factors and Self-Healing

In Chapter 2, we provided you evidence that the availability of primary care is a predictor of a community's health status. In stark contrast, access to specialist care does not reveal the same positive outcomes. There are several likely explanations for the primary care effect.

One powerful explanation for the primary care effect is that a relationship with your primary care provider allows for trust. Trust encourages more open communication, which then facilitates a more accurate diagnosis of medical problems. Trust also enhances compliance with scientifically validated medical treatment. Finally, and, most importantly, trust enhances the motivation of patients to improve their health behaviors and Life Ecology Factors. We now know that Life Ecology Factors and health behaviors have the most profound effects on preventing disease and premature death. Remember, it's better to keep the dam in ship-shape form rather than trying to patch it after it starts leaking.

We can take the argument regarding the power of primary care and apply it to alternative medicine practitioners as well. The medical community ridicules alternative medicine under the guise that they have not been scientifically demonstrated to improve health. Talk about the pot calling the kettle black! How ironic that modern medicine *itself* has little scientific basis for maintaining this self-righteous position. Even more ironic, is that alternative medicine undoubtedly works through Life Ecology Factors which *are* scientifically validated!

We've already provided you extensive evidence that the scientific foundation for healthcare decision-making in modern, and especially American, medicine is extremely weak. Worse yet, even when there are occasional randomized controlled trials for medical technology, they are often biased or utilize weak comparisons. Weak or false science is even worse than no science because the health benefit of the medical technology is overestimated, and society let's its guard down because experts present their finds with undue certainty. On top of that, there are virtually no cost benefit analyses. In other words, the medical community is not asking if the health benefit is coming at a steep price. The risk of technology at a steep price is that it may prevent the medical community from employing one or more other treatment options that might have worked as well or better and cost less thus better utilizing resources.

Alternative medicine should have a substantial place at the healthcare table for multiple reasons. First, modern medicine is often a gamble because of the poor scientific discipline behind it. Second, alternative medicine is harnessing our own self healing power by directly and indirectly tapping in to the Life Ecology Factors. Alternative medicine is often based on a principle of facilitating self healing rather than being the cure, unlike modern medicine. Alternative medicine is much less expensive and produces fewer side effects compared to technology and interventional, based care. Certainly, alternative medicine probably has a powerful placebo effect similar to modern interventions, but at a much lower physical and financial cost.

Summary of Root Cause #2

As we discussed earlier, there is a clear correlation between various inner-body elements in excess and the development of disease. Furthermore, there is clear causal connection between an improvement in Life Ecology Factors and a reduction in those excess inner-body elements. It makes perfect sense that Life Ecology Factors have a powerful effect on reducing the development of disease and premature death because of their dramatic impact on excess inner-body elements. Therefore, it also makes sense that Life Ecology Factors should be the primary focus of intelligent healthcare systems, especially given the relatively minor impact of medical technology. The relatively minor impact of medical technology is made worse by its unintelligent use per Root Cause #1.

Thus far in our *Modern Medicine is Killing You* story, patients are suffering doubly at the hands of modern medicine.

First, we are stumbling on broken ladders as the medical community utilizes medical technology in an unintelligent manner that unleashes the "Dangers of Doing Too Much". There is no doubt that this negatively impacts peoples' life expectancy as the evidence demonstrates, hence the "Killing You" idea. Second, we are distracted away from the correct wall for health and healing, self healing through Life Ecology Factors. All of the Life Ecology Factors and healthy behavior together are so much more powerful than technology in effecting your health outcomes that life expectancy is also lower than it needs to be because we are climbing the wrong wall. Thus, Root Cause #2 (medical technology is the focus of modern medicine but has much less impact than Life Ecology Factors) represents another part of the healthcare system that is "Killing You" though not directly as with Root Cause #1 (medical technology is utilized quite unscientifically and therefore dangerously). Root Causes #1 and 2 make it clear that we need a revolution in our construction of healthcare delivery systems.

The only way to place Life Ecology Factors at the center of the healthcare delivery system is to establish the correct accountability and incentives for total health outcomes. The easiest, highest impact incentive to motivate a more ecological approach to health and healing is to establish a different reward model for healthcare providers rather than the currently predominant fee-for-service model. Innovative healthcare systems should be rewarded with better profit margins as they creatively harness their patient's Life Ecology Factors which, in turn, cause an improvement in average health outcomes including less demand on resources. Furthermore, the healthcare system will benefit from the positive attention of its patients' better health outcomes per our proposed accountability system. People will flock to the more effective healthcare systems as a result of their better health outcomes, which will drive up revenue. Profit will further rise due to the increased revenue in addition to better profit margins. There *should* be a reward for innovation or else innovation for the betterment of all will dwindle. There is currently NO INCENTIVE for healthcare systems to produce the best outcomes for the lowest cost! Profit should depend on your health being better, not the number of treatments and tests you are subjected to!

The fundamental problem is that accountability and incentives are not in place to encourage the best healthcare system performance possible. With health outcomes transparency, health outcomes science, and a reimbursement model that will encourage an innovate blend of ecology and technology, we can enjoy the fruits of automatically improving healthcare systems.

Our vision for the future of medical research includes a large shift towards Life Ecology Factors improvement studies. This will include a measurement of the corresponding improvement in health outcomes. For example, what health benefit is produced by an intervention that coaches patients on relationships or state of mind?

Life Ecology Factors, which empower self-healing, are the key to how long we live as well as how well we heal. Life Ecology Factors are the gifts that keep giving because they also improve happiness and quality of life! You just received the biggest HQ boost in the book. The beauty of Life Ecology Factors and self healing is that you can start working on these right now! The Life Ecology Factors evidence makes it clear that the keys to health and healing are in your control. It is madness to depend on the healthcare system to keep you healthy. Let's wrap things up with a couple more HQ boosts and then you'll be ready to really flex your muscle in designing your own health and healing program as well forcing the healthcare system to serve you better.

Part III

ROOT CAUSE #3 :
MODERN MEDICINE IS HARMFUL

Chapter Five

The Problems of Complexity, Errors, and Waste

It was bad enough that you were using a broken ladder, but even worse that you had the ladder up against the wrong wall. Unfortunately, there is still one more problem. It turns out that there is someone slashing at the rungs of the ladder below you which obviously increases your risk of falling and getting further away from goal of better health. Even *if* you place the ladder up against the proper wall, a broken and further deteriorating ladder will prevent you from the paradise of health and healing.

It's time to receive one more HQ boost as you learn to protect yourself from a system that is so complicated and wasteful that it harms you in multiple ways.

The healthcare system has become quite complex and wasteful as a result of the unintelligent use of medical technology as well as an explosion in administrative bureaucracy. The problem with complexity and waste is that several types of errors result. Errors and waste may directly and indirectly make you sicker and poorer.

After completing my training as a medical scientist, I was offered an opportunity to be the director of a medical department. Specifically, I ran an anesthesiology department in the arena of high risk obstetrics. This is a setting where mothers with various diseases are also delivering their babies. Being pregnant and delivering a baby can be very risky for these moms as these stages can worsen or create problems such as heart failure or deadly bleeding. This experience allowed me to experience the incredibly complex organizations that run healthcare. I was involved with matters such as interpersonal conflicts, patient service improvement projects, quality assessment programs, unit staffing, and a barrage of insurance and regulatory paperwork that grew year by year. I was also witness to the kind of technological waste explained by Root Cause #1 as well as the complexity, waste, and errors that we will present to you in this chapter with Root Cause #3. I was provided the opportunity to manage another unit simultaneously. Eventually, I helped build a medical department from scratch within a large medical system. This latter experience provided me an even deeper experience of healthcare system bureaucracy including the complexities of human resources, reimbursement matters, and even more regulatory hoop jumping. These were all eye opening experiences that led to the development of the Root Cause #3 idea.

What happens when the medical community just keeps doing and doing and doing things "for our patients"? The logical result is the "Dangers of Doing Too Much" in Figure 1 of Chapter 1. We have already discussed several of these dangers in the previous chapters including medical technology doing more harm than good and distracting ourselves from the power of Life Ecology Factors respectively. Direct harm is easier to see but, the other, indirect harm is much harder to notice. Difficulty in noticing poor performance also applies to the problems of Root Cause #3 which we will describe in this chapter. The inability of the individual to detect a *causal connection* between modern medicine and unnecessarily negative outcomes was the motivation for our title *Modern Medicine Is Killing You*.

Root Cause #3 encompasses the problems stemming from systems that are complex and wasteful. Complexity leads to many harmful and deadly errors and waste leads to a host of additional problems. Specifically, wasting resources blocks the medical community from employing technology that *is* valuable for health outcomes. Wasting resources also blocks the medical community from utilizing valuable non-technologic medical care options, and blocks it from exploring innovative educational/coaching programs that would improve patients' health behavior and Life Ecology Factors. In addition, wasting resources causes finan-cial strain and stress that has become devastating in the United States. Finally, the risk of financial devastation forces employees to stay in their current positions even though they might be much more produc-tive in another role. All of society suffers when people are not being as creative as they are capable of. This represents lost productivity for society, an even more subtle cost of a broken healthcare system.

Next we will provide the evidence for Root Cause #3. In the conclud-ing section of the book we will summarize the Three Root Causes and briefly describe how the entire mess called modern medicine was allowed to develop over the past 50 years. The first collection of Root Cause #3 evidence has to do with direct errors caused by modern medicine.

The Problem of Healthcare System Errors

Ten years ago, a famous study was published in one of the most impor-tant medical journals available, the Journal of the American Medical Association (JAMA). This study measured the incidence of hospital-based adverse drug events in the United States. Adverse drug events means patient injury or death resulting from a medication they received from the healthcare system. This study was followed up by a critical confirmatory analysis by the Institute of Medicine (IOM). The IOM is the most prestigious group of health care thinkers in the United States including scientists, intellectuals, captains of industry, and physicians. The JAMA study concluded that the American healthcare system pro-duced <u>100,000</u> deaths <u>every year</u> through adverse drug events (ADEs) as well as two million non-deadly injuries. ADEs mean mistakes with the delivery of medications to patients. This figure doesn't even take into account unreported errors. In fact, there are some experts who are estimating that there are as many as 200,000 deaths a year. The Institute for Healthcare Improvement (IHI), an organization developed by the healthcare reform pioneer Don Berwick, estimates that the actual in-jury rate in hospitals is 15 million per year versus the 2 million per year referenced earlier. The IHI analysis was a more thorough hospital chart analysis and therefore more accurate. Since the 15 million injuries figure is seven times greater than the 2 million injury figure presented by JAMA, is it possible that the death figure from ADEs are 700,000 per year?! The exact figure does not matter, it's a massive number of harmed patients no matter what!

The IOM followed up the JAMA study by systematically analyzing the American healthcare system and concluded with its famous work *To Err is Human*. The title tells it all. Obviously, adverse drug reactions represent another big hit on the quality of healthcare being delivered. It certainly doesn't help that the average American over the age of 65 is receiving more than eight different medications by some estimates! Are these being prescribed scientifically? Are these interacting with each other? Sometimes a patient will have multiple healthcare providers who are prescribing medications without any coordination.

Think back to Chapter 3 and our summary of the American healthcare system. Many people know that the American healthcare system is the most expensive in the world, but the vast majority of people have no sense of the failures of the system on the quality side of the equation. In Chapter 3 we provided evidence at the international level regarding an American system that produces poor life expectancy and poor infant mortality. We also went deeper and produced evidence of poor *access* to healthcare which could partially explain worse life expectancy. Another strong collection of evidence was from Dartmouth Medical School including the work of Dr. Fisher that we described in Chapter 3. Their work led to an ironic finding, the higher the spending, the *worse* the health outcomes! The evidence in this chapter, including the aforementioned ADEs, as well as the ""Dangers of Doing Too Much" list will help explain how it is possible to produce this higher spending/worse outcomes conundrum. The conclusion we must reach is that complete healthcare system reform is a must or we risk ongoing physical and financial damage at the hands of modern medicine.

Yet another category of healthcare system errors are medical injuries. An example of a medical injury would be a disoriented patient falling from bed while being cared for in the hospital which subsequently launched a series of problems that lead to death. Medical injury includes any harm caused to patients while in the hospital including wrong-site surgery or leaving an instrument inside you during a surgery. By some estimates there are some 30,000 deaths a year related to medical injuries. Another category of healthcare system errors is ADEs in the outpatient setting totaling some 40,000 deaths a year in addition to the 100,000 deaths from ADEs in the inpatient setting. We can keep going with this parade of death. Hospital acquired infectious disease represents another 100,000 deaths per year analogous in scale to inpatient ADEs. What's amazing is that the simple act of hand washing is still considered the best solution to the infectious disease problem.

The power of hand washing in reducing infections was discovered by Dr. Ignac Semmelweis in 1847. This discovery eventually had a profound effect in reducing infectious disease in the end of the 19th and beginning of the 20th centuries. Guess what the estimate is for hand washing rates within hospitals? Amazingly, we fail to fully implement *this* "technology" but go right on discovering and employing many more exciting and more expensive medical technologies with questionable benefit. What about applying the powerful knowledge that we already have? The answer, by the way, is that the medical community is still at a 50% rate for washing hands! That means that a doctor or nurse washes their hands only 50% of the time after touching someone else who may possess deadly germs. Knowing the sad end to Dad's coronary intervention fiasco, doesn't the prospect of hospital induced deaths make you mad? Can you understand why Americans can experience worse overall health outcomes despite spending two to three times more than any other wealthy nation? This sad knowledge adds to your HQ and your confidence to challenge the healthcare system at every step.

All these hospital acquired deaths are perfect examples of the vicious combination of system complexity causing the medical community to drop the ball as well as poor accountability for poor performance.

So far in the Root Cause #3 journey we have at least 300,000 *reported* deaths per year caused by the American healthcare system! Undoubtedly the figure crosses the half *million* mark in reality. Guess what? *American healthcare system related deaths approach the levels of heart disease and cancer related deaths at approximately half a million deaths per year*!

The Problems of Healthcare System Waste

We hope it is even more clear to you how Americans can suffer some of the worst bottom line healthcare results of any developed nation. Root Cause #3 does not stop there. Thus far we have only touched upon the harm that arises from the complexity and errors part of the Root Cause #3 equation. What about waste and the harm it can produce?

Our current financial crisis makes us more aware than ever that we have limited resources. From a health perspective, there are multiple "Dangers of Doing Too Much" if the medical community wastes resources. If the medical community squanders our healthcare dollars, <u>we</u> have got to pay a health outcomes price. Given that we have limited resources, using up resources on medical care that has no or a negative impact of health outcomes also results in the medical community not utilizing multiple valuable categories of healthcare interventions such as technologic, non-technologic, Life Ecology Factors, and health behaviors. This represent indirect harm compared to errors, but harm nonetheless. Let's look at a couple examples of this price.

One study followed 18,000 patients over 2 years and analyzed their specific medical care. The investigators discovered that the medical community was not providing <u>FIFTY PERCENT</u> of the preventative, acute, and chronic care that best practice guidelines recommended! This study appeared in the New England Journal of Medicine, another of the most prestigious medical journals in the world which only accepts the highest quality of analyses. There is a price for wasting resources as per Root Cause #1; it means a lack of resources for the medical community to do the things that should be done. The same study calculated that patients received a paltry 15-30 minutes per year with their healthcare providers compared to the recommended six hours!

Studies demonstrate a correlation between nurse to patient ratios and death rates. The more patients a nurse must take care of, the higher the patient death rate. Given what you have learned in Root Cause #3 about healthcare system errors, this makes sense. An interesting question is, "Why are we getting to the point of straining our nurses (and sadly their patients) to the point that we even know this threshold of death?!" The nurses are getting beat up by the system because we're trying to extract more and more productivity out of them. In fact, California was the first state to legislate a minimum required nurse-to-patient ratio. Problems with too many patients per nurse would certainly be less likely if the medical community had the resources to hire more nurses instead of wasting money on unproven medical technology. We can extend this argument of inadequate resources for the human side of medical care as evidence points out that the length of nurses' work shifts also has an impact on death rates! We need more resources for the human part of the care, the care that really matters in the trenches, where there is the greatest risk of errors.

The IOM produced another extensive report called *"Crossing the Quality Chasm"*. *"Chasm"* refers to fact that the medical community has a long ways to go in producing the best healthcare quality possible *based on the scientific evidence.* This is stark contrast to Root Cause #1 where too much care was being provided. The recent section of Root Cause #3 provided evidence that there are many instances when patients are *not* receiving the care they should! Again, too much of what patients do not need and too little of what they do need. What a mess! Specifically, IOM identified twenty key areas of care where improvements could be made. This IOM summary statement seals the deal for Root Cause #3, "The goal of this report is to break the cycle of inaction. The status quo is not acceptable, it cannot be tolerated any longer. It is simply unacceptable that patients can be harmed by the same system that is supposed to provide healing and coverage." Again, the IOM is a very smart group of people.

We can extend our "There's not enough care which means more harm than necessary" argument even further by including the tragedy of the uninsured in the United States. Just because we criticized modern medicine for being unintelligent (per Root Cause #1), does not mean it does nothing of value. As a practicing physician, I have witnessed the many things the medical community does do to improve health. The Institute of Medicine also analyzed the problem of having so many uninsured people in the United States. You see, the problem of the un-insured is *everyone's* problem and not simply because of moral reasons.

Certainly it would be the noble and compassionate thing to provide all our brothers and sisters with at least basic medical care. Guess what happens when the uninsured ignore their health? They receive care af-ter their dams are badly leaking. Now they start to fill up the emergency rooms and hospital beds when their problems could have been avoided in many instances. Guess who else is in the ER and hospital waiting for care? YOU! Guess who has a greater likelihood of delays or er-rors because of ER and hospital congestion as well as absorbed medi-cal resources since the uninsured are made to forgo basic care? YOU! Thankfully Americans are compassionate enough to insist that anyone showing up at the emergency room needing care gets it. The problem of denying basic care to millions in this country comes back to haunt even those with insurance because of Root Cause #3. We'll come back to the plight of the uninsured, first let's discuss one last cost of the broken American healthcare system.

Another negative by-product of the ineffective American health-care finance system is lost productivity. How sad is it when people are trapped in jobs they don't want to be in, in order to maintain health care coverage. This hurts all Americans when its citizens cannot manifest their work genius and creativity in the way they desire. This represents lost innovation for *everyone*. This represents lost joy and productivity for everyone.

More Sources of Waste-Bureaucracy

So far we have discussed many direct and indirect sources of medical harm as a result of modern medicine becoming unnecessarily complex and wasteful. Part of this waste was explained by Root Cause #1, the unintelligent utilization of medical technology. Root Cause #1 produces *direct* harm when unintelligent medical technology causes more harm than good. Root Cause #1 produces *indirect* harm by wasting resources and unleashing Root Cause #3. Root Cause #3 is harm, in part, produced by waste as health improvement opportunities are missed due to lack of attention from the healthcare providers. Healthcare provider attention is less available if there are inadequate resources to pay them. Sadly, the American healthcare system has another major source of *waste* besides Root Cause #1.

Guess what percent of healthcare expenditures go towards administrative costs for the average developed nation, as well as the United States specifically? As you ponder that question, think about the following perspective. Americans cringe with fear at the prospect of going the route of socialized medicine like the Canadians or the Europeans as a whole. Why do they fear socialism? They feel it will slow down innovation as the system becomes a bureaucratic tangled mess. They say, "Government can't do anything right!" Most Americans do not realize that <u>half</u> of their citizens receive government led healthcare and the majority of these recipients are satisfied with their plan! Americans also cannot point to any evidence that private healthcare does any better in the departments of cost, quality, or both (value) combined compared to government based programs such as Medicare, Medicaid, or the Veterans Affairs Hospitals! *Again*, we are not advocating a nationalized program but we are saying the marketplace for healthcare must be made to function MUCH better in order to justify a market-based approach. Please stop saying, "Government can't get it right" because governments around the world are doing much better than the current "free market" American healthcare system. As we will point out, the key is the development of a *functional* market not free market.

Do you remember our question? What percent of healthcare costs are absorbed by administrative activities? Stunningly, the figure is 10% for the average wealthy nation, (most of them "socialized" or government driven systems), and **30%** for the United States! This book will recommend market based strategies, but the real boogieman in your healthcare closet is a dysfunctional marketplace not government! Let's put the 20% difference in administrative spending in perspective. Given the American healthcare economy is 2.4 *trillion dollars* per year, 20% extra spending represents a staggering 500 billion dollars of waste *every year*. To put *this* in perspective, we can eliminate the problem of the uninsured for a mere 200 billion dollars and still give every single person in the United States a thousand dollars *every year!* This does not even address the concept that 30% of American healthcare spending is represented by non beneficial medical technology/interventions!

So 30% of the American healthcare dollar is spent on things that do not contribute to patient health outcomes. This represents remarkable waste. With your Root Cause #3 HQ boost, you now know that waste translates into worsened health outcomes because of many different categories of missed healthcare opportunity. This can certainly help explain the American healthcare paradox of highest spending and worst outcomes among the wealthiest nations. Furthermore, waste adds to financial strain which is no longer tolerable given the other sources of strain in the worldwide economy.

Where does this waste emanate from? The source is a combination of insurance payment and hospital regulation related bureaucracies. The insurance companies and healthcare system battle with each other for their piece of the healthcare financial pie. Both sides have built armies of individuals to confirm that payment is due (or not due) and the complexity of the billing process is mind-blowing. At the same time, society has been uncovering one problem after another with the performance of the healthcare system ever since the famous "To Err is Human" report by the IOM. As a result, one piece of legislation and regulatory mandate after another is levied upon the healthcare system. This takes up time and money. The question is, "Is the net effect of regulation better health outcomes?" We do not know! Let's discuss several problems with *regulating* the medical community into better performance.

First, there is a tendency for healthcare systems to perform to the level of the test instead of building systems for continuous self-improvement. The latter awareness comes from personal experience. Having worked in several large healthcare systems, it is frustrating to see how much time and effort goes in to pleasing the regulators rather than building systems and teams that hold themselves accountable for excellence in health outcomes and efficiency. When the regulators are coming, everyone scurries about knowing what needs to be done to please them, but when the cat's away, the mice are back to play. As soon as the regulators leave, there is little incentive to improve the system. In the next section we will describe our suggestions for intelligent accountability and incentives so there IS a constant drive to improve the healthcare system.

Another problem with regulating the medical community to better performance is reflected in the cliché, "You can drag a horse to water, but you can't make him drink". When the ideas for improvement do not derive from within, people simply do not put their heart and soul into it. Instead, if the incentives are properly established, people will launch into virtuous cycles of *continuous* improvement, *not* just improvement when there is a test that needs to be crammed for.

Yet one more problem with achieving bold improvement is the nature of large bureaucracies. Again, it is ironic that we fear government bureaucracy running healthcare when the American healthcare system already has an unparalleled bureaucracy of its own! We again speak from experience, bureaucracies tend to be conservative and resist risky change. The vast majority of the American healthcare system is non-profit. As long as the system is on budget there is no need to take on more risk than necessary, even if it means better health outcomes, better service, and lower cost! The lack of profit motive slows the bureaucracy down. When there is a lack of accountability for business efficiency, it is very easy for the bureaucrats to say, "Leave me alone, I know what I'm doing, please do not tell me how to do my job." There is a tendency for people within bureaucracies to be very territorial for fear of accountability including being exposed for doing a less than ideal job. There is not much flow of ideas and creativity and much less entrepreneurship, meaning intelligent risk taking to produce better results for people. Furthermore, the bureaucrats keep pushing one new program after another to prove that they are being good leaders and workers. Unfortunately, there is typically little accountability for "closing the deal" on these ideas. Again, I have experienced the frustrations of trying to introduce new ideas only to be pushed off because of the latest regulatory or system mandates that first "must" be attended to.

An explosion in bureaucracy to combat ineffectiveness cannot work. I can tell you from personal experience that it's quite frustrating getting anything done in a large bureaucratic healthcare organization. My experiences have included building a medical department and trying to get many medical providers through the credentialing maze; trying to get people to work well together in the care environment; trying to get providers to serve their patients with greater kindness and consideration; trying to get the department to produce better outcomes and avoid bad outcomes like infectious disease; trying to eliminate waste whether that be technology that's used inappropriately or a care delivery process that's too complicated and prone to mistakes and inefficient flow. These experiences have shown that *things move excruciatingly slowly in healthcare systems.* This is one of our many motivations in putting this book together.

Can you imagine how many layers of bureaucracy have built up within the American healthcare system given the lack of proper accountability and incentives? How fixed people must be in their ways after literally *decades* of not being held accountable for how they serve patients , how they spend money, how efficiently they deliver care, what kind of health benefits are actually being produced, and what errors are developing?

It is human nature for people to resist change. They *especially* don't like change when they've had it so good for so long. How do you expect to get the medical community to work better without a significant shock to the system? My experience with the tremendous resistance of people inside the system tells me we must make a dramatic change in people's thinking AND the reward system so that we can not only lower the system's resistance to change, but also get people in the system excited about change because of the improvements they can produce.

Sadly, the current American healthcare reform debate is misguided. It's fine to provide insurance coverage for all citizens but this is where the debate and reform proposals go off the rails. People are at war in town hall meetings because they do not want to be saddled with even more government debt and taxes. One of our goals with this book is to point out that there is already so much waste and inefficiency in the system *NOW* that American citizens should have NO fear of <u>comprehensive</u> reform. Remember the government bureaucracy boogieman Americans fear lurking in their closet? He's already in the room, just turn around!

In the next section we will put together the Three Root Causes of poorly functioning healthcare systems. We will tie these back to the American healthcare system specifically as an example of the Three Root Causes in extreme, resulting in the worst healthcare system in the world. We will then get down to the basics of accountability and incentives in order to explain how this mess developed and how we can work out of it.

Part IV

PUTTING IT ALL TOGETHER

Chapter Six

The Problems Created by Poor Accountability and Incentives

Recap of the Three Root Causes

Earlier, we presented the symptoms and disease analogy to represent the problems of modern medicine. Most healthcare reform books and proposals stay at the level of diagnosing the symptoms of an ineffective healthcare system. These symptoms include inadequate insurance coverage, high costs, and poor quality of care. Few (if any) authors have completely dealt with the cause of these symptoms: the disease itself. If we do not address this underlying disease, the symptoms will return and potentially worsen.

The previous chapters have built the case for the Three Root Causes of poor healthcare system performance. Root Cause #1 states that modern medicine is *unintelligent* due to poor scientific discipline. Root Cause #2 states that modern medicine is *overrated* because medical technology's impact on health outcomes is less than people realize and, worse, the hope projected upon modern medicine distracts us from the power of self healing through Life Ecology Factors. Finally, Root Cause #3 states that modern medicine is *harmful* because it is complex and wasteful which can result in errors and missed opportunities that directly and indirectly hurt people. These Three Root Causes are the actual disease that has been overlooked in almost all healthcare reform discussions. American healthcare has descended the farthest in allowing the Three Root Causes to grow, and thus achieved the dubious distinction of having the most expensive AND least effective system amongst the thirty wealthiest nations.

The American Healthcare and Financial System Crises

The correlation between the American healthcare crisis and the recent financial crisis is both interesting and exasperating. In the financial system we had a tool or technology that got ahead of us and caused a lot of damage. When we say "got ahead of us" we mean society did not fully comprehend the benefits versus the risks of the new technology.

In this case, the primary trouble making technology was securitization. Securitization is a method for sharing risk when an investment might be too expensive or risky for an individual. A group of people invest money, receive a stock certificate as proof of their ownership percentage, and the money adds up to an amount large enough to make an investment an individual could not normally afford on their own. The idea of sharing risk is a reasonable concept and has been the underpinning of western civilization for the past 600 years. For example, it is too risky for an individual to build an airplane, fund a mass-production automobile company, or launch an oil and gas exploration enterprise. Short of government investment, these large-scale and risky discoveries and products would not come to market without the technology of securitization.

Any technology, though, can become too complex and exceed our ability to fully determine the *net and relative* benefit. Remember those terms from Chapters 2 and 3? We must ask if the benefits of the new technology exceed the side effects after comparing it to technology that's already available.

If we can't measure a technology's total benefit AND risk for *society*, then we've got a potential problem; we could be overpaying and/or taking on too much risk. In the case of the recent financial crisis, the technology that got us in trouble was the securitization of home mortgages. Given the size of the recent mortgage securities and their rapid trading, we surrendered our ability to understand the true value of the technology.

We now know the rest of the story. The securitization technology got out of control. Americans didn't realize how much risk they were taking on and a severe economic crisis resulted. People with poor credit bought homes, real estate values were artificially inflated, and people spent beyond their means as they overestimated their financial worth in part due to inflated home values. Increased spending made companies feel that the good times would keep on rolling, so they themselves expanded somewhat recklessly. Jobs were plentiful, which gave people even more confidence to spend. The economy was artificially pumped up due to excess spending which artificially increased profits which artificially inflated the stock market which further induced a feeling of high financial worth. The cycle kept recurring.

Eventually, the music stopped and people began realizing that home and stock prices were too high; they started running the other way. A lot of people were hurt by excess credit. They saved very little due to a false sense of their net worth. Now, people suffer as home values have plunged below purchase prices and have left them with debt and bankruptcies. Job losses have piled up. The stock market and therefore people's pensions have also suffered. All these factors have combined to create levels of economic and psychological stress that we have not experienced since the Great Depression. This is the problem with using technology without having the discipline to fully understand its implications or without having the proper checks and balances to detect problems when they start to develop.

This is basically how the financial disaster has unfolded. We had a sophisticated financial technology that exceeded our ability to understand the true benefits and risks. Furthermore, the system that was supposed to measure the benefit and risk of this large scale securitization failed.

You can certainly see the analogies between the financial crisis and the healthcare system mess. Root Cause #1 is about the unintelligent use of medical technology which is similar to large-scale mortgage securitization. We were excited about the prospects of the technology but did not have the discipline to confirm that the benefit actually justified the costs, especially over the long-term. Per Root Cause #2 (Modern Medicine is Overrated) we must ensure that we are using the most value-oriented technology available to us. In the financial case, we could have utilized a modified and thus safer version of securitization. Finally, as per Root Cause #3 (Modern Medicine is Harmful), the system became so complex that it was hard to notice errors. In the case of securitization, the error was allowing people with poor credit to purchase homes they could not continue to afford, and financial institutions placed too many risky loans on their books which ultimately caused a severe crisis in confidence. In the case of the healthcare system, the lack of transparency means errors such as adverse drug events, medical injuries, hospital-acquired infectious disease, and missed opportunities for valuable healthcare interventions.

So How in the World Did We Allow this Healthcare System Mess to Develop?

As a result of my interest in healthcare leadership, I started taking many business courses. It soon became apparent that not only had the medical community not structured its medical thinking scientifically (per Root Causes 1 and 2), but the United States had failed to structure its healthcare system in an intelligent manner including the correct accountability and incentives to motivate improving outcomes. Many other areas of the economy *have* employed effective accountability and incentives leading to increasing value for consumers. The healthcare marketplace was not set up so that healthcare providers and systems would compete to out-innovate each other in improving healthcare value.

Thinking Tool—The Importance of Accountability and Incentives

Now we are going to go even deeper into the modern medical mess by explaining how the Three Root Causes *themselves* were allowed. Let's delve into the basics of human nature. Many expect the profession of medicine to function in a noble manner. This is unrealistic as long as humans run the system. The only way to motivate the healthcare system to optimally serve its people is to harness the keys to human motivation. People are generally driven by accountability and incentives. This book is a story about the problems that can arise from poor accountability and the wrong incentives.

In this discussion, accountability is defined as a measurement of performance and price and incentives are a reward for good performance or a penalty for poor performance. Before we examine these further, let's first take a little detour and talk about the meaning of "free market".

Thinking Tool—Functional Free Market Compared to Free-for-All Free Market

Another vital concept being overlooked in the healthcare reform debate is the meaning of **free market** as applied to healthcare. The United States is built on the idea that a free market is the key to a successful society. People will work hard because they can earn a reward. Consumers will benefit from innovation if businesses feel they will be financially rewarded for introducing valuable products to the marketplace.

We often hear the quip, "The free market has already been tried in healthcare and it hasn't worked." This is typically an attempt to justify more government based or single-payor approaches to healthcare. We argue, "Correct, free market has been attempted but this does not matter!" The real goal should be a *functional* free market, NOT the free-for-all free market American healthcare is currently trapped in. When we say "functional", we mean it works properly. What do we mean by the marketplace "works" properly and what are the keys to it working?

The promise of functional marketplaces is better selection of products and ever improving quality and prices. We can look at quality and price together and refer to this as value. In other words, if quality improves and the price stays the same, value has increased. If quality stays the same but the price is reduced, value, again, increases. The best increase in value is when both the quality improves AND price is reduced. Functional marketplaces consistently deliver better value as producers try and outdo each other to win or keep customers' business.

When does a free market function properly and thus deliver on its promise? Three key conditions must be present for automatic and continuous improvement in value to appear: <u>transparency in the price</u> being charged for the product, a <u>measure of the benefit</u> being delivered by the product, and an <u>ability and desire to switch who we purchase the product from</u>. This desire stems from an improvement in our lives when we switch who we purchase our product or service from. Of course, the *ability* to switch producers requires true choice. Choice includes enough options and minimal barriers to change who we purchase from.

These three conditions generate real competition which, in turn, motivates the producers to constantly improve the value they deliver to customers. Wonderfully, the value keeps improving without direct pressure from the consumers. Every once in a while, one of the competitors makes a discovery that significantly increases value by either substantially improving the benefit with a smaller increase in cost or producing the same benefit but in a much less costly manner. Either way, value takes a big jump and shakes up the industry. This is called "disruptive innovation".

If we can set up our marketplace properly, value keeps improving *by itself* because the producers are motivated to innovate in order to increase their customer base and improve profits. A functional marketplace can be a beautiful thing spurring much creativity in improving product quality and cost and making people's lives better.

Let's look at a small personal example of a functional market in action. There was a video store that I rented movies from quite frequently. Suddenly, they had a serious competitor who provided videos through the mail. Without my doing anything, the company that owned my store said, "Guess what, we will also send you movies through the mail, from a larger catalogue than the local store can maintain, and at the same price!" I said, "Cool! I'm not paying any more than I did before and now I get more benefits" Then, without any prompting, they provided another benefit with no change in cost, they eliminated late fees. This move was presumably to respond to the new competitor whose customers could hold on to their movies as long as they desired. I was now able to hold the movies much longer. This represented another improvement in benefit with the price staying unchanged, in other words, further improved value. This improved value just showed up. Then my store added <u>another</u> benefit. They said, "Not only can you obtain another movie from the store when you return the first movie, but, we will also send you one in the mail". So now I received even more benefit with no change in the cost! Finally, my video rental company started offering other movie plans for a lower cost but, of course, with less benefit. However, if I wasn't using all the benefits of the more expensive plan in the first place, the lower cost was great and I had just the benefits I wanted. Once again, this was an improvement in value! If you think about various product lines including cars, computers, appliances, and so on, you have undoubtedly noticed constantly improving quality and features with costs staying fixed or even dropping. This is the power of a true *functional* free market NOT a free-for-all market. In a free-for-all market, the lack of value transparency and/or poor ability of consumers to switch who they buy their goods and services from, blocks producers from the pressure to constantly improve their product. Consumers can get hurt due to excess cost and deteriorating quality.

Let's tie together accountability and incentives with the three requirements of a functional market. The first two keys to a functional market were transparency in outcomes and prices. These two conditions are the same as accountability for the healthcare system's delivery of value *(Fig. 6.1)*. In the case of healthcare, we have added another element of accountability not found in most marketplaces: scientific discipline *(Fig. 6.1)*. By now you understand why we must ensure an intelligent basis for a <u>particular</u> medical intervention given the "Dangers of Doing Too Much". Scientific discipline is accountability at the <u>individual</u> decision level whereas benefit and cost transparency is ac-

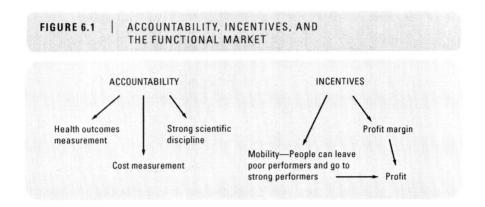

FIGURE 6.1 | ACCOUNTABILITY, INCENTIVES, AND THE FUNCTIONAL MARKET

ACCOUNTABILITY — Health outcomes measurement / Strong scientific discipline / Cost measurement

INCENTIVES — Profit margin / Mobility—People can leave poor performers and go to strong performers ⟶ Profit

countability <u>overall</u>. The latter includes the total outcome of *hundreds* of patient care steps.

Finally, there is the third requirement of a functional market, the desire and ability to change who we purchase our product or service from. We are calling this third requirement mobility. Mobility falls under the category of incentives since poorly functioning healthcare systems will be penalized by losing business and well functioning systems will be rewarded with more customers *(Fig. 6.1)*. Another incentive we can structure is better profit margins to motivate healthcare system efficiency and error reduction. There is nothing wrong with healthcare system profits as long as these are tied to improved customer value!

Intelligent incentives require accountability to judge value and the ability and desire to reward strong producers. Strong producers will not appear without profits. The desire to switch producers will not appear if consumers cannot benefit by more savings and/or better healthcare. Without intelligent incentives, Americans can count on more premature death at the hands of the Three Root Causes.

The Current State of American Healthcare System Accountability and Incentives

Let's explore the state of American healthcare system accountability and incentives to understand how the Three Root Causes themselves may have been allowed to develop. Guess how many of the three conditions of a *functional* free market have existed in American healthcare for the past 40-50 years? NONE! It is unfair to say that a free market approach has not worked in American healthcare because the United States has not introduced ANY of the conditions necessary for a functional or intelligent free market.

Until recently, Americans have not measured the performance of healthcare systems or healthcare providers! Some will argue that Americans have launched quality measurement and reward initiatives within the healthcare system. This is true, there have been some attempts to measure the quality of healthcare systems, but these efforts are thoroughly inadequate. Currently, quality is determined by whether the medical community is performing *some* of the things that best practice guidelines suggest. For example, the best practice guidelines might suggest that four interventions are important for a patient that gets admitted to the hospital for heart failure. If a hospital does all four things on a consistent basis, they will receive a top rating for "quality". Meanwhile, their patients often do not *stay* out of heart failure for very long and are right back to the hospital. Is this success? It is as far as quality is currently measured! *This will not suffice for health outcomes accountability on multiple levels.*

First, these quality initiatives typically do not get to the bottom line: how did the patient's health fare in terms of the primary problem that caused them to enter the healthcare system? Secondly, the positive and negative financial incentives from current quality programs are too small and, in effect, do not create an incentive for either good or poor outcomes. Investigators have recently expressed concern that despite the famous Institute of Medicine report, "To Err is Human", in

1999, there has been little progress in reducing system-related patient injury! Third, the healthcare *insurance* marketplace is not set up for consumers to freely switch their healthcare provider. For example, a family may want to change healthcare institutions if their quality seems below average. Typically, individuals and families suffer large out-of-network penalties for traveling out of their employer's network. Furthermore, there are no clear price AND health outcomes information to guide consumers in switching. Fourth, it is not good enough to do a few things properly when there are potentially hundreds of steps involved in helping a patient heal. Finally, how about preventing the patient from having to be treated in the hospital in the first place?!

We must measure bottom-line health outcomes. This will help identify and reward truly effective healthcare systems. Current quality initiatives must go *much* further and *much* faster. The second condition of a functional market, transparency of price, has certainly been absent *(Fig. 6.1)*.

Patients have not had the accountability tools to challenge the system. There has also been an absence of science to validate much of the medical community's healthcare recommendations per Root Cause #1 *(Fig. 6.1)*. In summary, there has been little health outcomes transparency, an absence of healthcare price transparency, little health outcomes science, and a lack of healthcare partnership to keep the system honest.

What about incentives? Positive incentives depend on performance measurement and mobility. Mobility means consumers can reward the better performing systems with their business. Currently, there is no accountability nor mobility to pressure the American healthcare system to continuously improve its healthcare value. Of course, value is the most important measure of a business' level of service to its customer. In other words, the American healthcare system is not setup to serve its patients in the best manner possible.

Choice, an aspect of mobility, has been eliminated by large healthcare purchasing agreements between employers and healthcare systems. These arrangements prevent employees from changing who they purchase healthcare services from because of heavy "out-of-network" charges. Choice has also been limited due to a poor ability of individuals to judge the value being delivered by healthcare systems. Furthermore, actual choice has been restricted by significant limitations on healthcare insurance companies selling their coverage across state lines due to anti-trust *exemptions* for this industry. Also, employees are not typically rewarded for being value conscious, which diminishes their <u>desire</u> to shop and create the consumer pressure that is so vital for a functional market. Finally, consumers are frozen in place due to the risk of denied coverage based on "preexisting conditions".

American consumers are caught in a "worst of all worlds" scenario as their costs are rising in the form of surging co-pays, deductibles, and premiums while not possessing proper mobility or value transparency to shop for the best healthcare quality for the best price. This is where free market or capitalism is at its worst; the absence of a *functional* market allows a free-for-all market to develop. In the worst case scenario, large monopolies develop which, in turn, become non-responsive and even abusive by charging exorbitant prices and delivering poor quality.

Again, it is ironic that Americans shudder at the prospect of government run healthcare fearing it will become a big bureaucracy that will lack the motivation to improve quality or price. American's worst fears have *already* happened, they just don't realize it! A poorly functioning or free-for-all healthcare market has produced a system that is destructive of value. The American healthcare system lacks the drive to constantly improve price and quality. To our conservative/Republican friends, (as well as much of the United States), you can't have it both ways; you can't complain about government involvement in healthcare but do very little to force the marketplace to function better. By the way, we ARE advocating a functional market set of solutions, *not* a government-based approach.

Interestingly, even the father of capitalism, Professor Adam Smith, did *not* believe in a *free* market. He stated that appropriate functioning of the market was dependent on checks and balances given the selfish nature of human beings. He developed the now-famous idea of the "invisible hand" which magically caused value to improve as the market functioned properly. He also insisted that government, the people, and the business class must keep a check on each other.

A market without self-disciplined participants and intelligent checks and balances is really a free-for-all market, hence the wild ride we have experienced over the past 30 years in the world of finance as well as the past 50 years in American healthcare. Americans should lobby for an *intelligent* or functional free market *not* the free-for-all market they currently possess. It does NOT *matter who pays for the healthcare*, whether it be consumers, government, or corporations, if the marketplace is not structured with the proper accountability and incentives. The result will be continued large-scale failure. The current healthcare reform debate focuses on who should be covered with healthcare insurance and who will pay but there is virtually NOTHING about making the marketplace work better to serve the people. This is why we have characterized the current healthcare reform debate in the American Congress as useless. There is no need to fear government-run healthcare given how destructive the free-for-all free market has been thus far. The United States can and must do much better to justify a market-based approach to healthcare.

The effectiveness of *functional* markets is the reason some analysts passionately advocate so-called "consumer driven healthcare". Analysts (and we the authors) anticipate the same virtuous cycle of constantly and self-improving value being delivered by healthcare systems IF there is enough consumer demand for value.

Let's get back to the foundation of accountability and incentives. Human nature is driven by accountability and incentives, plain and simple. Markets function better when they create effective accountability and incentives for the producers of goods and services. With effective accountability and incentives in place, producers stay on their toes and constantly improve their product. Improvements include lower prices through improved efficiency and/or better quality without an increase in price. American healthcare has been a marketplace disaster.

FIGURE 6.2 | WHERE THE VALUE LEAKS

Value decreases by health outcomes worsening and/or costs increasing.

Root Cause #1: Unscientific use of medical technology increases the cost and possibly worsens health outcomes.

Root Cause #2: An overemphasis on medical technology and ignorance of Life Ecology Factors causes health outcomes to be much worse than they need be.

Root Cause #3: System complexity and waste results in direct worsening of health outcomes through errors and indirect worsening of health outcomes because wasted resources cause missed care opportunities. Errors also cause more cost and wasted resources.

THE THREE ROOT CAUSES ATTACK VALUE FROM BOTH SIDES OF THE EQUATION, BENEFITS AND COSTS

This is astonishing since the United States is the ultimate example of functional markets in action!

Poor accountability and incentives for delivering the best health outcomes for the best price has caused the American healthcare system to produce some of the worst outcomes for the highest cost! When the accountability and incentives are set up poorly, value will leak from many locations. This results in higher prices and worse quality than necessary *(Fig. 6.2)*.

We just completed a discussion about the current state of accountability and one element of the incentive structure, mobility. What is the predominant motivation or incentive in the current American healthcare system? In other words, what determines where the money is going to flow? As we have mentioned several times in earlier chapters, it is fee-for-service. To refresh your memory, fee-for-service means that if the healthcare system performs an intervention, it gets paid. It's so simple and, yet, so wrong. If there isn't accountability to keep the system honest, what prevents the system from doing everything possible when it gets paid for doing so? Nothing! There is no accountability and the incentives are to do things, NOT produce healthier patients! <u>There should be no trust of the current American healthcare system because</u>

<u>there is neither accountability nor the reward for what truly matters, patients getting healed as quickly, safely, and efficiently as possible</u>!

Thinking Tool—The Perfect Storm of Lost Checks and Balances

So far we have Three Root Causes of ineffective healthcare systems that were allowed to grow like weeds because of poor accountability and incentives that currently exist in American healthcare. It is interesting to study how the United States, in particular, could have *allowed* such poor accountability and incentives. We will describe this as The Perfect Storm of Lost Checks and Balances *(Fig. 6.3)*.

The "perfect storm" of poor checks and balances has developed in the American healthcare system over the past 50 years. The first problem was the introduction of so-called "third party payment". Third party payment means someone other than the patient is paying for healthcare insurance and healthcare costs. During World War II, corporations increasingly provided coverage for healthcare costs. Up until then, only 3% of Americans even purchased healthcare insurance. World War II created inflation which forced the government to impose price and wage freezes. Creative corporations, desperate to attract and retain employees, looked to healthcare insurance as a tool to reward current and prospective employees. Businesses also convinced the American government to make these contributions tax deductible. The problem with third party payment is that people did not directly feel healthcare spending. Thus, the United States lost the major functional marketplace requirement of value consciousness. In the 1960's, the federal and state governments also became involved in healthcare coverage through the programs of Medicare and Medicaid. Progressively, even more individuals and families were relieved from the *direct* effect of healthcare costs while they paid indirectly via higher taxes and stagnant wages.

Why didn't the 3rd party payers *themselves* demand value from the healthcare system? Of course, the payers for healthcare (corporations, government, and healthcare insurance companies) would have demanded value *unless* there was an easier way out. There was! They simply passed the costs on in the form of higher premiums which, in turn, were paid through higher taxes and lower wages. The latter stemmed from business dollars going to benefits costs rather than income. Insurance companies take a percentage of total cost and thus *benefit* from prices going up! <u>Nobody</u> had an incentive to be value conscious. This produced an insane, uniquely American, market situation.

A second reason that the United States lost the drive to create a functional marketplace was its historic economic boom over the past 60 years. The United States became the dominant economic force in the world by getting through the two World Wars relatively unscathed, having an environment that supported business development, and experiencing an unprecedented explosion of productivity-enhancing technological advancement. The 3rd party payers passed on healthcare costs to society, which we were able to absorb because of plentiful resources. Again, accountability and intelligent incentives were pushed to the side.

A third reason for loosening checks and balances was modern society's complete belief in technology's benefits, ingrained over the past 500 years. Certainly society has experienced many wonderful scientific and technological advancements in the past couple hundred years such as the Internet, computers, communication devices, and transportation systems, so our faith in technology is understandable. Yet, an unchecked belief in anything is ultimately problematic as the American healthcare mess illustrates. Medical technology was assumed to be good until proven otherwise. This was a disastrous attitude without the scientific discipline to confirm technology's health outcomes value let alone harm. This is, in part, how society allowed Root Cause #1 to develop.

A fourth reason society did not demand accountability and incentives was due to the information explosion. The combination of technologic advancement and rising computer processing speed produced so much information that society in effect said, "Doc, you make the decision. I don't even want to think about it!" What patients often do not realize is that their healthcare provider is *also* overwhelmed with too much information, not to mention an absence of the *right* kind of information delivered to them *while* they are making decisions. An example of the right kind of information includes health outcomes research to establish best practices and confirm the value of proposed medical interventions. No wonder the Three Root Causes were allowed to develop in a system where there is no mechanism to consistently move healthcare providers in the right direction.

Thus far, we have described general reasons for Americans to not demand effective healthcare accountability and incentives. The fifth problem in this Perfect Storm of poor accountability and incentives is specifically related to incentives. Starting in the late 70s and early 80s, the government-derived medical payment system progressively favored more interventional care rather than a focus on overall patient outcomes. This was problematic as the medical community responded by overemphasizing medical technology without the scientific discipline to prove the value of most of these interventions. This explains the explosion in healthcare spending as a percent of U.S. GDP after the 1960s *(Fig. 3.1)*.

Strangely, the worse the patient's outcome, the more procedures the medical community needs to conduct allowing it to get paid more in the process. In other words, *the worse the health outcomes, the more the medical community gets paid!* This is the worst possible incentive structure imaginable.

The specialist model of care encourages the use of interventions, medications, and diagnostic tools. This is especially true if the intervention is reimbursed more than time spent with the patient. It's ironic that large studies can only demonstrate a community health benefit from primary care, which requires time spent with the patient, yet this is the least financially rewarded of the care options. On the other hand, specialist care is the least proven to be beneficial but the most highly financially rewarded!

Given the changing reward system, it was natural for the medical community to move towards greater specialized care. This resulted in a

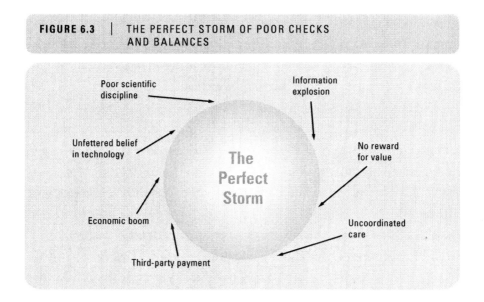

FIGURE 6.3 | THE PERFECT STORM OF POOR CHECKS
AND BALANCES

fragmentation of healthcare as the natural conductor, the primary care provider, was effectively pushed out of the picture. The left hand did not know what the right hand was doing which in turn facilitated more expensive, repetitive and unnecessary care throughout the system (For a more vivid depiction of this problem, please view the November 22nd, 2009 *60 Minutes* episode). This fragmentation of care is in effect a sixth source of poor accountability and incentives. We summarize this perfect storm in Figure 6.3.

System in Crisis

With a combination of poor accountability and incentives allowed by multiple lost checks and balances, the Three Root Causes especially grew within the American healthcare system. The result is the worst healthcare system in the developed world with near-bottom performance in most health outcomes categories combined with the highest cost of any system by far. The lack of accountability is starkly highlighted by many parties misbehaving in every corner of the healthcare system. Rather than describing these examples of inappropriate and even fraudulent behavior in gory detail, we ask you to scan and explore the list of references pertaining to this section.

The bottom line is this: misbehavior in the American healthcare system has been widespread and pervasive. The examples in the reference section will infuriate you. Our goal is to motivate you to *completely* distrust the American healthcare system so that <u>thorough</u> and <u>effective</u> reform will be the only answer you will accept. Poor habits including the Three Root Causes and inappropriate profiteering are so prevalent that only a shock to the system will get it out of its current pattern of value destruction.

Americans must implement complete transparency in healthcare prices and outcomes, as well as liberate and motivate the consumer to be more value conscious with enough healthcare choices to select from. Most examples of inappropriate healthcare system behavior will disappear as a result of the system reforms we are suggesting.

Despite the evidence of misbehavior, please be careful about blaming insurance companies and profiteering CEOs for the healthcare crisis. This is inaccurate for several reasons:

- Profits are a minor problem compared to the waste generated by the unscientific use of medical technology.

- Profit in and of itself is not a problem as long as these are connected to consumer value. We must be realistic, innovation will not occur without some degree of profit incentive.

- Scapegoating entities like insurance companies also distracts from an even more important healthcare system problem: modern medicine is overrated and self healing is under appreciated. We need to reassert control of our own health outcomes through Life Ecology Factors which are currently not being supported by the healthcare system.

- Americans ALL allowed this environment of poor accountability and misaligned incentives. It takes many to create a mess like the American healthcare system and Americans had their hands off the wheel for too long. Until just recently, insurance companies and healthcare systems have not been held accountable for the quality and efficiency of their health outcomes. Furthermore, health providers have had a blank check for utilizing resources.

Americans have not pushed for accountability, and there are plenty of pulls to do too much such as the hero status achieved by introducing an exciting new piece of technology to "save the day". There is also a compulsion to do something tangible rather than spending time with our patients. The final pull to do too much is the seduction of earning large sums of money.

Modern medicine and especially the American healthcare system have allowed the development of the Three Root Causes, including widespread misbehavior, due to poorly designed accountability and incentives. These poor accountability and incentives, in turn, were allowed by the "Perfect Storm" of poor check and balances. American medicine is the ultimate example of how badly people can get physically and financially hurt when there are poor accountability and incentives combined with powerful and expensive medical tools used unintelligently. From top to bottom, the American healthcare system is a mess. The current American Congressional debate is nowhere close to helping with the real problems within the American healthcare system.

In the next chapter we will introduce a more powerful collection of accountability and incentives to drive more effective healthcare system performance.

Chapter Seven

Transformational Healthcare Reform Through Powerful Accountability and Incentives

Getting Motivated by the Savings Potential

The Three Root Causes of ineffective healthcare systems should motivate a restructuring of the current systems of accountability and incentives. Before we start listing a powerful collection of accountability and incentives, let's review the potential savings that can be extracted from comprehensive American healthcare system reform.

If the United States dropped its healthcare spending to the level of other wealthy nations, it would experience a nearly 60% reduction in spending! For a couple reasons, we will be more conservative in predicting potential savings. The United States will always tend towards the discovery and use of technology, thus driving costs higher. This is acceptable as long Americans have some key checks and balances in place to prevent the abuse of such tools. Secondly, we are recommending substantial investments in outcomes and science infrastructures which will absorb some of the savings. These investments, though, will produce significant health outcomes improvement and cost savings in the long run.

60% is one estimate of the savings potential. Another estimate is to combine two figures we have already detailed. The first figure is based on Dr Fisher's analysis as described in Chapter 3: approximately 30% of American healthcare interventions provide little or no health outcomes value. Given what you know about Root Causes #1 and 3, this figure is quite plausible. The second figure is derived from the insurance payment and system related waste including layer upon layer of bureaucracy built up over the past five decades. The United States spends 31% of its healthcare dollars on administrative costs, which is three times that of the other developed nations. Other developed nations average only 10% of healthcare spending for administrative costs. The difference is a whopping 20%.

Combining the intervention (30% healthcare dollar waste) and bureaucracy waste (20% of American healthcare dollars) figures yields a 50% savings potential!

Above, we arrived at a 60% savings potential if Americans reduced their per-person healthcare spending to the level of other developed nations. These two figures validate each other. If Americans structure their accountability and incentives systems properly, hundreds of billions of dollars will be returning to consumers.

One argument against the following reform proposal is that jobs will be lost as the healthcare system will be naturally trimmed. Our counterargument is that the saved money will go *somewhere* in the economy. Other sectors of the economy will put the money to better use and produce jobs because of their more functional markets. The reason for the latter is that most sectors of the American economy demand value and thus yield better benefit for less cost. Why not create jobs *and* be as productive as possible? Thus, do not be deceived by the argument that we should maintain healthcare spending at its current levels so that jobs will be maintained.

The U.S. is currently spending approximately 2.4 trillion dollars per year on healthcare costs. A conservatively estimated 40% reduction in spending would represent nearly a one *trillion dollar, or one thousand billion* dollars, saved *per year.* This staggering amount of savings could literally eliminate all current problems with American healthcare accountability, incentive, and coverage. The United States can comfortably eliminate its problem of 50 million uninsured with coverage costing approximately 200 billion dollars. The United States can build a health outcomes science system to drive the intelligent use of medical technology by investing billions of dollars annually to build this vital foundation of accountability. Yet, this investment will still only represent a small percentage of total healthcare spending. The United States must also build a health outcomes tracking system which will provide another layer of accountability and also cost a small percentage of total spending. Americans can *also* put thousands of dollars back into people's pockets to motivate them to become active participants in the new healthcare marketplace. Specifically, cash or vouchers can be placed directly in individual's hands so that they will reward healthcare systems and healthcare insurance companies that are innovative in their delivery of healthcare value.

Voucher plans can be structured so that minimum healthcare coverage levels will be required while retaining a savings potential to encourage value purchasing. At the same time, the amount provided to individuals can be less than current spending levels, putting more money in government and corporate accounts to help them become more financially stable. The prospect of greater financial stability will encourage all Americans to move to a more functional marketplace. There is more than enough money within the American healthcare budget to achieve all the goals of accountability, incentives, and improved finances!

Some More Perspective Before the Reform Proposals

The recommendations for reform that follow may seem complicated. There may also appear to be a lot of controls being imposed. These changes, however, are vital to prevent the healthcare system from hurting you. Remember, the Three Root Causes can trap you regardless of your insurance coverage or wealth. Furthermore, these reforms are necessary for an effective free market approach to the American healthcare system crisis. The past couple years in the financial markets should have convinced you that unregulated markets eventually *do* cause harm.

There must be checks and balances to protect the consumer.

Let's make the need for checks and balances more clear with an analogy. Imagine you are going to a food market inside a large building similar to a local farmer's market or a flea market. The better the building is structured, the more comfortable consumers would be in entering the marketplace. Furthermore, if the vendors displayed their prices quite clearly and there are many vendors to choose from, even more consumers will be drawn to the marketplace. Finally, a rating system for quality would truly put the consumer in the driver's seat. For example, if you can access vendor ratings (evaluations by experts and/or fellow shoppers), you can find the right balance between quality and price *for you*.

A marketplace with physical safety and transparency in price and quality is quite inviting to consumers. The more consumers appear, the greater the business prospects are and more vendors would set up shop to take advantage of the dynamic marketplace. The more vendors that compete, the more these vendors feel pressure to improve prices and quality. Better prices and quality attract even more potential customers and a virtuous cycle is launched. The key, though, to creating this win-win type of marketplace is establishing physical, financial, and quality safeguards.

The reforms we are proposing are intended to allow you the maximum flexibility in selecting a healthcare plan, provider, and system in pursuing the optimal healthcare value for you. The prospect of designing your own healthcare program starts with a healthcare provider that approaches your care scientifically, ecologically, and with simplicity. It will be important to choose a provider and healthcare system based on evidence that they will address the Three Root Causes. This will include a willingness to spend more time to educate and support patients. You do not necessarily have to make healthcare decisions yourself, but rather you should be able to pick the best healing environment for you and ask smart questions to protect yourself. This chapter will address *system* changes that will support you in obtaining high-value healthcare by fixing the healthcare marketplace, while the next chapter will discuss steps you can take *right now* that will make you healthier and wealthier.

Summary of the Reform Proposals

Thus far, the American healthcare system provides the worst value of any healthcare system in the world, the Three Root Causes produce most of this value leakage, and society allowed for such value destruction due to poor accountability and incentives. We will conclude with a comprehensive healthcare reform proposal motivated by the desire to deliver the best healthcare value to society.

We are proposing 3 building blocks to motivate continuously improving healthcare systems *(Fig. 7.1)*. The Building Blocks consist of the following elements:

- **Wide-spread education** to teach the Three Root Causes of poor healthcare system performance. These educational programs will motivate individuals and families to assume control of their own healthcare program and the healthcare system as a whole (*motivation* for reform, Building Block #1).

- **A mechanism to *independently* measure healthcare system prices and outcomes** (*accountability*, Building Block #2).

- **A much larger investment in health outcomes science** (*accountability*, Building Block #2).

- **Incentives to motivate consumer-driven pursuit of value** which will produce a functional market and force the healthcare system to continuously improve value (*incentives*, Building Block #3)

- **Incentives to improve Life Ecology Factors.** For example participation in wellness educational programs and financial rewards for meeting certain health behavior benchmarks (*incentives*, Building Block #3).

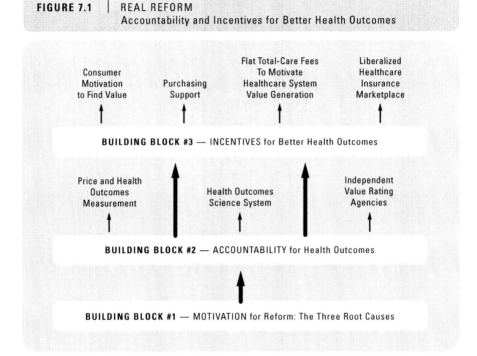

FIGURE 7.1 | REAL REFORM
Accountability and Incentives for Better Health Outcomes

- **Agencies that help consumers identify and reward healthcare systems with good value** (*incentives*, Building Block #3).

- **Rewards for healthcare systems that improve efficiency and health outcomes** (*incentives*, Building Block #3).

- **An open healthcare insurance marketplace** to force competition within this sector (*incentives*, Building Block #3).

Building Block #1: Getting Motivated by the Three Root Causes

The American healthcare system is highly ineffective in delivering value. We have exposed the Three Root Causes of lost value. These Three Root Causes are rarely, if ever, discussed in the same location and collectively should motivate a more profound healthcare reform movement via wide-spread education.

Building Block#2: Accountability for Health Outcomes and Costs

The most critical foundation for an effective healthcare system is accountability for health outcomes. Lacking this piece, most healthcare reform proposals are virtually useless. No accountability means no functional marketplace. No functional marketplace results in the worst of all worlds: blind spending on interventions, higher costs, and, paradoxically, worse outcomes.

We recommend the creation of a standardized healthcare ratings system. Potential mechanisms are already in place including insurance companies and agencies such as The Joint Commission on the Accreditation of Healthcare Organizations (JCAHO) as well as the National Committee for Quality Assurance (NCQA). These entities would be granted government-mandated access to healthcare system charges and medical records in order to measure prices and outcomes.

We are now acutely aware of the risk of ratings agencies that are paid by the very groups they are rating. One key element in the recent financial system disruption was the lack of independent ratings agencies. How could they issue critical reports on the very companies who were paying their bills? In retrospect, it was the most preposterous arrangement imaginable! Ratings agencies *must* be truly independent lest we make the same mistake in healthcare. A functional marketplace depends upon accurate price and cost transparency.

These healthcare ratings agencies would be paid from a pool of funds derived from a tax on existing healthcare spending. The funds available to these agencies must be generous enough to entice multiple competitors. Again, there are more than enough resources in the American system. Reducing revenue will simply force the healthcare system to spend its healthcare dollars more intelligently. There is more than enough waste to be eliminated from the system

At the same time, these ratings agencies must themselves be held to a performance standard. We could create a "rate-the-rater" system by having patients, providers, and healthcare systems rate the accuracy and reliability of the various ratings agencies. We can also measure whether poor ratings motivate performance improvement.

Ratings agencies would be required to employ standard measurement systems. These systems would be derived through a national forum. In this manner, we are comparing apples to apples in utilizing the ratings to select a prospective system or provider for our own care. Once the first two building blocks are in place, consumers can more confidently enter the marketplace and move the United States from a free-for-all free market to a functional free market.

Building Block #2 also requires a health outcomes *science* system. Science is another type of accountability. Whereas health outcomes tracking measures overall patient outcomes, health outcomes science confirms that individual healthcare interventions are truly valuable. Medical technology is too advanced, expensive, and dangerous to not confirm its true value. Healthcare science is challenging to produce but the alternative is suffering from Root Cause #1. Americans must make a substantial investment in clinical science. Health outcomes science allows the medical community to discover and emphasize the interventions (ecological or technologic) that have the best impact on healthcare outcomes for the lowest cost. Healthcare systems will be unlikely to perform the type of large-scale research that is necessary to *scientifically* determine the best pathways to health and healing. There is

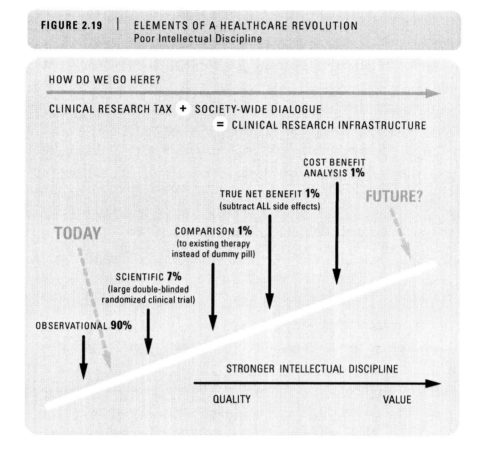

FIGURE 2.19 | ELEMENTS OF A HEALTHCARE REVOLUTION
Poor Intellectual Discipline

HOW DO WE GO HERE?

CLINICAL RESEARCH TAX **+** SOCIETY-WIDE DIALOGUE
= CLINICAL RESEARCH INFRASTRUCTURE

COST BENEFIT
ANALYSIS **1%**

TRUE NET BENEFIT **1%**
(subtract ALL side effects)

FUTURE?

TODAY

COMPARISON **1%**
(to existing therapy
instead of dummy pill)

SCIENTIFIC **7%**
(large double-blinded
randomized clinical trial)

OBSERVATIONAL **90%**

STRONGER INTELLECTUAL DISCIPLINE

QUALITY   VALUE

just too much financial risk to expect individual healthcare systems to perform this function properly in the increasingly price competitive environment of a functional marketplace. The implementation of research must be driven by government given its scale and risk.

Most healthcare providers are not trained as scientists, they're trained as technologists. They know their products, they know how the technology has been developed or how the technology *theoretically* works. However, they're *not* trained as health outcome *scientists* that can verify the net and relative benefit of their treatments and tests.

As we described in Chapter 2 *(Fig. 2.19)*, health outcomes science is like a series of hurdles that must be cleared before we can be truly confident in the value of the proposed medical treatment or test. Unfortunately, most of the medical community's healthcare decision making is based on little or no evidence. The first or "observational" hurdle represents virtually no science and includes the tendency of healthcare providers to base their healthcare decisions on personal experience. The latter is not scientific since many confounding factors can easily explain positive outcomes. This poor science would not be as problematic if it weren't for the expense and risk of modern medical tools.

In the current state of modern medicine, decisions are guided by only a few randomized trials, virtually no comparison trials, virtually no studies looking at the true long-term net benefit of the medical community's therapies, and almost no cost-benefit analysis studies. In other words, almost *none* of the other healthcare science hurdles are even attempted! How can we push the medical community to the stronger side of the science and value spectrum?

Let's put some numbers on the current state of healthcare science investment in the United States. Again, the American healthcare budget is over two trillion dollars or stated differently, two thousand billion dollars. Guess what the budget is for the National Institute of Health (NIH)? The NIH is the primary American institution for producing health science. The hopes for an intelligent approach to healthcare decision making rests on this entity. As you think about the answer, remember that science is a pursuit of the truth and in the absence of the truth we risk the "Dangers of Doing Too Much". The Three Root Causes should have convinced you that the "Dangers of Doing Too Much" are clearly occurring.

The answer to our question is that the NIH budget is approximately 30 billion dollars which is just over <u>one percent</u> of total American healthcare spending! Does this make sense? There's even worse news than this.

Approximately two thirds of the NIH budget is for basic science (think molecules, genes, etc.), *not* health outcomes research. Thus, we can effectively chop the American health outcomes budget down to a paltry ten billion dollars, less than half of one percent of total American healthcare spending! This figure does not include industry funded trials since these are biased and focused on promoting the companies' products. In fact, the NIH was starting to be criticized in the early-to-mid 1990s for not spending enough on health outcomes research.

The United States also possesses a government mechanism called the Agency for Healthcare Research and Quality (AHRQ) whose name reveals its valuable function. What do you think its budget is? Remarkably, AHRQ, until recently, had an even smaller and inexcusable budget of 300 *million* or just 0.3 billion dollars! Luckily, the United States Congress recently appropriated 4 billion dollars for AHRQ, so there is some hope, but a much larger investment is required to establish a strong foundation of outcomes and science accountability (Building Block #2).

The United States must invest *tens* of billions of dollars to produce both an outcomes analysis infrastructure (the electronic database and people to gather/analyze the data) and a clinical science system (the people to conduct and analyze large clinical trials exploring all potential medical interventions). In summary, the United States currently only spends a few billion dollars to intelligently guide the use of thousands of billions of dollars every year. This simply doesn't make sense! Health outcomes transparency and health outcomes science investments will pay for themselves by substantially reducing the Three Root Causes, thus saving hundreds of billions of dollars and improving outcomes!

Building Block #3: Incentives

Building Block #2 represents accountability, a critical check and balance for creating a functional market. Once Building Block #2 is in place, consumers can more confidently enter the marketplace and move things from a free-for-all free market to a functional free market. The real force driving functional markets, though, are incentives.

Incentives need to be created so that individuals and families will *want* to enter the healthcare marketplace. This would cause the marketplace to be more dynamic and effective. Furthermore, incentives need to be structured so that healthcare systems focus on patient health outcomes. Just having to utter this last statement seems ridiculous, but such is the state of modern and especially American medicine. Finally, we also need to create incentives for the healthcare purchasing agents to assist healthcare consumers in producing scientific and value conscious healthcare packages.

You see, for the past 50 years, healthcare insurance agencies, whether private or government-based such as Medicare and Medicaid, have been *passive* agents. Insurance entities have traditionally passed costs on to the consumer in the form of higher premiums, lower wages, and/or higher taxes. Therefore, healthcare consumers were not being value sensitive due to third party payment. The third party payers themselves weren't paying attention to value because they could pass the costs on! What a disaster!

Let's step back for some more functional market perspective. Why do we need as many consumers as possible? If there are just a few large customers such as Ford or Pepsi, then there is much less need for the healthcare system to compete for customers once contracts have been established with these large purchasers. Thus, the healthcare system has much less drive to improve its healthcare value, the problem of the past four decades. The marketplace cannot function if there are not enough consumers to maintain continuous pressure on healthcare systems and insurance companies to satisfy consumers who can easily leave.

Americans must create a system whereby consumers *want* better healthcare value and healthcare systems *want* to generate improving healthcare value. This contrasts with the current state of affairs where price is unattended to and quality is only somewhat mandated through regulations. Systems can receive incentives to naturally and continuously improve value. To summarize, strong incentives are required for consumers, healthcare systems, and insurance companies to deliver better health outcomes in the most efficient manner possible.

Consumer Incentives

The consumer needs a financial incentive to value shop. Increased consumer sensitivity to value will force the marketplace to generate health outcomes innovation. One aspect of value is cost, and consumers will want to venture on their own if they can put more money in their pockets. This would be achieved by providing the healthcare insurance funds to consumers to purchase their own coverage rather than the employer doing so. Another bonus of consumer control of healthcare insurance purchasing is the satisfaction of selecting the healthcare provider and approach that they believe in.

Given the power of many value-conscious consumers to activate the marketplace, we endorse HSAs or Healthcare Savings Accounts as an incentive for consumers. An HSA is dedicated to healthcare costs and contributed to by individuals and/or their employer or government. HSA legislation was only recently passed in 2004. These accounts are structured to require catastrophic care insurance, a high deductible, and tax-free contributions. Furthermore, the funds in this account can be rolled over from year to year and are available for retirement purposes. In the past, medical accounts were a "use it or lose it" arrangement, but now these are, in effect, the individual's own funds. With HSAs, consumers will have a desire to use their healthcare funds in a value-conscious manner which will pressure the healthcare system to continuously improve its product in order to attract these dollars.

Given the impact of Life Ecology Factors, flexibility in healthcare purchasing can yield better health outcomes in addition to forcing the market to be more responsive to consumers. HSAs also represent an instant revolution because the mechanism is already in place and it is fairly easy to convert to this type of coverage. You will benefit from the confidence of a high HQ in making the switch from total coverage provided by the employer to HSA coverage driven by you. There are currently a few million people enrolled in these plans but once tens of millions are enrolled, the healthcare marketplace will have to honor *mobile* consumer pressure!

Earlier, we calculated 50 to 60 percent waste in the American healthcare system. One way for Americans to send a message that they will not tolerate this state of affairs is to effectively disengage from the healthcare system and only purchase what they need based on scientific demonstrations of healthcare value. This is where insurance companies and healthcare systems can produce there own revolution. As we discussed earlier, insurance companies have essentially been inactive by passing on the costs and taking their cut. With a substantial pool of mobile, value-conscious consumers, there will be more demand for *active* insurance agents. These agents will help to design intelligent healthcare packages based on science, yet allowing for flexibility in customizing plans to harness self healing.

From the consumer's perspective, disengaging from traditional healthcare coverage may seem daunting, but hopefully the Three Root Causes have provided you the inspiration and motivation to make bold changes to enhance your life. Given that healthcare providers are often flying blind, there is not very much risk in disengaging from the system and reengaging it selectively.

HSA Plans should be structured to provide more healthcare coverage than currently available plans given the need to improve Life Ecology Factors. We will refer to bolstered HSA plans as HSA *Plus.*

The risk with simple HSAs is that people will skimp on necessary care including support to enhance Life Ecology Factors. There are at least three solutions to this problem of purchasing too little care. First, individuals and families can be legislatively mandated to purchase not only catastrophic coverage but also a core package with substantial allowances for preventative care. This will ensure a greater emphasis on the most powerful aspects of health and healing, Life Ecology Factors. Second, insurance companies and healthcare systems can structure plans that provide progressively more covered treatments and tests based on the scientific evidence.

For example, let's imagine there are a total of 500 treatments and tests available to the medical community. It turns out that 50 of these procedures have been scientifically proven to be essential for people's health. These 50 could be included in a so-called "HSA Plan A" or catastrophic-only coverage. HSA Plan B might include the next 100 most scientifically validated treatments and tests and so on and so forth. Again, these modifications of simple HSA plans are intended to prevent people from hurting themselves by short-cutting coverage in order to save money.

A third approach to the basic HSA plan would be even more revolutionary. In this approach to modifying HSAs, participants would purchase different tiers of flat-fee coverage instead of fee-for-service plans. Let's revisit the advantages of flat-fee, or global, reimbursement. Root Cause #1 would be reduced because the healthcare system will be less motivated to perform treatments and tests as these will not be paid for individually. Root Cause #2 will improve as an ecological approach to health and healing will produce the best return on investment. Finally, the complexity aspect of Root Cause #3 will be reduced as the motivation to do more will disappear. Performing less treatments and tests will preserve resources and reduce missed care.

Innovative incentive programs need to be produced within a flat-fee world in order to motivate a range of healthy behaviors. Examples of incentives include financial rewards for attending self-care educational courses as well as Life Ecology Factors support groups. Patients with evidence of poor health would be naturally charged a risk-adjusted premium, but these patients could be financially rewarded for improvements in the various inner-body elements per Chapter 4. Furthermore, key improvements in dietary behaviors can be measured and rewarded such as improvements in cholesterol, long-term glucose, and inflammation levels just to name a few.

Healthcare insurance in its current form doesn't make sense. Do you purchase auto insurance that covers any possible expense? This would probably encourage the mechanic to do anything and everything to your car and then provide you a higher bill the next year. This is exactly what has occurred within American medicine, exacerbated by expensive and dangerous medical technology. Total coverage, paid for *indirectly*, in a fee-for-service arrangement with the presence of "advanced" medical technology and absence of science and health outcomes accountability have combined to produce a disaster. Unfortunately, this disaster has been difficult to see. The Three Root Causes demonstrate how the American healthcare system has been a disaster, none the less.

HSAs and HSA Plus types of programs would be a revolution in moving Americans towards healthcare functional markets. Consumers would have incentives to shop for the best healthcare plan for them including more savings and more satisfying and effective healthcare plans. An active and mobile consumer will keep insurance companies and healthcare systems under pressure to continuously improve healthcare value, benefiting all of society. Now that we understand the incentives for the consumer, let's turn to incentives for the healthcare system.

Healthcare System Incentives

You cannot trust a healthcare system that does not have the right accountability and incentives. The American system as a whole is undisciplined and ignorant about the best approaches to health and healing because of a lack of science to guide it (Root Cause #1) and the wrong incentives to utilize the best, <u>scientifically proven</u> approaches to patient care (Root Causes #2 and 3). Given the failings of the American healthcare system through the Three Root Causes, we come to one of the most dramatic and important conclusions of this book.

Fee-for-service reimbursement for healthcare interventions has been a disaster in conjunction with complete insurance coverage. In the absence of science and given the "Bias to Do Things" and the Three Root Causes, fee-for-service just doesn't make sense!

The most important conclusion of this book is that Americans need to switch to a fixed or flat-fee budget healthcare model and eliminate fee-for-service. Of course, the budgeted amount would be adjusted for patient risk factors.

Flat-fee payment might sound like an HMO or managed care system on a national scale, but we would build several checks and balances that did not exist within the 1990's HMO movement. The failure of the 1990's HMO movement stemmed, in part, from poor buy-in from consumers and healthcare providers as well as poor quality and service accountability. Poor buy-in was grounded in society feeling entitled to "the best" care possible including as much technology as possible. Little did they realize the growing problems of the Three Root Causes. In addition, poor accountability allowed excess profiteering by managed care companies that lacked the check and balance of health outcomes measurement. Thus, if managed care organizations provided less care to improve their profit margins, it was difficult to detect any compromise in the quality of care they delivered.

The first problem of poor buy-in can be addressed by educational programs explaining the Three Root Causes. With widespread education, we as a society will now agree that restraint in care is *a good idea* in the absence of science, given the bias to do things and the "Dangers of Doing Too Much". People will be especially open to the idea of managed care if we also address the problem of poor accountability. We can build a better fixed-budget healthcare model by first laying down Building Block #2. With performance accountability in place, it will be apparent if a healthcare system is cutting corners, and consumers will run in the other direction.

With a fixed budget per patient and a robust accountability mechanism, healthcare systems will need to truly innovate from a value perspective. This will serve to both reduce costs while maintaining or improving service and quality. The *incentive* for healthcare systems to produce lower costs in a fixed budget scenario is that efficient systems will have a better profit margin. Furthermore, health outcomes tracking will help to identify which healthcare systems are being efficient <u>and</u> effective, thus drawing more customers and even greater profits.

Some feel that profit should not be involved in health matters at all. However, as long as human beings are driving healthcare, profit is an important motivator in a functional market. The vital check and balance of Building Blocks #2 and 3 will prevent excess profiteering as it would cause quality to suffer and customers would leave. Given price and quality transparency and a mobile consumer, savvy healthcare systems will keep reducing their profit margins in order to attract customers with lower prices. Despite a lower profit margin, *total* profits will increase as the number of customers increases. This pattern has occurred in many other areas of the economy.

Profits and improved consumer value are certainly not inconsistent as long as there are cost and benefit transparency in the system, as well as consumer mobility. In fact, a profit-based system will motivate better value for society than a non-profit system. I have spent 20 years in several non-profit healthcare systems and I can tell you there is little to motivate efficiency or effectiveness other than the threat of reduced revenue. With the prospect of profits, there will be a constant industry-wide drive to improve systems of delivery resulting in both lower premiums (to attract more customers) and higher profit margins. Health outcomes will improve due to simplified systems and the intelligent use of medical technology. The latter, of course, tackle Root Causes #1 and 3! Truly visionary healthcare systems will also make Root Cause #2 investments in Life Ecology factors that will pay off with even better long-term outcomes and profit margins.

Let's revisit the mobility piece of the functional marketplace puzzle. In order for the healthcare marketplace to be functional, we *simultaneously* need price and outcomes transparency and a *desire* and *ability* of customers to switch who they purchase their healthcare from. We have already discussed transparency and consumer incentives. Consumer incentives produce a *desire* to switch healthcare providers, but now we need to work on the consumer's *ability* to switch.

The other side of the mobility equation is the availability of enough healthcare plans to pick from. It is *vital* that we alter the interstate healthcare insurance laws. Currently, state-based healthcare insurance entities are exempt from anti-trust regulations. Thus, virtual healthcare insurance monopolies operate *within* most states preventing true competition from large national vendors. The latter usually grow large because of their organizational effectiveness which, in turn, allows the delivery of value to customers. Restrictions in the ability of healthcare insurance vendors to sell their products across state lines greatly reduce the amount of choice available.

Even if Americans maintain fee-for-service payments and the current healthcare insurance system, the insurance industry must be opened up to national competition. Opening the healthcare insurance marketplace represents a vital method of increasing consumer choice.

Building Block #2 will automatically produce another source of increased choice. A healthcare price and outcomes monitoring system will make it apparent if substantial value can be gained by traveling to a healthcare system outside of one's immediate area. There will already be increased consumer incentive to shop as we will have placed dollars in their hands. By expanding the "shopping" territory because of value visibility and a motive for consumers to put savings in their pockets, we will, in effect, increase choice and therefore mobility.

Building Blocks 2 and 3 will create the first large-scale *functional* healthcare marketplace in the United States! Then healthcare value "magic" will appear as value continually increases and the Three Root Causes melt away!

The last piece of Building Block #3 *(Fig. 7.1)* is the creation of agents to help consumers to find the best healthcare value in their region. These agents, whether they are insurance companies or a new type of consumer advocate, can provide services such as investigating the quality, safety, and cost effectiveness of prospective healthcare systems. They can also help consumers *limit* the menu of healthcare services included in their healthcare packages based on strong science and demonstrations of added value relative to existing therapy. This discernment will drop healthcare costs. Agents can also provide guidance for purchasing healthcare services that are not on consumer's customized menus. Agents can provide ongoing educational programs for improving Life Ecology Factors. Finally, healthcare decision making tools can be developed to help consumers become equal partners as they engage the healthcare system for care.

Consumers, with the guidance of *active* support agencies, can customize their coverage to include more premium packages. Experts can certainly agree on a core package that everyone should have, such as the HSA Plan A we described earlier.

Don't be alarmed by all the American rationing and death panels scare tactics. It will NOT be difficult to design packages that contain all the proven, essential care items for a modest cost compared to current expenditures. What is not in these packages can just as easily harm you per the "Dangers of Doing Too Much". All the scare tactics make one large mistaken presumption: additional care is good until proven otherwise. The Three Root Causes should prove that this is wrong! We should *collectively and intelligently* decide on core packages that contain essential care based on science not based on theory or fantasy. These core packages can be highly effective and yet cost 60-70% less than current average costs! As an aside, consumers who choose lower coverage levels can still obtain non-covered services with the accumulated funds within their HSAs.

Let's put some numbers on this core package idea. The problem of the uninsured in the United States should be relatively easy to eliminate *without any more spending* in contrast to the nearly one trillion additional dollars being attached to current Congressional proposals for expanded coverage! We can produce a basic-care insurance plan with significantly tighter scientific and value standards for at least 50% of the current average cost for American healthcare coverage. Instead of spending $7,500 per person, we can achieve an effective package for half or $3,750, nearly a $4,000 per-person savings!

Remember that the United States governments (Federal and State) provide healthcare insurance coverage for approximately 40% of its citizens or about 120 million people. A savings of $4,000 for each of these 120 million people would represent approximately $500 billion dollars saved! How much would it cost to cover the 50 million uninsured citizens at $4,000 per person? Only 200 billion dollars! There is so much waste in the system that the more intelligent use of healthcare resources can yield hundreds of billions of dollars in savings. These savings can, in turn, eliminate American healthcare coverage issues; ease family, corporate, and government financial problems; and provide funds for solid Building Blocks # 1, 2, and 3. Of course, we need to allow several years for the healthcare system to adjust to these large changes, but the outcome will be more than worth this time investment.

There is precedence for this type of "core package" within a free market system, including the approach which was recently developed in the Netherlands. In the Dutch case, the government specified a core package that all insurance companies are required to provide their members. People have the ability, though, to switch who they purchase their coverage from which represents the mobility required for a functional market!

Summary of Proposed Accountability and Incentives System

In summary, most of the current American healthcare reform proposals deal with either covering more people or shifting who pays, but almost none deal with the really tough question: how do individuals and families find the best healthcare value AND push the system to produce more healthcare value? The HSA pathway can be fruitful IF there is a robust accountability system in place as well as a functional marketplace that allows more competitors to come in, enticed by dollars they can earn. There are a LOT of dollars in the American system thus producing incentives is not difficult *as long as they are tied to healthcare value, NOT simply performing interventions!*

Figures 7.3 and 7.4 summarize the current and desired state of accountability and incentives. Even if you choose not to instigate a revolution at the national level, these concepts will remind you of what to look for in constructing your own value-oriented healthcare plan. Our proposal seeks the optimal balance of cost and value generation given

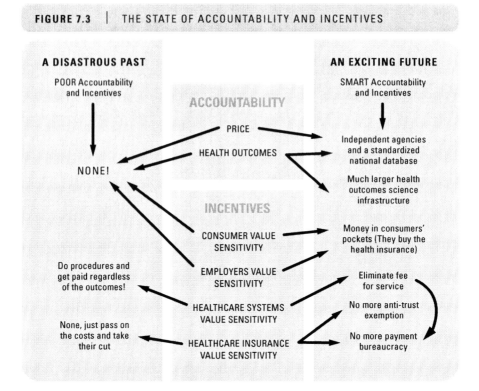

FIGURE 7.3 | THE STATE OF ACCOUNTABILITY AND INCENTIVES

the staggering amount of waste, complexity, and missed opportunity that exist in the current American system.

Let's expand on Building Block #1 now that you have a more thorough understanding of Building Blocks #2 and 3. The key to achieving societal acceptance for Building Blocks #2 and 3 is an education regarding the Root Causes of lost healthcare value and the mechanisms for recapturing this value. The following Building Block #1 educational elements should motivate reform:

1. Examples of many, large-scale failures in medical scientific discipline

2. The relatively minor impact of technology on overall health outcomes

FIGURE 7.4 | WHAT SHOULD PEOPLE DO WITH *THEIR* MONEY?

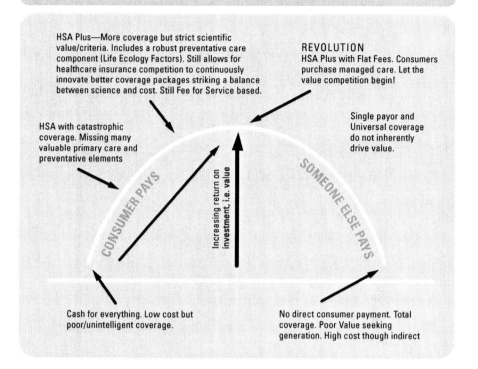

3. The dangers of engaging a broken healthcare system

4. The power of self-healing through Life Ecology Factors

5. The superiority of a functional free market over a free-for-all market

6. The only way to tackle the Three Root Causes is to fundamentally change   accountability and incentives

7. Individual consumer involvement is vital to force value generation

8. The only way to drive a constant improvement of value from within the healthcare system is to pay for total care and total outcomes NOT individual interventions

9. There is no way other than a flat-fee or global payment structure to encourage: the intelligent and conservative use of technology to counter Root Cause #1; the incorporation of life ecology factors into the care plan to counter Root Cause #2; and the constant move towards intelligent, efficient, and *self*-improving care *processes* to counter Root Cause #3.

Current Healthcare Reform Proposals Reviewed

Current healthcare reform proposals have been completely off the mark given the importance of value, a deeper awareness of where value is being lost, and the presence of misaligned incentives. Let's review the current proposals through the value and functional market lenses.

1. More or universal coverage. This is the primary focus of the current American healthcare debate. It is noble to cover all Americans with basic healthcare protection. For the first time in recent history, the United States is confronted with *severe* resource limitations as its economy has deflated and its total debt burden is at an all-time high. Covering more people with a healthcare system that is financially and physically destructive is far from ideal. Americans will continue to throw away *trillions* of dollars while falling far short of the level of health they are capable of. In some ways, universal coverage without substantial reform to correct the Three Root Causes is like throwing more fuel into the fire of poor accountability, waste, system complexity, and generally poor performance. Sadly, the United States can no longer afford to throw money at the problem. Universal coverage does not even consider accountability, incentives, and forcing the healthcare system to deliver the best value possible. Universal coverage is where current American legislation rests. This is by no means *reform.*

2. Transfer costs. This is represented by increased co-pays, premiums, and deductibles for individuals and families. This category also includes typical Healthcare Savings Accounts (HSAs) recommendations.

The objective with transferring financial responsibility is to encourage individuals and families to be more value sensitive, thus moving the American healthcare towards a more competitive or functional market. The hope is that functional market induced competition will spur the healthcare system to generate more value. The problem is that these proposals shuffle the costs while the underlying problems rage on.

Our proposal submits that HSAs are a *part* of the solution, but they are thoroughly inadequate by themselves given the value destroying nature of the healthcare system. Standard HSA proposals do not address important issues including: poor scientific discipline, limitations of technologic approaches to medical care, an ignorance of ecological factors in creating more complete healthcare programs, system waste, and poor performance stemming from poor value accountability.

HSA plans also fall short with their main promise, the development of more *functional* marketplaces. The fundamental problem is that HSA proposals have not sufficiently addressed the current lack of outcomes and price transparency. HSA proposals also do not help with the creation of consumer support mechanisms for finding the best healthcare value in the region (choice/mobility) nor the proper healthcare financing innovations necessary to motivate greater healthcare value (incentives). In summary, basic HSA proposals are too superficial to address accountability and only improve incentives from the consumer perspective.

3. Single payer or public option. The rallying cry of the single payer advocates is that the free market in healthcare has failed AND we need to eliminate the insurance industry in order to reduce bureaucracy and profiteering. A free market has been tried, but it was not allowed to transition into a functional market.

As attractive as eliminating insurance payment related bureaucracy sounds, a single payer system is also doomed to rising inefficiency if Americans do not introduce intelligent checks and balances. The following is a vital point missed by almost all healthcare reform proposals; no matter what the system, whether it is HSAs, a single payer system, or universal coverage, if the foundation is not complete and solid, American healthcare is doomed to continuing failure. We must include ALL the elements of an intelligent marketplace to motivate improving value. Otherwise, the United States should go ahead and switch to a single payer system. The worst Americans can do is to stay in the middle, neither a centralized system nor a functional market.

Let's be realistic. Americans will always be strongly tilted towards a free market approach. It supports the principles on which the United States was founded. But let's not talk about healthcare reform if the conditions for the intelligent use of resources are not created. That is the intent of our proposal; to shock people into a more complete discussion about health, healing, and functional markets. Only then will societies move towards more comprehensive healthcare system reform.

A Review of the Current Prospects for a Functional Market in American Healthcare

The American healthcare system is starting to measure and post its **performance** due to corporate and governmental pressure, but as we discussed earlier, this is nowhere close to truly serving patients.

In contrast, **price transparency** is currently not to be found since healthcare systems are stuck in a vicious cat-mouse game with either insurance companies or the government. The payers for healthcare (corporations, government, and insurance companies) pay an ever smaller percentage of the healthcare system's charges. The healthcare system or providers counter by charging more to compensate. Given these circumstances, it would be financial suicide for a healthcare system to reveal its true prices.

A sad victim of this pricing gamesmanship are the uninsured. Healthcare systems are forbidden by insurance companies from charging different amounts to its customers. This ensures that if the healthcare system is raising its charges, it is going to truly stand behind those charges. As a result, the uninsured, paradoxically, get charged ridiculous amounts when, in fact, healthcare systems DO provide contractual discounts for their larger customers! This is just one more example of destructive American bureaucracy and games within the healthcare system. Does it seem like Americans can really fix this system by tinkering with it at the margins?

Mobility and, therefore, choice has been restricted in several ways. Most importantly, employers have structured purchasing arrangements with healthcare systems in order to reduce costs. Ironically, there has been no pursuit of *value,* meaning best costs with best quality, in these agreements. Furthermore, costs have risen anyways due to a lack of comparison shopping and a tendency to pass the costs on to employees and customers. Unfortunately, these purchasing arrangements have also taken the *individual* customer out of the equation because of prohibitive out-of-network charges. Mobility has also been blocked by a lack of value transparency, thus not allowing a functional marketplace to form. If one cannot measure price and outcomes, on what basis would one switch providers?! Also, active agents have not been available to guide value-based healthcare decisions, let alone construct value-oriented healthcare coverage packages. Of course, the number of competitors in the healthcare marketplace has also been reduced by anti-trust exemptions.

With almost all current healthcare reform proposals, we simply change the name but deliver the same poor performance! Let's conclude in the final chapter with a list of what you as an individual can currently do to transform your healthcare program and healthcare system.

Chapter Eight

Start YOUR Healthcare Revolution NOW!

A Recap of the Thinking Tools for Building Your HQ

A rising HQ will allow you to intelligently and confidently take control of your healthcare program as well as drive the creation of more effective healthcare systems. Your HQ is being built upon the foundation of several thinking tools that we will now briefly review.

The **first Thinking Tool** is the **"Dangers of Doing Too Much"**. This list highlights why healthcare decision making cannot be taken lightly. There are many sources of harm if decisions are not made intelligently. We cannot simply say more tests and treatments are better until proven otherwise. We hope that the Root Cause #1 evidence has countered the false, especially American, assumption that more technology is better. *It most certainly is not!*

The **second Thinking Tool** is **scientific thinking**. Only scientific thinking can deliver truly *intelligent* healthcare decisions. This tool also allows you to recognize the relatively poor scientific discipline behind much of modern medicine. You can turn the tables by demanding more science before being subjected to medical technology. More scientifically disciplined healthcare decisions reduce resource waste and injury. They also ensure that the health benefit of a proposed treatment or test justifies the likely physical and financial risk.

Your **third Thinking Tool** is the understanding that **technological advancement does not mean scientific advancement.** Technological advancement without scientific advancement is actually unintelligent and potentially dangerous. We call this **Root Cause #1, "Modern**

Medicine is Unintelligent". We have highlighted this unintelligence with multiple examples of large-scale healthcare mistakes that have produced more harm than good. The example of the American health-care system highlights the poor performance that can result, in part, from Root Cause #1.

The **fourth** and the most powerful **Thinking Tool** is the concept of **Root Cause #2, "Modern Medicine is Overrated" and self healing is underrated**. This taught you that the technology behind modern medicine is overemphasized (ladder against the wrong wall) and, in fact, the undeniable key to health and healing is YOU! Future effective healthcare systems *must* harness the power of self healing through improved Life Ecology Factors. Ideally, you are inspired to use this power now.

The **fifth Thinking Tool** is **Root Cause #3, "Modern Medicine is Harmful"**. This includes the idea that large systems have a mind of their own and become error prone and wasteful. Errors and waste are a significant element of the "Dangers of Doing Too Much" and a silent killer that most people are unaware of.

The **sixth Thinking Tool** was a back-to-basics discussion of human motivation: **accountability and incentives**. We simply cannot expect the healthcare system to serve us well if we have virtually no accountability and the wrong incentives! Societies need to work from the ground up and construct proper accountability and incentives in order to motivate better health-producing behavior by healthcare systems and patients themselves.

We also developed the **seventh Thinking Tool** of **functional free markets**. Functional markets are dependent on not only the right accountability and incentives but also the availability of multiple vendors and the ability to switch who we purchase our healthcare services from. If we desire competition that will continuously launch healthcare innovation, consumers must be able to measure what they are receiving, have an incentive to pursue the best value, and have enough healthcare providers to select from. Amazingly, *none* of these conditions currently exist within the American system!

An **eighth Thinking Tool** was **"The Perfect Storm of Lost Check and Balances"** which allowed modern societies and especially the United States to produce the wrong accountability and incentives. Poor accountability and incentives led to incredible misbehavior, whether intentional or unintentional, including the growth of the Three Root Causes.

The **ninth and final thinking tool** was the **three Building Blocks of a transformational healthcare reform plan**. These Building Blocks start with educational programs to achieve buy-in for reform. Then we build much more powerful accountability and incentives systems. We then applied the Building Blocks thinking tool to analyze the inadequacies of current healthcare market function and healthcare reform proposals.

What Can YOU Do?

There you have it! In some ways the failures of modern and especially American medicine are fairly easy to understand. There were poor checks and balances that led to poor accountability and incentives. The poor accountability and incentives allowed the Three Root Causes to grow like weeds. You can reverse this process as your HQ rises!

There are two types of revolutionary action you can take right now. One category is the steps you can immediately take in structuring your health and healing program. The other category is steps you can take to force the healthcare system to serve you better.

First let's discuss your health and healing program. Root Cause #1 informs you that it is not wise to engage in a healthcare intervention just in case it might help. Much harm and wasted resources can result from unscientific decisions. **Most** healthcare decisions are unscientific because the healthcare system has not been held accountable for scientific discipline. Even if you have complete healthcare insurance, there is a risk from loosely accepting healthcare interventions. Review the types of questions we suggested at the end of Chapter 3 in order to flex your HQ muscle and protect yourself. There are already easy-to-access decision-making guidelines for various health scenarios and undoubtedly more consumer friendly versions of these guidelines will appear. These guidelines need to be strengthened to include an explanation of the scientific evidence behind various branches on the decision trees.

Root Cause #2 means YOUR Life Ecology Factors are by far the dominant predictor of whether you will develop disease and how well you will recover from existing disease. Do not fall under the spell of modern medicine, thinking it will save you when things get bad. The analogy of the dam, and specifically the inner-body elements evidence, proves that modern medicine can rarely help you by itself. Only you can heal yourself, but modern medicine can give you a little breathing room when applied scientifically.

It is vital that you constantly work on improving your state of mind, relationships, and other Life Ecology Factors. The latter includes exercise, adequate sleep, and a diet with plenty of fruits, vegetables, modest calories, and key nutrients. It is also critical to reduce toxins such as smoking and unhealthy additives within food. Any participation in religious or spiritual activities can promote Life Ecology Factors. In the least, be disciplined in devoting time daily for Life Ecology Factors improvement. This is not just about living longer but living a higher quality of life including more happiness! Can there be a better investment than living both a longer and better life?!

You must also protect yourself against healthcare decision making errors by watching every step the healthcare system takes in caring for you. Root Cause #3 demonstrated the opportunity for many healthcare system errors. One specific and simple example of protecting yourself is insisting that ALL the healthcare providers that enter your room wash their hands. Also make sure you completely understand the purpose, amount, and rate of injection for medications received in the clinical setting. Ask questions until you truly understand why your healthcare provider is recommending a particular intervention or test.

Root Cause #3 also means not getting the care that you should including the primary or preventative care that *science* recommends. Decision-making guidelines can also be helpful. In addition to Root Cause #1, where decision-making guidelines help you avoid healthcare interventions with weak scientific justification, guidelines can help to advocate interventions that you *should* be receiving based on the evidence.

That was just a brief overview of the types of personal action available to optimize your health and healing now. You can also more confidently force your healthcare system to serve you better. A rising HQ helps you to ask the right questions about healthcare system accountability and incentives. Specifically, you can push your healthcare system or legislator to increase healthcare system outcomes and science accountability as well as structuring the correct incentives to motivate constantly improving healthcare value.

For true accountability, the United States must make an annual multibillion dollar investment in a standardized electronic health record system and an independent system for tracking healthcare outcomes and prices. This can be funded with a tax on *existing* healthcare dollars. In other words, there is more than enough money in the system. Americans do not need to spend more, just squeeze out the waste. The healthcare system will complain, but there is <u>plenty</u> of waste in the system and they can easily tighten their belts to fund this accountability system.

In addition, Americans must compel their governments to make an annual multibillion dollar investment in a health outcomes science system. We need to create the electronic and human infrastructure to design, conduct, analyze, and report many, large, multicenter clinical trials so we can *prove* that there is a good health outcomes return on investments. This system will also be paid through a healthcare system tax and will also pay for itself through reduced waste per Root Cause #1.

Besides accountability, it is also important to push your government and employers to structure proper incentives to motivate the healthcare system to constantly improve healthcare value. You must ask for the insurance premium money to be placed in *your* hands rather than in the hands of your employer or government doing the shopping. The

Three Root Causes should inspire you to take control in order to save money for yourself AND create a more effective and satisfying healthcare plan. We just dealt with consumer incentives but let's now tackle the healthcare system's incentives

A flat-fee or global payment system will prevent healthcare providers from constantly performing unnecessary interventions just because they can get paid. Healthcare providers would be paid a salary with some reward for productivity. If we only pay a salary, some healthcare providers will drag their heals since they get paid anyways. Yet, with a flat-fee system we will remove most of the incentives to do as many medical interventions as possible. Furthermore, medical technology will be used more sparingly because it impinges on profit margins. On the other hand, our Building Block #2 accountability systems will prevent healthcare establishments from cutting corners for the sake of profits as some did during the 1990s. Healthcare systems that are avoiding valuable care will see their relative performance decline and customers will start to flee.

The healthcare insurance system must lose anti-trust exemptions, which will generate more competition and then force companies to constantly improve health outcomes and drop prices in order to attract customers. Now that healthcare purchasing power is in your hands, you will be much more value sensitive, thus adding more pressure to the insurance companies and healthcare system to perform by *continuously* improving value.

In summary, you must push the government and your employer to use their power to force the development of:

- A health outcomes tracking system

- A health outcomes science system

- Cash in your hands to purchase healthcare coverage including the HSA approach

- Flat-fee reimbursement models for total care

- More open insurance markets

To not do so will allow the Three Root Causes to keep haunting you. There is no need for this degree of failure. Americans have the resources and ingenuity to produce excellence!

Dreaming About Tomorrow

What value can we imagine generating in the United States as a result of these comprehensive reforms? We can save *hundreds* of billions of dollars AND create better health outcomes. The focus must be on value. Americans must create value transparency and reward, and the rest will happen automatically. The principles are that simple. This does not have to be complicated! These changes are achievable within a few years. Some of the savings and healthcare improvement can start immediately for individuals.

Let's reiterate some critical numbers. The American healthcare system costs 2.4 trillion dollars per year and, even at a conservatively estimated 40% reduction in waste, Americans can generate a <u>trillion</u> dollars of savings <u>every year</u>! This is equal to a bank system bailout <u>every year</u>! This staggering level of savings can be used to:

- Place money directly into consumer's pockets as an incentive for making the shift from total healthcare coverage, which is expensive and relatively ineffective, to an intelligent, value-oriented coverage approach such as the HSA Plus programs

- Place funds into consumer's healthcare savings accounts

- Reduce the healthcare financial burden on corporations and government to improve their financial stability

- Build an accountability infrastructure including the electronic and human resources required for health outcomes tracking and scientific investigations

- Create incentives for value-purchasing support agencies; for example, insurance companies that play a more active role in discovering the best health outcomes for the lowest cost in the region and then structure packages with just what the customer needs

- Eliminate the tragedy of millions of uninsured people in the United States

Restructuring American healthcare accountability and incentives is analogous to putting a man on the moon. Americans can do this. The United States is blessed with sufficient resources. It needs the correct vision and the commitment to see it through. Let's boost our collective HQ and then drive the personal and system change that will make people healthier and wealthier!

APPENDIX | THE ROLE OF THE VARIOUS PLAYERS IN THIS TRANSFORMATION

If the healthcare system has fixed payments per patient, it can improve its profits by becoming more efficient and by attracting more customers. The healthcare system would be held accountable for its performance per Building Block #2, and have enough potential customers and competing producers per Building Block #3. Once Building Blocks #2 and #3 start to appear, the magic of the *functional* marketplace will take hold. Prices will drop and outcomes will improve.

We will soon describe how healthcare systems will succeed in an era of intelligent accountability and incentives. One tool for forcing the intelligent use of medical technology will be standardization of care. In other words, medical science experts will agree on best practices that will also be validated by healthcare outcomes databases. These guidelines will NOT be produced by medical societies that tend to promote the interventions of their own subspecialty. Rather, teams from various medical and non-medical fields will develop balanced and objective practice guidelines. These guidelines will be more conservative in utilizing medical technology until strong scientific evidence justifies their utilization. These guideline development committees will be funded by the health outcomes science investment we are recommending.

In summary, standardized care serves multiple purposes including:

1. Less wasteful or unintelligent care (Root Cause #1).

2. The systematic and scientific introduction of Life Ecology Factors improvement (Root Cause #2).

3. Holding healthcare providers accountable for compliance with best practices (Root Cause #3).

4. The simplification of the healthcare delivery environment (also addresses Root Cause #3).

Healthcare Providers

One of the key barriers to the utilization of best-practices or standardized care guidelines is the healthcare providers. Doctors and other healthcare providers may resist an adherence to practice guidelines. Healthcare providers will guard their independence to remain unique and maintain a monopoly. There's a saying that, "Absolute power corrupts absolutely." Power without checks and balances is destructive with the American healthcare disaster as a prime example. Now society is discovering how ineffective and inefficient the American healthcare system is, and the backlash will start. We believe it is important for healthcare providers to keep the enclosed perspectives in mind so they can be a part of the solution rather than an impediment.

Healthcare providers will complain about practicing "cookie cutter" or "one size fits all" medicine. They may also claim that they are the experts and should be allowed to apply this expertise on a case-by-case basis. We have several responses to these potential complaints which will also address the unfounded fear of rationing.

The world of modern medicine has become too complex, as demonstrated by the fallout of the Three Root Causes. Healthcare providers' decision-making independence no longer makes sense due to the information explosion, poor science, complexity of medical technology, complexity of healthcare delivery environments, the "Dangers of Doing Too Much", and the "Bias to Do Things". It is time for physicians to relinquish themselves to a new role as the captain of a *team* that cares for patients.

There's another problem with physicians having too much autonomy: defensive medicine. The problem with not practicing standardized care is that physicians feel they are on their own in making decisions. Being alone, they feel compelled to use every tool at their disposal lest they be blamed for malpractice. Defensive medicine is a major source of expense and wasted resources (Root Cause #1). Interestingly, the amount of money paid out for malpractice lawsuit *losses* is approximately five billion dollars per year in the United States; this is the amount Americans spend on pet food! In contrast, the amount spent on defensive practices is at least sixty billion dollars. The reaction to fear is much greater than the problem of the lawsuit itself. This is particularly problematic given the expensive tools utilized by the medical community.

If healthcare providers would relinquish *technical* decision independence and agree to standardized practices within their institutions, malpractice fears would drop substantially. A healthcare provider is much less likely to be criticized or sued if they have directly followed a guideline. When we say "technical" decisions, we are referring to the decision to use any medical technology including medications, tests, and interventions.

Standardized practice also creates accountability for all healthcare providers to deliver the care that is deemed necessary (Root Causes #2 and 3) and not provide wasteful and potentially dangerous care (Root Cause #1). If the healthcare provider's organization functions with such accountability, they feel assured that they are part of a successful environment and also benefit financially. Standardized practice drives consistent and simplified delivery processes which reduce errors and waste and improve quality of care (Root Cause #3).

Standardized practice can be facilitated at the point of care with decision-making computer systems which yield several advantages. These guidance systems bring collective wisdom right into the meeting between the healthcare provider and patient. Remember, it is too difficult for healthcare providers to assimilate the avalanche of information available, let alone sift through and find the scientific evidence. Another advantage of decision-making systems is that healthcare providers are protected from malpractice claims for two reasons. Providers will guide patients through the decision-making tree, and the *patient* will be making the decisions. These guidelines are also the most advanced thinking on medical matters, and thus backed by the provider's institution.

There's yet another powerful reason for providers to yield decision-making. Life Ecology Factors are much more powerful in producing health and healing than technology per Root Cause #2. Physicians are too enamored with technology. Frankly, all of society is enamored with technology, believing it will save the day. It is understandable that we have great belief in science, technology, and the never-ending march of progress, but now we've lost perspective and lost control. Ironically, Root Cause #2 can bring physicians back to the honorable role of healer. You see, unleashing the powers of self healing *cannot* be standardized. It requires time to form a connection with a patient, build trust, and then motivate compliance and Life Ecology Factors improvement. *There is nothing more gratifying than building a relationship of trust and then participating in the productive journey of another.* Healthcare providers need to reacquaint themselves with this source of joy and meaning. In a fixed budget or flat fee system, intelligent healthcare systems will emphasize time spent with patients rather than the often false-hope of medical technology.

There are several more reasons that healthcare providers should not be afraid to yield their decision-making autonomy. They will still retain autonomy for providing the clinical diagnosis. Healthcare providers will be needed to educate patients through the decision-making guidelines. They will be critical in building a relationship of trust with the patient. This relationship is vital to their patients' willingness to share important health information as well as comply with the prescribed therapy plan.

As a reminder, spending time with patients and working to improve their Life Ecology Factors is the most powerful rationale for changing the reimbursement model. Currently, Americans primarily reward technological interventions. Even if Americans do not go so far as to change from interventional reimbursement to total-care reimbursement, we could reward time spent with the patient *much more handsomely*. This would compensate primary care doctors for the key health and healing role they play. This just makes sense given the impact of primary care availability upon community health outcomes and the overall non-impact of specialists in their current mode of practice. Life Ecology Factors are undoubtedly the most important route for primary care and alternative medicine's impact. We can only tap into this power through time spent with patients. Patient interaction time will only be boosted with a substantial change in reimbursement.

To summarize, we are suggesting that it is critical for healthcare providers to surrender their independence for technical decision-making, allow a move towards decision-making guidance systems, participate in a shift to a self healing emphasis, recognize the power and joy of building a progressively deeper relationship with patients, and embrace a change in the reimbursement model to support more time spent with patients. Healthcare providers will give up one element of their autonomy, but the healthcare system will function more effectively due to better accountability and incentives. This improved functioning will paradoxically free up more resources which can support the more enjoyable aspects of patient care, not to mention sustain healthcare provider salaries which are currently being threatened by the healthcare fiscal crisis in the United States.

The future for successful healthcare systems will likely include support groups that encourage and coach improvements in Life Ecology Factors. Certainly we can create accountability and incentives for patient health behaviors. For example, we can measure smoking, obesity, participation in formal exercise programs, or participation in formal meditation programs. We can introduce reductions or increases in healthcare insurance premiums as incentives. However, incentives have their limits, which is why coaching or support groups are vital.

The effectiveness of support groups stem from multiple sources. It doesn't work to ridicule or judge another person for being overweight. When a person feels judged they generally shut down and give up. The alternative is to say, "We're all experiencing this challenge, so there is no judgment". This is the power of a support group focused on a particular challenge such as obesity. When non-judgment and genuine empathy are present, trust naturally builds. With trust, one starts to open up and understand the psychological and spiritual challenges that are blocking healthy behavior. Support groups can also get people excited about a collective mission and provide a sense of hope. Support groups introduce creative approaches to challenges based on collective experience. Finally, these groups also create accountability for healthy behaviors. The future of successful healthcare systems will rely less on doctor-patient relationships and more on support group-patient relationships.

Of course, healthcare providers can be the leaders of these groups, but the required skill set will be different than the stereotypical high IQ, high octane doctors we currently have. Rather, there will be a premium on emotional or spiritual intelligence in order to build healing relationships with patients. These stronger, high-trust relationships will be the key to unlocking health awareness, better targeted medical therapy, better compliance, and improving Life Ecology Factors.

One may argue, "Why would healthcare providers allow for the reforms suggested in this book given the risk to their salaries?" We argue that *average* salaries should remain the same. Healthcare providers' salaries only represent approximately 20% of the American healthcare budget. We would recommend a balancing of salaries so that primary and specialist salaries are more comparable. Of course, supply and demand will still apply in a functional market and specialists who are in short supply will be paid more handsomely.

In summary, our proposals would leave average healthcare providers salaries untouched or perhaps *increased* to accelerate their acceptance of these reform proposals. At the same time, healthcare providers will experience a more satisfying practice environment with less legal fear and a greater sense of joy and meaning as they play a more powerful role in their patients' lives. They will also be less trapped in a rat race trying to perform as many procedures as possible to generate revenue. The chairman of a very large surgery department recently said to me, "Just pay my surgeons as if they are doing the procedure but just have them <u>not</u> do the surgery. For every dollar they are paid, 4 dollars are charged by the system." In other words, if you pay healthcare providers handsome *salaries*, the American system will still come out way ahead due to a substantial improvement in the Three Root Causes AND a savings of hundreds of billions of dollars. Thus, a flat-fee system is quite feasible from a healthcare provider perspective if we can structure it to reassure them.

The Healthcare System

We just described the sacrifices that healthcare providers need to make in order to reverse the Three Root Causes. In particular, a move towards standardized practice will be a key to successful healthcare systems. Standardized practice will be even more vital if we switch to a fixed budget system. Let's briefly discuss what healthcare systems will need to do in an environment possessing the accountability and incentives we are recommending.

In an environment with greater health outcomes accountability and a fixed budget, healthcare systems will be motivated to reverse the Three Root Causes. First, they will use medical technology more sparingly in order to generate better profits as well as lower prices to entice more customers. This conservative approach to medical technology will be justified by Root Cause #1.

Second, per Root Cause #2, healthcare systems will become much more innovative in blending Life Ecology Factors and technology-based interventions to produce optimal health outcomes. This will include a significant shift in clinical emphasis to self healing. As a result of our Building Block #2 outcomes databases, healthcare system's performance will be placed under a microscope. Healthcare systems would be short-sighted not to tap into innovative methods for improving patient's Life Ecology Factors.

Finally, healthcare systems in a fixed budget environment would have an incentive to reduce complexity and waste as it improves profit margins and outcomes per Root Cause #3. Our accountability system would add pressure by identifying healthcare systems that produce a disproportionate rate of errors. Wouldn't it be great to have a healthcare system that is motivated to eliminate the Three Root Causes and work towards the same goals as patients have?!

Standardized practice will reduce the use of wasteful and dangerous technology. Standardized practice will reduce complex and wasteful care environments. Finally, standardized practice can also begin to incorporate more coaching tools to improve Life Ecology Factors. Still, standardized practice has another payoff. It allows us to be more scientific!

If we have a relatively consistent process or work flow, we can remove or rearrange a couple steps and measure what the effect is. This is a systematic or scientific approach. We can also measure how individual steps are being conducted and learn how to improve their execution. The work environment would be continuously simplified and made more consistent. Mistakes would drop and efficiency would improve. It makes sense that the less complex the care environment, the less likely we are to "drop the ball" by either doing something we shouldn't do or not doing something we should do. This applies to all the errors committed by the medical community including medication errors, medical injuries, hospital acquired infections, as well as the omission of valuable medical care.

Having witnessed such virtuous cycles in action, the entire American healthcare system must be engaged in continuous self-improvement. *Nothing* will make this happen faster than a fixed budget! This is not guess work! In addition to the limited examples of such virtuous cycles in healthcare, many sectors of the American economy have been displaying these types of process improvement for *DECADES!* While the tools have always been there, the accountability and incentives have not.

Furthermore, as healthcare systems become self-sustaining in their improvement, there will be much less need for a regulatory bureaucracy to bully them into better performance. Less bureaucracy will mean even less complexity and more cost savings.

Common sense tells us that it is *much* harder to get a human being or a system to perform if they aren't motivated from within by proper incentives. The correct incentives will produce inner motivation. Rules and regulations are often hoops to jump through; they waste time and produce questionable NET benefits. When people own the process of improvement, they feel a sense of accomplishment. Everyone wants to maintain the great feeling of accomplishment, creativity, and sense of purpose on top of the profit and accountability motives.

Speaking of bureaucracy, flat fees will also eliminate another *MAJOR* source of waste: the legions of people on the hospital and insurance side trying to either ensure or avoid payment. Hence, some experts advocate a single-payer system, similar to the system in Canada, in order to eliminate the healthcare insurance industry and the games they play. The problem is that a single-payer system with fee-for-service still in place does not prevent healthcare providers from doing too many procedures. It also doesn't prevent payment bureaucracy from developing with one *big* insurance company and several healthcare systems still trying to either avoid or ensure payment. A single-payer system would, in effect, be like Medicare on a larger scale. A single payer system also represents too much risk of a bureaucratic insurance system that will become inefficient once it has no competition. A flat fee system, though, truly eliminates the payment mess and waste.

Going to a flat fee system *eliminates* the need for those armies of people trying to decipher the payment mess. Flat fee payment also creates an incentive to eliminate the Three Root Causes as we discussed. Just eliminating the payment bureaucracy would save <u>hundreds</u> of billions of dollars! In contrast, a single-payer system with fee-for-service means the healthcare system can perform the accepted list of procedures and still get paid with much less incentive to innovate its approach to medical care.

It is very encouraging that Massachusetts is the first state to give serious consideration to the idea of a flat fee system. Several healthcare thinkers have also suggested a move towards a flat fee structure. With an intelligent accountability system as a foundation, there are many reasons why a flat fee system would be truly transformational.

Now, to be fair, we are not saying that it is impossible to make a fee-for-service system work better. The accountability system we are recommending would go a long way in order to keep the healthcare system honest and reduce excess interventions. Several of the fee-for-service problems would still remain, though, including being saddled with a payment bureaucracy and *much* less incentive to reverse the Three Root Causes.

Healthcare providers and healthcare systems will require unprecedented leadership to adapt to the new system of accountability and incentives. They will be limited in their ability to merely do more procedures to escape financial difficulty. They will have to implement industrial engineering tools as described above to eliminate waste and inconsistent performance within complex systems.

The American healthcare industry has had so little accountability and such poor incentives that it has allowed layer upon layer of inefficiency, waste, and poor performance to build. Healthcare leaders are not accustomed to the difficult conversations of holding healthcare providers accountable to the standard of continuously improving value. Due to a lack of incentives for producing value, many of the most talented leaders exited because a premium on team building or systems improvement did not exist. A hospital CEO only needed to make investments in advanced technology and the revenue would appear. There was *nothing* in the incentive structure to encourage the best health outcomes for the lowest price, which is much tougher to accomplish. Building truly effective healthcare systems will also require tremendous leadership to foster creative and ecological approaches to health and healing.

Modern medicine has been a remarkable misadventure. It will require the best leaders to unravel this mess. Their job will be facilitated by the correct accountability and incentives.

The Healthcare Insurance Companies

We do NOT advocate the elimination of the healthcare insurance industry, but our proposals will alter their role. They would no longer be passive agents simply taking their cut of the action. A flat fee system would eliminate a large part of the current insurance function and bureaucracy: reconciling payment. On the other hand, the healthcare insurance industry could become an active agent, finding the best healthcare value available for consumers. They can help structure more science-based healthcare coverage packages including flat-fee models. This brings us to another vital aspect of the healthcare reform discussion.

Recall our earlier functional market discussion. The three critical components of a functional market are price transparency, quality transparency, and a mobile consumer. Mobility means there's enough pressure on producers to keep improving their product or risk losing business. Pressure depends on the first two conditions, price and quality clarity, as well as having enough consumers and producers. We will generate plenty of consumers if they are rewarded for value shopping. We will generate enough value-producing healthcare systems if there is a flat fee system with sufficient accountability. The last piece in this functional market puzzle is allowing healthcare insurance companies to sell their products across state lines. This is presently a *major* impediment to a functional marketplace. Insurance companies have near monopolies in most states because competitors are restricted from entering their territories.

Another potential solution to the competition puzzle is the public insurance option. However, the public insurance option is *useless* without the proper accountability and incentives in place. If, as many believe, "Government can't do anything right" and the public insurance entity becomes too bureaucratic, then there is nothing to fear on the part of private insurance companies. Public insurance WILL represent another competitor forcing the marketplace to be more functional. Healthcare insurance companies complain that this entity will unfairly cut prices, but our accountability system will prevent this. Either prices are cut due to a willingness to take less profit (good for consumers and a functional market) or because the payment is truly inadequate. In the latter case, healthcare systems can simply refuse to take this payment. If the payment is adequate to cover costs and allow a slight profit margin, there will be a "taker" because a small profit margin multiplied by millions of customers means *billions* of dollars of profits. Sam Walton employed this model with great success in building Wal-Mart, and many consumers benefited from the value they received. Either the public insurance option will not serve as a threat or it will produce real competition. We can't go wrong by having more competitors. The best situation for producing a functional market is the presence of more than ONE competitor.

A critical element of the functional healthcare marketplace is liberalization of the healthcare insurance industry to include interstate sales. Another approach to improving competition within the healthcare insurance market is an insurance exchange. This mechanism allows small purchasers to pool their resources to buy healthcare coverage which then attracts multiple healthcare vendors. Again, this marketplace needs to be open for multiple vendors to enter. We still need to build these marketplaces on top of strong accountability and incentives. There are plenty of references to explain this approach in detail, but national insurance exchanges are one more attractive method to establish a functional market for American healthcare.

Employers

The role for employers is straightforward. Employers should help with the cultural transformation of employees *wanting* to be on their own for healthcare purchasing for the multiple reasons we listed earlier. Once employees are on their own, businesses can focus on their core mission. So how can American companies facilitate this transition?

Employers can encourage their employees' independence in several ways. First, the Three Root Causes should convince consumers that they can't simply accept what the healthcare system provides them. Given that there is approximately 60% waste in the American healthcare system, doesn't it make sense to purchase healthcare insurance that doesn't cover everything? Coverage for everything is what employers typically provide their employees. Why not make an agreement to provide employees a fixed, lower sum of money than their current healthcare insurance costs?

Employees can then purchase their own cost-effective healthcare insurance. This allows them to put more money back in their pocket while obtaining better, more satisfying healthcare. Why should corporations provide their employees a <u>lower</u> sum than the current costs of healthcare insurance? We're making a fairly safe assumption that there is at least 40% waste in current packages, and that the transition to a new system will be smoother if *everyone* has something to gain. By providing employees a lower amount than current premium costs, government and corporations would immediately benefit from the upcoming savings. Therefore, they will be motivated to encourage the various elements of our proposed reform movement.

For example, employees could receive cash in an amount that is 10% less than the total healthcare insurance costs currently paid by their employer. The employer would no longer have healthcare insurance costs as an annual worry. The employee stands to gain a substantial amount, but should be required to do a few things with the money.

First, a specific amount of the funds will need to be placed in a **Healthcare Savings Account.** Employees should be required to purchase a minimum level and type of coverage as we described with the HSA Plus example. These are still the <u>employee's</u> funds. Eventually, with excess funds, consumers can use the HSA for retirement purposes. More immediately, these funds are used for the higher deductible/lower premium coverage that is part of the HSA structure. A higher deductible means that the employee is using their own money and will be more active in seeking value. This will put more money in the employee's pocket and create a more dynamic healthcare marketplace.

This, in turn, will force producers to keep upping the ante in delivering healthcare value. Greater discretionary healthcare dollars will also allow employees to customize their healthcare plans consistent with an approach that improves their Life Ecology Factors.

Why hasn't this already happened? First, employees have had limited awareness of the Three Root Causes, and thus assumed that if they had healthcare insurance coverage they're better off leaving things alone. Second, the vast majority of people do not realize how precarious their healthcare insurance coverage is and how the healthcare financial burden is continuously being transferred to them without any value input from them. Third, there has been no value transparency in the form of price and health outcomes visibility. Thus, our proposal insists on a solid accountability program. Finally, there have been limits in employees' mobility. This is where Building Block #3 comes in with the incentives to stimulate a functional marketplace. A critical aspect of mobility is choice, which is why liberalization of the healthcare insurance industry is critical.

Moving employers out of the role of healthcare insurance purchaser is a win-win proposition. Corporations can focus on their core mission and serve the public as they are best fit. Employees can place more money in their pockets and create customized and therefore more satisfying and effective healthcare packages. Finally, the production of a true, dynamic healthcare marketplace will benefit everyone by launching a vigorous competition between healthcare systems and between healthcare insurance entities. A functional marketplace will, in turn, deliver continuously improving healthcare value to everyone through a progressive reversal of the Three Root Causes.

REFERENCES

INTRODUCTION

The Current State of Affairs

1. Brooks, David. "Whip Inflation Now." *NYTimes.com* 10 July 2009. (This is a wonderful summary of the inadequacies of current federal healthcare reform legislation. Mr. Brooks and other New York Times authors have issued several very intelligent analyses regarding healthcare reform as a whole, as well as specific topics within the debate. In fact, you will notice an extensive array of New York Times articles listed in this references section. You will find these quite helpful in understanding various healthcare reform matters)

2. Brooks, David. "Kill the Rhinos!" *NYTimes.com* 24 July 2009.

3. Herbert, Bob. "This Is Reform?" *NYTimes.com* 18 Aug. 2009.

Part I Root Cause #1—Modern Medicine is Unintelligent

Chapter 1
SCIENTIFIC THINKING WILL BOOST YOUR HQ

My Story—Anesthesiology Residency and Witnessing the Explosion of Technology

1. Li, Guohua. "Epidemiology of Anesthesia-related Mortality in the United States, 1999-2005." *Anesthesiology* 110 2009:759-65.

The Problem of Bias

1. Mann, Charles C. "Epidemiology Faces Its Limits." *Science* 269 1995:164-166. (Regarding the "discovery" of many "causes" of cancer including the LA Times reference)

2. Taubes, Gary. "The Soft Science of Dietary Fat." *Science* 291 2001.

3. Ebrahim, Shah, and Davey, Smith G. "Data Dredging, Bias, or Confounding." *British Medical Journal* 325 2002: 1437-1438.

A Call for the Elimination of Certain "Science" Departments

1. Le Fanu, J. The Rise and Fall of Modern Medicine. NY: Caroll&Graf, 2000.

The Placebo Effect, a Special Type of Confounding Factor

1. Ernst E., and K. L. Resch. "Concept of True and Perceived Placebo Effects." *British Medical Journal* 311 1995: 551-553.

2. Grenfell, Raymond. "A Double-Blind Study of the Treatment of Hypertension." *JAMA* 15 April 1961.

3. Kaptchuk, Ted J. "Do medical devices have enhanced placebo effects?" *Journal of Clinical Epidemiology* 53.8 2000: 786-792.

Chapter 2

TECHNOLOGICAL ADVANCEMENT WITHOUT SCIENTIFIC ADVANCEMENT IS HARMFUL TO YOUR HEALTH

What Went Wrong with NHS? (Hormone Replacement Therapy Fiasco)

1. Waters, David, and Edwin Alderman. "A Randomized Controlled Trial- Effects of Hormone Replacement Therapy and Antioxidant Vitamin Supplements on Coronary Atherosclerosis in Postmenopausal Women." *JAMA* 228 2002: 2432-2440.

2. Beral, Valerie. "Evidence from Randomized Trials on the Long-term Effects of Hormone Replacement Therapy." *The Lancet* 360 2002: 942-944.

3. Quindlen, Anna. "And Now for a Hot Flash." *Newsweek* A223 29 July 2002.

4. Singer, Natasha and Wilson, Duff. "Menopause, as Brought to You by Big Pharma." *NYTimes.com* 13 Dec. 2009. (How ironic that a class-action lawsuit has now been launched by 13,000 women who took LHT and have now developed breast cancer)

Supplements are Medications, Buyer Beware

1. Editorial. "The Hazards of Vitamin E." *NYTimes.com* 14 Nov. 2004.

2. Khaw, Kay-Tee. "Relation between Plasma Ascorbic Acid and Mortality in Men and Women in EPIC-Norfolk Prospective Study: a Prospective Population Study." *The Lancet* 357 2001 (observational study that found a correlation between vitamin C levels and heart disease and cancer death)

3. Heart Protection Study Collaborative Group. "MRC/BHF Heart Protection Study of Antioxidant Vitamin Supplementation in 20,536 High-risk Individuals: a Randomized Placebo-controlled Trial." *The Lancet* 360 2002: 23-33. (NO benefit of E, C, and Beta Carotene for heart disease or cancer. A randomized controlled trial!)

4. The Alpha-Tocopherol, Beta-Carotene Cancer Prevention Study Group. "The Effect of Vitamin E and Beta-Carotene on the Incidence of Lung Cancer and Other Cancers in Male Smokers." *New England Journal of Medicine* 330.15 1994: 1029-1035. (Randomized controlled trial in Finland of patients *already* having lung cancer but the results were much more negative for overall cancer and other health problems for the vitamin groups compared to the placebo group!)

5. US Preventive Services Task Force. "Routine Vitamin Supplementation to Prevent Cancer and Cardiovascular Disease: Recommendations and Rationale." *Annals of internal Medicine* 139.1 2003: 51-55. (Important scientific group cannot recommend the use of E, C, beta carotene, or folic acid for cancer or heart disease prevention based on the entire body of evidence)

6. Kmietowicz, Zosia. "Food Watchdog Warns against High Doses of Vitamins and Minerals." *British Medical Journal* 326 2003: 1001. (Not only no benefit but also the risk of harm. A systematic 4 year British analysis of vitamins with the discovery of risk for overdosage with multiple different vitamin classes)

7. Kolata, Gina. "Vitamins: More Maybe Too Many." *NYTimes.com* 29 Apr. 2003.

The Miserable State of Medications Science

FALSE SCIENCE OR SCIENCE MANIPULATION

1. Bhandari, Mohit. "Association between Industry Funding and Statistically Significant Pro-industry Findings in Medical and Surgical Randomized Trials." *CMAJ* 170.4 2004: A168.

2. Dobson, Roger. "Industry Sponsored Studies Twice as Likely to Have Positive Conclusions about Costs." *British Medical Journal* 327 2003: 1006.

3. Elias, Marilyn. "Psychiatric Drugs Fare Favorably when Companies Pay for the Studies." *USA Today* 24 May 2006: A267.

4. Noonan, David, and Geoffrey Cowley. "Prozac vs. Placebos." *Newsweek* July 2002: 48-49.

5. Greenberg, Gary. "Is That Prozac? Or Placebo?" *MotherJones* November/December 2003.

6. Harman, Steve. "The making of a disease: female sexual dysfunction. Concerns over Drug Industry Creation of New Diseases." *JAMA* 326 2003: 45-47.

7. Stephenson, Joan. "New Drugs' Dosages Often Too High." *JAMA* 288.13 2002: 1578. (Medications are tested at the highest possible doses to encourage greater sales, often requiring post-approval reductions because of side effects on average)

8. MacPherson, Kitta. "Pharmacia Denounced for Halting Drug Study." *The Star-Ledger News* 23 April 2003.

9. Editorial. "Many Questions about Vytorin." *NYTimes.com* 5 Sept. 2008. (Vytorin passed with very few, small studies. Subsequent studies indicated no effect of coronary plaque or heart attacks. Then some concern about cancer risk. Again no net or relative benefit established but drug becomes a blockbuster)

10. Singh, Debashis. "Drug Companies Advised to Publish Unfavorable Trial Results." *British Medical Journal* 326 2003: 1163.

11. Grady, Denise. "Study questions value of big doses of hard drug." *NYTimes.com* 31 Aug. 2004.

WEAK SCIENCE—POOR NET BENEFIT (MUCH LESS EFFECTIVE AND/OR MUCH GREATER SIDE EFFECTS THAN BENEFITS)

1. Berenson, Alex. "For Widely Used Drug, Questions of Usefulness Is Still Lingering." *NYTimes.com* 2 Sept 2008. (Not only no benefit regarding heart attacks BUT also *an increased risk of cancer*)

2. Berenson, Alex. "Heart Risks Seen in Drug for Anemia." *NYTimes.com* 16 Nov. 2006. (Much higher risk of heart problems and death due to higher dosage. Label warns against higher dose, yet doctors prescribe at higher levels than the Europeans who also have a lower death rate. American doctors *make more money by selling more drug. There is no scientific evidence of quality of life benefit from the higher dose,* the excuse provided for the higher doses)

3. Berenson, Alex and Pollack, Andrew. "Doctors Reap Millions for Anemia Drugs." *NYTimes.com* 9 May 2007.

4. Meier, Barry. "Medicine Fueled by Marketing Intensified Trouble for Pain Pills." *NYTimes.com* 19 Dec. 2004. (Billions made on these drugs, FDA can't keep up, significantly more *deaths from Celebrex and* because of heart disease and bleeding ulcers)

5. Grady, Denise, and Harris, Gardiner. "Overprescribing Prompted Warning on Antidepressants." *NYTimes.com* 24 Mar. 2004.

6. Grady, Denise. "Seeking to Shed Fat, She Lost Her Liver." *NYTimes.com* 4 Mar. 2003.

7. Kolata, Gina. "A Widely Used Arthritis Drug Is Withdrawn." *NYTimes.com* 1 Oct. 2004.

8. "Study: Wide Use of Drug Caused Deaths." *CNN on the Web* 5 Aug. 2004.

Raising the Bar for Medications?

WEAK SCIENCE—POOR RELATIVE BENEFIT

1. Editorial. "Two More Blockbusters Fall Short." *NYTimes.com* 18 Sept. 2008.

2. Davis B. "Major Outcomes in High-Risk Hypertensive Patients Randomized to Angiotensin-Converting Enzyme Inhibitor or Calcium Channel Blocker vs Diuretic: The Antihypertensive and Lipid-lowering Treatment to Prevent Heart Attack Trial (ALLHAT)." *JAMA* 288 2002: 2981-2997.

3. Petersen, Melody. "Diuretics' Value Drowned Out by Trumpeting of Newer Drugs." *NYTimes.com* 18 Dec. 2002.

4. Pollack, Andrew. "The Minimal Impact of a Big Hypertension Study." *NYTimes.com* 28 Nov. 2008.

NO SCIENCE—RAMPANT OFF-LABEL MEDICATION USE

1. Steinman, Michael A. E. "Changing Use of Antibiotics in Community-Based Outpatient Practice, 1991-1999." *Annals of Internal Medicine* 138.7 2003: 525-533. (The overprescribing of so-called "Superdrug" antibiotics for infections which then risks antibiotics resistance)

2. "Study: Doctors Over Prescribing Super Drugs; Doctors Unwisely Over Prescribing New Super Drugs for Common Ailments, Study Says, Living." *Associated Press* 31 Mar. 2003.

3. Pollack, Andrew. "Talking Up a Drug for This (and That)." *NYTimes.com* 27 Apr. 2003. (Evidence wasn't good enough for approval but showed some positive results and MDs started prescribing based on "science")

4. Noonan, David, and Geoffrey Cowley. "Prozac vs. Placebos." *Newsweek* July 2002: 48-49.

5. Editorial. "Medicare and 'Off-Label' Cancer Drugs." *NYTimes.com* 10 Feb. 2009.

WEAK FDA

1. "FDA to Make Changes to Boost Drug Safety." *Reuters on the Web* 30 Jan 2007. (IOM criticizes poor FDA performance and FDA responds with promises to change)

2. Representative Henry Waxman report on January 29th 2004 ("FDA not taking enough action against false claims in prescription drug ads")

3. Harris, Gardiner. "FDA to Expand Scrutiny of Risks From Drugs After They're Approved for Sale." *NYTimes.com* 23 May 2008. (Now. after all these decades of medications being allowed in the medicine cabinet. Now we're going to scrutinize for long-term side effects!)

4. Editorial. "Industry a Distortion of the FDA.." *NYTimes.com* 8 Dec. 2004. (Already short budgeted, funds diverted to new medication approval rather than tracking long-term side effects)

5. Editorial. "Substantial Complications." *NYTimes.com* 11 May 2009. (FDA even less present for device safety monitoring)

6. Editorial. "Not What You Call Due Diligence." *NYTimes.com* 13 Jan. 2009. (HHS review of FDA found stunning omissions by the FDA in approving drugs and devices)

7. Goozner, Merrill. "Overdosed and Oversold." *NYTimes.com* 21 Dec. 2004.

8. Petersen, Melody. "Who's Minding the Drugstore?" *NYTimes.com* 29 Jun. 2003.

9. Opinion. "Blocking Medical Product Suits." *NYTimes.com* 1 Aug. 2004.

CORPORATE MISBEHAVIOR—DISCLOSURE PROBLEMS

1. Vedantam, Shankar. "Antidepressant Makers Withhold Data on Children." *Washington Post on the Web* 29 Jan. 2004. (Complaints about refusal of pharmaceutical companies to disclose study results despite concern about higher suicide rates in younger individuals taking these drugs. Part of criticism was the prediction that *many* of the studies likely showed no benefit vs. placebo and thus undermined the value of antidepressants. This also highlights the ability of pharmaceutical companies to eliminate unfavorable studies and simply highlight the favorable ones as with the assessment bias section of Chapter 2).

2. Berenson, Alex. "Despite Warnings, Drug Giant Took Long Path to Vioxx Recall." *NYTimes.com* 14 Nov. 2004.

3. Berenson, Alex. "Merck Admits a Data Error on Vioxx." *NYTimes.com* 31 May 2006.

4. Harris, Gardiner. "FDA Says Bayer Failed to Reveal Drug Risk Study." *NYTimes.com* 30 Sep. 2006.

5. Harris, Gardiner. "Judge Says Maker of OxyContin Misled Officials to Win Patents." *NYTimes.com* 6 Jan. 2004.

LOBBYING

1. Pear, Robert. "Drug Companies Increase Spending on Efforts to Lobby Congress and Governments." *NYTimes.com* 1 June 2003.

2. Stolberg, Sheryl Gay. "Drug Lobby Pushed Letter by Senators on Medicare." *NYTimes. com* 30 July 2003. (Pharmaceutical companies in effect wrote the legislation which is analogous to them ghost writing medical journal articles!)

MARKETING TRUMPS SCIENCE

1. Meier, Barry. "Medicine Fueled by Marketing Intensified Trouble for Pain Pills." *NYTimes.com* 19 Dec. 2004. (Billions made on these drugs, FDA can't keep up, significantly more <u>deaths from Celebrex and</u> because of heart disease and bleeding ulcers)

2. Spence, Michelle M. "Direct-to-consumer Advertising of COX-2 Inhibitors: Effect on Appropriateness of Prescribing." *Medical Care Research and Review* 62.5 2005: 544-559.

3. "Impact of Direct-to-Consumer Advertising on Prescription Drug Spending." *Kaiser family Foundation* 2003: B 100.

4. Hensley, Scott. "As Drug Sales Teams Multiply, Doctors Start to Tune Them Out 'Arms Race' by Pfizer and Rivals Boost Pill Prices, Ire, but No One Dares Retreat." *Wall Street Journal* 13 July 2003: A164.

5. Newswire, Ivanhoe. "Drug Reps Play Role in Overprescribing." *British Medical Journal* 326 2003: 1178-1179.

6. "Misleading Drug Ads Slip Under Regulators' Radar." *USA Today on the Web* 6 Jan. 2003.

7. Pear, Robert. "Investigators Find Repeated Deception in Ads for Drugs." *NYTimes.com* 4 Dec. 2002.

8. Vedantam, Shankar, and Marc Kaufman. "Doctors influenced by Mention of Drug Ads." *Washington Post* 27 April 2005: A206.

9. Kowalczyk, Liz. "Drug Companies' Secret Reports Outraged Doctors." *Boston Globe* 25 May 2003: A274.

10. Grady, Denise, and Gardiner Harris. "Overprescribing Prompted Warning on Antidepressants." *NYTimes.com* 24 Mar. 2004.

11. Lavoie, Denise. "Whistle-blower to Get $24.6 million, Pfizer Also Will Pay Civil, Criminal Fines." *CBS News on the Web* 13 May 2004.

12. "Pfizer Settles with Maryland, 18 Other States, It Must Change How It Promotes Antibiotic for Child Ear Infections." *Associated Press* 7 Jan. 2003.

CONFLICT OF INTEREST—HEALTHCARE PROVIDERS AND MEDICATIONS

1. Fava, Giovanni A. "Long-Term Treatment with Antidepressant Drugs: The Spectacular Achievements of Propaganda." Editorial. *Psychotherapy and Psychosomatics* 71 2002: 127-132.

RESEARCHER PAY AND PHYSICIAN GIFTS

2. Harris, Gardiner. "Researchers Fail To Reveal Full Drug Pay." *NYTimes.com* 8 Jun. 2008.
3. Harris, Gardiner. "Drugmakers are Still Giving Gifts to Doctors, FDA Officials Says." *NYTimes.com* 4 March 2005.
4. Petersen, Melody. "Court Papers Suggests Deal of Drugs Use." *NYTimes.com* 30 May 2003.
5. Editorial. "Industry's Role in Hypertension." *NYTimes.com* 30 May 2006.
6. Ross, Brian, and David W. Scott. "How Pharmaceutical Companies Use Enticement to "Educate" Physicians." *ABC News on the Web* 23 Mar. 2002.
7. Harris, Gardiner. "As Doctors Write Prescriptions, Drug Company Writes a Check." *NYTimes.com* 27 Jun. 2004.
8. Editorial. "Hidden Drug Payments at Harvard." *NYTimes.com* 10 June 2008.
9. Editorial. "No Mugs, but What About Those Fees." *NYTimes.com* 5 Jan. 2009. (Loopholes still allowing gifts to doctors which then creates conflict of interest in doctors prescribing)
10. Editorial. "(Generic) Drug Resistance." *NYTimes.com* 10 Dec. 2008. (Powerful marketing and advertising prevents healthcare providers from using less expensive generic medication options)
11. Bekelman Justin E. "A Systematic Review." Scope and Impact of Financial Conflicts of Interest in Biomedical Research. *JAMA* 289.4 2003: 454-465.
12. Psaty, Bruce M. "Clinical Trial Investigators and Their Prescribing Patterns, Another Dimension to the Relationship Between Physician Investigators and Pharmaceutical Industry." *JAMA* 295.23 2006: 2787-2790.

MEDICAL JOURNALS BOUGHT OFF

1. Editorial. "Our Conflicted Medical Journals." *NYTimes.com* 23 July 2006.

PRICE MANIPULATION

1. Abelson, Reed. "How Schering Manipulated Drug Prices and Medicaid." *NYTimes.com* 31 Jul. 2004.
2. Pear, Robert. "Investigators Say Drugmakers Repeatedly Overcharged" *NYTimes.com* 30 June 2004.

3. "Drug Makers to Pay Medicaid Settlement; Bayer, Glaxo Smith Kline to Pay Record Medicaid Fraud Settlements to Resolve Alleged Overcharges." *Associated Press* 16 April 2003.

4. Jewell, Mark. "Express Scripts to Pay $9.5 Million in Settlement." *Associated Press* 27 May 2008.

TWO FORMER EDITORS OF THE PRESTIGIOUS *New England Journal of Medicine* BLAST THE PHARMA INDUSTRY

1. Angell, Marcia. "Is Academic Medicine for Sale." *New England Journal of Medicine* 342.20 2000: 1516-1518.

2. Wente, M. "Who Will Take on the Pushers?" *The Globe and Mail on the Web* 19 Dec. 2002.

3. Marcia Angell, "The Pharmaceutical Industry-To Whom Is It Accountable?" *The New England Journal of Medicine* 342.22 June 2000:1902-1904.

4. Relman, Arnold S. and Angell, Marcia. "America's Other Drug Problem: How the Industry Distorts Medicine in Politics." *New Republic* 16 Dec. 2002: A 325.

5. Relman, Arnold S. "Your Doctor's Drug Problem." *NYTimes.com* 18 Nov. 2003.
(The pharmaceutical companies do NOT pay for most of the research that discovers new, innovative medications. These are primarily funded by the government and universities. Further, the relative and net value of new medications is almost never established. In the absence of science, the industries manipulation through marketing and advertising including control of the medical establishment message is quite powerful and steering decision-making)

OTHER SUMMARIES OF THE PHARMACEUTICAL INDUSTRY PROBLEM

1. Greider, Catherine. "The Big Fix: How The Pharmaceutical Industry Rips Off American Consumers." New York: Public Affairs, 2003.

2. Krugman, Paul. "A Serious Drug Problem." *NYTimes.com* 6 May 2005.

3. Judd, Jackie. "Pharmaceutical Profiteers, Drug Company's Net Federal Funds While Developing New Products, Taxpayers End Up Funding Drug Companies." *ABC News on the Web* 9 June 2003.

Coronary (Heart) Artery Interventions—Disaster Because of Poor Science

1. Kenny, James J. "Bypassing the Evidence: A Critical Analysis of Several Questionable Medical Treatments for Atherosclerosis." *A Continuing Medical Education Series* 10 Sept. 2003.

2. Kolata, Gina. "Heart Pump and Brain Injury: a Riddle Deepens the Time." *NYTimes.com* 13 May 2003.

3. King III, Spencer B. "Why Have Stents Replaced the balloons? Underwhelming Evidence." *Annals of Internal Medicine* 138.10 2003.

4. Meier, Barry. "Removing Heart Cables is Hard Choice." *NYTimes.com* 7 April 2009.

5. Pembrook, Linda. "Post-CABG Cognitive Decline Linked to Long-term Impairment." *Anesthesiology News on the Web* 2001.

6. Editorial. "The Limits of Opening Arteries." *NYTimes.com* 28 March 2004.

7. Grady, Denise. "Study Questions Angioplasty Use in Some Patients." *NYTimes.com* 15 Nov. 2006.

8. Kolata, Gina. "New Studies Question Value of Opening Arteries." *NYTimes.com* 21 Mar. 2004.

9. Feder, Barnaby J. "Doctors Rethink Widespread Use of Heart Stents." *NYTimes.com* 21 Oct. 2006.

10. Newman, Mark F. "Longitudinal Assessment of Neurocognitive Function after Coronary Artery Bypass Surgery." *New England Journal of Medicine* 344 2001: 395-402.

11. Ornish, Dean. "Intensive Lifestyle Changes for Reversal of Coronary Heart Disease." *JAMA* 280.28 1998: 2001-2007.

12. Esselstyn, Caldwell B. and Favaloro, Rene G. "Introduction: More than Coronary Artery Disease." *The American Journal of Cardiology* 26 Nov. 1998. (A wonderfully honest and insightful article by cardiac surgeons regarding the misguided modern medical approach to treating coronary artery disease in general, *written over a decade ago*)

Other Examples of Science Exposing Surgical Procedures

1. Moran, Mark. "High-Cost medical Advances Need to Prove Value." *Psychiatric News* 38.24 2003: 11.

2. Maddern, Guy. "Safety and Efficacy of Interventional Procedures." Editorial. *The British Medical Journal* 326 2003: 347-348.

3. Moseley, Bruce J. et al. "A Controlled Trial of Arthroscopic Surgery for Osteoarthritis of the Knee." *New England Journal of Medicine* 11 July 2002. (Knee arthroscopic surgery was no better than a sham comparison surgery!)

4. Kolata, Gina. "A Study Revives a Debate on Arthritis Knee Surgery." *NYTimes.com* 11 Sept. 2008. (and yet, knee surgeries just continue despite even more evidence demonstrating their lack of relative benefit!)

5. Veronesi, Umberto. "20-Year Follow-up of a Randomized Study Comparing Breast Conserving Surgery with Radical Mastectomy for Early Breast Cancer." *New England Journal of Medicine* 347.16 2002: 1227-1232.

6. Fairbank, Jeremy. "Randomized Controlled Trial to Compare Surgical Stabilization of the Lumbar Spine with an Intensive Rehabilitation Program for Patients with Chronic Low Back Pain: the MRC Spine Stabilization Trial." *Bridge Medical Journal* 330 2005: 1233.

7. Kolata, Gina. "Study Questions Need to Operate on Disc Injuries." *NYTimes.com* 22 Nov. 2006.

8. Kolata, Gina. "Lumpectomies Seen As Equal in Benefit To Breast Removals." *NYTimes. com* 17 Oct. 2002.

9. Meier, Barry. "New Effort Reopens a Medical Minefield." *NYTimes.com* 7 May 2009.

10. Editorial. "Substantial Complications." *NYTimes.com* 11 May 2009. (FDA even less present for device safety monitoring)

11. Meier, Barry. "Costs Surge for Medical Devices, but Benefits Are Opaque." *NYTimes.com* 5 Nov. 2009. (Stunning example of how Medicare strikes deals to reimburse medical interventions with little or no science to justify the procedure)

Screening Tests—Inappropriate Screening including Poor/No Benefit Examples

1. "Task Force Recommends Against Routine Coronary Heart Disease Screening." *Annals of Internal Medicine* 140 2004: 24. (Whereas the American Heart Association and American College of Cardiology both DO recommend the screening!)

2. Grady, Denise. "Less Screening Urged for Some for Cervix Cancer." *NYTimes.com* 18 Dec. 2002.

3. "Colonoscopies Overdone, US Study Suggests." 16 Aug. 2004. < http://sci.tech-archive.net/Archive/sci.med.diseases.cancer/2004-08/0164.html>

4. Fuhrman, Vanessa. "Overuse of Medical Scans is Under Fire, as Billings for CT Scans, MRI Sore, Medicare Panel to Recommend More Scrutiny." *Wall Street Journal* 12 Jan. 2005: A34.

5. Moss, Michael, and Jennifer Steinhauer. "Mammogram Clinic's Flaws Highlight Gaps in US Rules." *NYTimes.com* 24 Oct. 2002.

6. Whiteford, John, and Whiteford, John Ryan. "Screening for Breast Cancer." *Annals of Internal Medicine* 138.9 2003: 768-770.

7. Editorial. "A Fallible Prostate Cancer Test." *NYTimes.com* 30 July 2003.

8. "Study: Prostate Test Misses a Majority of Tumors." *Reuters* 24 July 2003:A302.

9. Jody, Jane E. "Questions Outnumber Answers on PSA Test." *NYTimes.com* 18 Feb. 2003.

10. Kolata, Gina. "Prostate Test Found to Save Few Lives." *NYTimes.com* 19 March 2009.

11. Kolata, Gina. "10 Million Women Who Lack a Cervix Still Get Pap Tests." *NYTimes.com* 23 June 2004.

12. Berenson, Alex. "Weighing the Costs of a CT Scan's Look Inside the Heart." *NYTimes.com* 29 June 2008.

13. Kolata, Gina. "Good or Useless, medical Scans Cost the Same." *NYTimes.com* 2 Mar. 2009.

14. Law, Malcolm. "Screening Without Evidence of Efficacy." Editorial. *British medical Journal* 328 2004: 301-302.

15. Kolata, Gina. "Early Detection of Cancer: Nothing is Black and White." *NYTimes.com* 24 Dec. 2002.

16. Duenwald, Mary. "Putting Cancer Screening to the Test." *NYTimes.com* 15 Oct. 2002.

17. Kolata, Gina. "Cancer Society, in Shift, Has Concerns on Screenings." *NYTimes.com* 21 Oct. 2009. (Stunning admissions by the American Cancer Society that breast and prostate cancer screening and screening in general have been overrated in their value. Also, screening in general has not been approached in a scientifically sophisticated manner.)

18. Sack, Kevin and Kolata, Gina. "Screening Policy Won't Change, U.S. Officials Say." *NYTimes.com* 19 Nov. 2009. (Concern about new mammography recommendations and government getting involved in decision-making. What these fears do not recognize is the lack of science and healthcare providers that are incapable of making scientifically disciplined decisions because of information overload. There MUST be some central body whose role it is to cull through all the information and produce an intelligent guideline to get the most health benefit out of our resources. *The unintelligent use of resources KILLS more people*)

19. Collins, Gail. "The Breast Brouhaha." *NYTimes.com* 19 Nov. 2009. (A nice listing of many large-scale medical decision-making errors by the medical community)

20. Grady, Denise. "Guidelines Push Back Age for Cervical Cancer Tests." *NYTimes. com* 20 Nov. 2009. (15 million cervical cancer screens a year in the United States *in women without a cervix* when guidelines already stated this wasn't necessary. Also more evidence that the medical community was performing too many screenings with no evidence of mortality benefit and a higher incidence of complications from cervical procedures including premature birth and cesarean sections during pregnancy)

21. Kolata, Gina. "Scientists Begin to Question Benefit of 'Good' Cholesterol." *NYTimes.com* 15 Mar. 2004.

22. "Radiation Overexposure From CT Scans May Be More Widespread Than Previously Estimated." *ACPE Daily Digest* 15 Dec. 2009. (based on 2 articles from the Archives of Internal Medicine that indicate as many 29,000 *excess* cancers and 18,000 *excess* deaths because of CT scan radiation exposure in one year!)

The Sad State of Chemotherapy—Poor Science and Conflict of Interest

1. Haney, Daniel Q. "Cancer Wonder Drugs are Not Working Miracles." *Associated Press on the Web* 27 July 2003.

2. Ezekiel, J. Emanuel. "Chemotherapy Use among Medicare Beneficiaries at the End of Life." *Annals of Internal Medicine* 138.8 2003: B 60.

3. Nesi, Tom. "False Hope in a Bottle." Editorial. *NYTimes.com* 5 June 2003.

4. Harris, Gardiner. "Medicare Curbs on Payment for Cancer Drugs." *NYTimes.com* 30 Jan. 2004.

5. Kolata, Gina. "Advances Elusive in the Drive to Cure Cancer." *NYTimes.com* 24 April 2009.

6. Kolata, Gina and Pollack, Andrew. "Costly Cancer Drug Offers Hope, but Also a Dilemma." *NYTimes.com* 6 July 2008.

7. "Doctors Say Futile Cancer Treatment Rising." *USA Today on the Web* 2 June 2006.

8. Friend, Tim. "Chemotherapy Use Rises among Terminal Patients." *USA Today* 3 June 2003.

9. Abelson, Reed. "Drug Sales Bring Huge Profits, and Scrutiny, to Cancer Doctors." *NYTimes.com* 26 Jan. 2003.

10. Clancy, Carolyn M. "Is Outcomes Research on Cancer Ready for Prime Time?" *Medical Care* 40.6 2002: 92-100. (*NOW* ready for prime time after decades of extensive use?)

11. Singer, Natasha. "Cancer Center Ads Use Emotion More than Fact." *NYTimes.com* 19 Dec. 2009.

GENERAL THOUGHTS ON THE POOR STATE OF SCIENCE IN AMERICAN AND
MODERN MEDICINE

1. Woolf, Stephen. "The Breakeven Point: When Medical Advances Are Less Important Than Improving The Fidelity With Which They Are Delivered." *Annals of Family Medicine* 3 2005: 545-552.

2. Steinberg, Earl P. "Evidence-Based? Caveat Emptor!" *Health Affairs* 24.1 2005:80-92. (Even the label of "EBM" is unfairly attached to many healthcare endeavors. EBM is only as good as the evidence, and the evidence is not very good for the most part)

3. Abramson, John. "Overdosed America: The Broken Promise of American Medicine." New York: HarperCollins, 2004.

4. Singh, Debashis. "Drug Companies Advised to Publish Unfavorable Trial Results." *British Medical Journal* 326 2003: 1163.

5. Sandars, John. "Improving the Implementation of Evidence-based Practice: a Knowledge Management Perspective." *Journal of Evaluation in Clinical Practice* 12.3 2006: 341-346.

6. Friedman, Lawrence M and DeMets, David L. <u>Fundamentals of Clinical Trials</u>. Springer; 3rd edition, 1999. (Excellent book by some of the pioneers of medical science including Dr. DeMets whose class was inspirational to the author of this book. The Intro chapter includes many excellent examples of the history of and rationale for a scientific to healthcare decision making)

7. Smith, Richard. "Doctors are not Scientists." *British Medical Journal* 328 2004. (This is correct based on my own experience and the reason standardization of care must be encouraged and enforced. Otherwise resources are wasted and patients are directly and indirectly harmed.)

8. Genuis, Stephen J. "Diagnosis: Contemporary Medical Hubris; RX: a Tincture of Humility." *Journal of Evaluation in Clinical Practice* 12.1 2005.

9. Ebrahim, Shah and George Davey Smith. "Data Dredging, Bias, or Confounding." *British Medical Journal* 325 2002: 1437-1438.

10. Timmermans, Stefan. "The Promises and Pitfalls Of Evidence-Based Medicine." *Health Affairs* 24.1 2005: 18-28.

11. Bodenheimer, Thomas. "Is Evidence-Based Medicine Evidence Based?" *Health Affairs* 24.2 2005:562-563.

12. Goel, Vijay. (No title) American Medical Student Association Health Policy Group. 3 Jun. 2003. (interesting point about the dearth of subjects included in the Cochrane database and the many holes within expert opinions, and guidelines primarily based on case studies or opinions)

TERRIBLE FUNDING FOR HEALTH OUTCOMES RESEARCH AND NEXT STEPS
FOR SOCIETY

1. Robeznieks, Andis. "The Bush Administration Proposes $24.7 Million Budget Cut for Healthcare's 'Apple Pie' Agency." *AMNews on the Web* 12 May 2003.

2. Landers, Susan J. "Are the Good Times Over at National Institutes of Health?" *AMNews on the Web* 24 Feb. 2003. (It's outrageous that *clinical* research is threatened by cuts because the National Institute of *Health* is primarily a basic science outfit. Health is most affected by clinical research NOT basic research)

3. Wilson, Duff. "Research Uproar at a Cancer Clinic." *NYTimes.com* 23 Oct. 2009. (Another example of how poorly funded and porous the American clinical research infrastructure is)

Chapter 3

HAUNTED BY UNINTELLIGENCE: EVIDENCE FOR A BROKEN AMERICAN
HEALTHCARE SYSTEM, THE FINAL CULMINATION OF ROOT CAUSE #1

Problem Number 1: The American Healthcare System is Too xpensive

1. Anderson, Gerard. "Researchers Rule out Supply Constraints and Litigation as Cause. US Still Spends More on Health Care than Any Other Country." *Johns Hopkins School of Public Health on the Web* 12 July 2005.

2. Anderson, Gerard F. "It's the Prices, Stupid: Why the United States is So Different from Other Countries." *Health Affairs* 22.3 2003.

3. Organization for Economic Cooperation and Development, Heath Data, 2000.

4. Dorschner, John. "Sticker Shock: Extras Drive up Costs of US Healthcare." *Miami Herald on the Web* 28 Apr. 2003.

5. Abelson, Reed. "Weighing Medical Costs of End-of-Life Care." *NYTimes.com* 23 Dec. 2009.

Problem Number 3: Where's the Improved Quality of Life Delivered by the American Healthcare System (International Comparisons)?

POOR QUALITY AT THE BIG PICTURE LEVEL DESPITE EXPENSE

1. Kristof, Nicholas D. "Health Care? Ask Cuba." *NYTimes.com* 12 Jan. 2005.

2. Davis, K. "Mirror, Mirror on the Wall: An International Update on the Comparative Performance of American Health Care." *Common Wealth Fund on the Web* 15 May 2007.

3. Stein, Rob. "Survey Says US Patients Pay More, Get Less Than Those in Other Western Nations." For Americans, Getting Sick Has Its Price. *The Washington Post on the Web* 4 Nov. 2005.

4. Schoen, Cathy. "US Health System Performance: A National Scorecard." *The Commonwealth Fund on the Web.* 20 Sep. 2006.

5. Editorial. "World's Best Medical Care?" *NYTimes.com* 12 Aug. 2007.

6. Spithoven, A. "Why US Health Care Expenditure and Ranking on Health Care Indicators Are So Different From Canada's." *Int. J. Health Care Finance Economics* 31 July 2008.

7. Gerard. "Cross-national Comparisons Can Determine Whether Additional Health-care Spending Results in Better Outcomes. Comparing Health System Performance in the OECD Countries." *Health Affairs* 20.3 2001: 80.

8. Scheffey, Daniel. "Rising Hospital Costs: The Value quandary." *US Newswire on the Web* 11 Dec. 2002.

9. Editorial. "The Wrong Place to be Chronically Ill." *NYTimes.com* 18 Nov. 2008.

10. Anderson, Gerard F. "Health Spending in the United States and the Rest of the Industrialized World." *Health Affairs* 24.4: 903-914.

11. Moran, Mark. "Quantity of Medical Care doesn't Guarantee Quality." *Psychiatric News* 38.6 2003.

12. Starfield, B. "The Effect of Specialist Supply on Populations' Health: Assessing the Evidence." *Health Affairs on the Web* 15 March 2005.

13. Balcker, Katherine, and Amitabh Chandra. "Medicare Spending, the Physician Workforce, and Beneficiaries' Quality of Care." *Health Affairs* 2004.

14. Editorial. "Doctors and the Cost of Care." *NYTimes.com* 14 June 2009.

15. Pear, Robert. "Health Care Spending Disparities Stir a Fight." *NYTimes.com* 9 June 2009. (Legislators initial responses to the Medicare Variation with no benefit and the war high-spending states are ready to fight)

16. Anderson, Gerard F. "Comparing Health System Performance in OECD Countries." *Health Affairs* 24.4 May/June 2001.

17. Grumbach, Kevin. "Specialist, Technology, and Newborns Too Much of a Good Thing." Editorial. *The New England Journal of Medicine* 346.20 2002: 1574-1575.

18. Comarow, Avery. "Are Hospitals Overdosing on Intensive Care?" *U.S. News & World Report on the Web* 2 June 2008.

19. Phelps, Charles E. "What's Enough, What's Too Much?" *Annals of Internal Medicine* 138.4 2003: 348-349.

Problem Number 4: Americans Do NOT Wait Less to Receive Healthcare

REAL ACCESS DATA INCLUDING THE UNINSURED, PRIMARY CARE

1. "53% of US Residents Say Family Cut Back on Health Care in Past Year Because of Costs, Poll Finds." *Kaisernetwork.org.* 26 Feb. 2009.

2. Bindman, AB. "Diagnostic Scope of and Exposure to Primary Care Physicians in Australia, New Zealand, and the United States: A Cross Sectional Analysis of Results from Three National Surveys." *BMJ* 334.7606 2007: 1261.

3. Pear, Robert. "When a Job Disappears, So Does the Health Care." *NYTimes.com* 7 Dec. 2008.

4. Pallarito, Karen. "Medical Problems Cause Half of Personal Bankruptcies." *Healthday on the Web* 2 Feb. 2005.

5. Institute of Medicine. <u>Hidden Costs, Value Lost: Uninsurance in America</u>. National Academies Press, 2003.

6. Stencel, Christine. "IOM Report Calls for Universal Health Coverage by 2010; Offers Principals to Judge, Compare Proposed Solutions." *Institute of Medicine* 14 Jan. 2004.

7. Edelson, Ed. "More Young People going without Health Insurance: Study Finds 13.7 Million without Coverage, Mostly because of Costs." *Healthday on the Web* 2 June 2008.

8. Finkel, David. "A Slave to Health Insurance: More Older Women Must Work for Money and Benefits." *Washington Post on the Web* 4 Oct. 2003.

9. Abelson, Reed. "Small Business Is Latest Focus in Health Fight." *NYTimes.com* 10 July 2008.

10. Starfield, B., Shi, L., and Macinko, J. "Primary Care Impact on Health Outcomes: A Literature Review." *Milbank Quarterly* 83.3 2005: 457-502.

Regional Evidence of Waste and Poor Performance

1. Fisher, Elliot S. "More Medicine Is Not Better Medicine." *NYTimes.com* 1 Dec. 2003.

2. Wennberg, John E. "Geography And The Debate Over Medicare Reform." *Health Affairs* 13 Feb. 2002.

3. Wilensky, Gail R. "The Implications of Regional Variations in Medicare - What Does It Mean for Medicare?" *Annals of Internal Medicine* 138.4 2003.

4. Shine, Kenneth I. "Geographical Variations in Medicare Spending." *Annals of Internal Medicine* 138 2003: 347-348.

5. Fisher, Elliot S. "The Implications of Regional Variations in Medicare Spending." Part 2: Health Outcomes and Satisfaction with Care. Editorial. *Annals of Internal Medicine* 138 2003: 288-298.

6. Yasaitis, L. and Fisher, E. "Hospital Quality and Intensity of Spending: Is There An Association?" *Health Affairs, Web Exclusive* 21 May 2009.

Part II Root Cause #2: Modern Medicine is Overrated

Chapter 4
THE POWER OF SELF-HEALING AND LIFE ECOLOGY FACTORS

Modern Medicine Is Overrated

1. McKinlay, Sonja M. and John B. "The Questionable Contribution of Medical Measures to the Decline of Mortality in the United States in the 20th Century." *MMFQ Health and Society* 55.3 1977: 405-428.

The Relationship Factor

1. Berkman, LF. "Social Networks, Host Resistance, and Mortality: A Nine-year follow-up Study of Alameda County Residents." *American Journal of Epidemiology* 109.2 1979: 186-204.

2. Miller, Karl E. "Can Family Support Improve Stroke Recovery?" *American Family Physician on the Web* 15 Jan. 2001.

3. Dickinson, Emma. "Good Friends, Rather Than Close Family Ties, Help You Live Longer In Older Age." *Journal of Epidemiology and Community Health* 59 2005:574-579.

4. Russek, Linda G. "Perceptions of Parental Carrying Predict Health Status in Midlife: A 35-year follow-up of the Harvard Mastery of Stress Study." *Psychosomatic medicine* 59.2 March/April 1997: 144-149.

5. Ellias, Marilyn. "Study: A Happy Marriage Can Help Mend Physical Wounds." *USA Today on the Web* 6 March 2005.

6. Gupta, Sanjay. "Happy Marriage Good for the Heart." *CNN on the Web* 16 Sep. 2003.

7. Gardner, Jonathan, and Andrew Oswald. "How is Mortality Affected by Money, Marriage, and Stress?" *Journal of Health Economics* 23.6 2004: 1181-1207.

8. Friedman Eric L, and Sue A. Thomas. "Pet Ownership, Social Support, and One-year Survival after Acute Myocardial Infarction in the Cardiac Arrhythmia Suppression Trial." *American Journal of Cardiology* 76.17 1995: 1213-1217.

9. Gorkin, Larry. "Psychosocial Predictors of Mortality in the Cardiac Arrhythmia Suppression Trial-1." *American Journal of Cardiology* 71 1993: 263-267.

10. Yan, Lijing. "Psychosocial Factors and Risk of Hypertension: The Coronary Artery Risk Development in Young Adults (CARDIA) Study." *JAMA* 290.16 2003: 2138-2148.

11. Friedman, Howard S. "Psychosocial and Behavioral Predictor is of Longevity, the Aging and Death of the 'termites.'" *American Psychologist* 1995: 69-78.

12. House, James S. "Social Relationships and Health." *Science* July 1988: 241.

13. Dimsdale, Joel E. "Social Support-a-lifeline in Stormy Times." Editorial. *Psychosomatic Medicine* 57.1 1995: 1-2.

14. Cohen, Sheldon. "Social Ties and Susceptibility to the Common Cold." *JAMA* 277.24 1997: 1940-1944.

15. Eng, Patricia M. "Social Ties and Change in Social Ties in Relation to Subsequent Total and Cause-specific Mortality and Coronary Heart Disease Incidence in Men." *American Journal of Epidemiology* 155.8 2002: 700-709.

16. Oxman, Thomas E. "Lack of Social Participation or Religious Strength and Comfort as Risk Factors for Death after Cardiac Surgery in the Elderly." *Psychosomatic Medicine* 57.1 1995: 5-15.

17. House, J.S. "The Association of Social Relationships and Activities with Mortality: Prospective Evidence from the Tecumseh Community Health Study." *American Journal of Epidemiology* 116 1982:123-140.

18. O'Neil, John. "Aging: Help Others, for a Longer Life." *New York Times* 13 Dec. 2002.

The State of Mind Factor (Including the Placebo Effect)

1. "Live Longer With Transcendental Meditation." *Ivanhoe's Medical Breakthroughs on the Web* 4 May 2005.

2. Schneider, Robert H. "Long-term Effects of Stress Reduction on Mortality in Persons > 55 years of Age with Systemic Hypertension." *American Journal of Cardiology* 95 2005:1060-1064.

3. Robb, Vicki. "New Scientific Study Finds Forgiveness a Factor into Decreasing Spread of AIDS." *EurekAlert.org* 13 Oct. 2003.

4. Everson, Susan A. "Hopelessness and Risk of Mortality and Incidence of Myocardial Infarction and Cancer." *Psychosomatic Medicine* 58.2 1996: 113-121.

5. Fawzy, F.I. "Malignant Melanoma: Effects of an Early Structured Psychiatric Intervention, Coping, and Affective State on Recurrence and Survival Six Years Later." *Archives of General Psychiatry* 50.9 1993.

6. Roberts, Alan H. "The Power of Nonspecific Effects in Healing: Implications for Psychosocial and Biological Treatments." *Psychology Review* 13 1993: 275-391.

7. Kawachi, Ichiro. "Coronary Heart Disease/Myocardial Infarction: Prospective Study of Phobic Anxiety and Risk of Coronary Heart Disease in Men." *Circulation* 89.5 1994: 1992-1997.

8. Turner, Judith. "The Importance of Placebo Effects in Pain Treatment and Research." *JAMA* 271.20 1994: 1609-1614.

9. Margo, Curtis E. "The Placebo Effect." *Survey of Ophthalmology* 44.1 1999: 31-44.

10. Elliott, Victoria S. "Pursuing the Placebo Effect: What Exactly Is It? The Use of Placebo Has Been Associated by Patients with Trickery or Losing Out, but Some Researchers Are Looking for Something about It That Can be Harnessed to Heal." *AMNews on the Web* 20 Dec. 2004.

11. "Study: Placebos Make People Feel Better." *Associated Press* 24 Aug. 2005.

12. Brody, Howard. "The Placebo Response: Recent Research and Implications for Family Medicine." *Journal of Family Practice* 49.7 2000: 649-654.

13. Duenwald, Mary. "Power of Positive Thinking Extends, Its Scenes to Aging." *NYTimes.com* 19 Nov. 2002.

14. Neergaard, Lauren. "Power of the Placebo: Simply Expecting Relief from Pain Can Help." *MyTELUS health on the Web* 19 Feb. 2004.

15. Goldschmidt, Debra. "Study Says Patients is More Than a Virtue." *CNN on the Web* 20 Nov. 2002.

16. Kubzansky, Laura D. "Is Worrying Bad for your Heart? A Prospective Study of Worry and Coronary Heart Disease in the Normative Aging Study." *Circulation* 95.4 1997: 818-824.

17. Greenberg, Gary. "Is It Prozac? or Placebo?" *Mother Jones on the Web* Nov./Dec. 2003.

18. Ernst E. and Resch, K. L. "Concept of True and Perceived Placebo Effects." *British Medical Journal* 311 1995: 551-553.

19. Cohen, Sheldon. "Types of Stressors that Increase Susceptibility to the Common Cold in Healthy Adults." *Health Psychology* 17.3 1998: 214-223.

20. Williams, Redford. "Resolved: Psychosocial Interventions Can Improve Clinical Outcomes in Organic Disease-rebuttals and Closing Arguments." *Psychosomatic Medicine* 64.4 2002: 564-567.

The Inflammation Factor

1. Goode, Erica. "The Heavy Cost of Chronic Stress; Some Can Be Benign, But Too Much Can Be Lethal." *New York Times* 17 Dec. 2002.

2. Gorman. "The Fire is Within." *Time* Feb. 2004: 8.

3. "Anti-Inflammatory Diet." *UWhealth.org/Integrativemed* 1.2 2003.

The Diet Factor

1. Stein, Rob. "Low-calorie Diet May Lengthen Life: Regimen Reduces risk of Disease is Associated with Aging." *Washington Post* 20 April 2004: A03.

2. Rimm, E. B. "Vegetable, Fruit, and Cereal Fiber Intake and Risk of Coronary Heart Disease among Men." *JAMA* 275.6 1996: 447-451.

3. Stein, Rob. "Daily Alcohol Cuts Risk of Heart Attack." *Washington Post* 9 Jan. 2003: A01.

4. "Obesity Cuts Lifespan for Young Adults, New Study Shows Being Obese at Age 28 Can Cut up to 20 Years off a Persons Life." *Associated Press* 7 Jan. 2003.

5. Fox, Maggie. "Obesity as Unhealthy as Heart Failure-Study." *Yahoo News on the Web* 7 Nov. 2004.

6. Jenkins, David J. A. "Effects of a Dietary Portfolio of Cholesterol-lowering Foods versus Lovastatin on Serum Lipids and C-reactive Protein. *JAMA* 290.4 2003: 502-510.

7. "Nuts (and Fiber) to High Cholesterol, Who Needs Statin Drugs When You've Got the Grocery Store?" *Time Magazine* Aug. 2003.

8. Editorial. "Study Hailed as Convincing in Tying Fat to Cancers." *NYTimes.com* 24 Apr. 2003.

9. Walford, Roy L. "Calorie Restriction in Biosphere 2." *The Journals of Gerontology Series A* 57 2002: B211-224.

10. Johnson, Rachel K., et al. "Dietary Sugars Intake and Cardiovascular Health. A Scientific Statement From the American Heart Association." *Circulation* 24 Aug. 2009.

11. Esselstyn, Caldwell B. "Resolving the Coronary Artery Disease Epidemic Through Plant-Based Nutrition." *Preventive Cardiology* Fall 2001. (An evidence-based argument that dietary interventions are far superior to technological approaches to treating coronary artery disease)

12. Lustig, Robert H. "The Fructose Epidemic." *The Bariatrician.* 24.1 2009.

The Exercise Factor

1. Johnson, Carla K. "Study: Exercise Can Add Three Years To Life." *Associated Press on the Web* 14 Nov. 2005.
2. Squires, Sally. "Lean Plate Club: More Activity, Less Achoo!" *Washington Post* 18 Nov. 2003.
3. "Studies: Walking May Ward Off Alzheimer's." *Associated Press on the Web* 22 Sept. 2004.

The Sleep Factor

1. Wheeler, Timothy B. "High Price of Cheating Sleep." *Sunspot on the Web* 5 May 2003.
2. Adams, Amy. "Stanford Research Builds Link Between Sleep, Cancer Progression." *Eurekalert on the Web* Oct. 2003.
3. White, Geoffrey. "Sleep and Balance Linked to Heart Disease." *Washington Post on the Web* 27 Jan. 2003.
4. Kantrowitz, Barbara. "In Search Of Sleep." *Newsweek on the Web* 15 July 2002.

When Life Ecology Factors Work Together...

1. Jonas, Wayne B. "Investigating the Impact of Optimal Healing Environments." *Alternative Therapies* 9.6. 2003.
2. Frank, Aimee. "Lifestyle Changes Clinically Effective." *Eurekalert on the Web* 28 Oct. 2003.
3. Ivanhoe Newswire. "Lifestyle Changes May Prevent Disease." 14 Nov. 2005. (Harvard head of Nutrition estimates that 80% of coronary artery disease and 90% of diabetes can be eliminated with exercise and optimal diets!)
4. "Health for Life, Living Longer, Living Better." *Newsweek* Fall/Winter 2001.
5. Ornish, Dean. "Intensive Lifestyle Changes for Reversal of Coronary Heart Disease." *JAMA* 280.28 1998: 2001-2007.
6. Hickman, Belinda. "Lifestyle Tips Key to Cutting Health Costs." *The Australian News* 27 Nov. 2004.
7. *Khaw et al.* "Combined Impact of Health Behaviors and Mortality in Men and Women: The EPIC-Norfolk Prospective Population Study." PLoS Medicine5 (1) e12. doi:10.1371/journal.pmed.0050012. 8 January 2008 and http://www.srl.cam.ac.uk/epic/findings/index3.html. (a 14 year improvement in life expectancy from only minimal exercise, 5 servings of fruits and vegetables per day, non-smoking, and moderate alcohol! This website has a very nice collection of evidence about key lifestyle factors and their impact on life expectancy)
8. Jonas, Wayne B. and Rakel, David P. "Putting Healing Into Healthcare Reform: Will Physicians and Healthcare Practitioners Lead?" *Alternative Therapies* Nov/Dec 2009. (Very nice summary of the inadequacies of current reform discussions in the context of key predictors of health and healing)
9. Walker, Lou Ann. "We can control how we age." *Parade Magazine* Sept. 2001.

The Religion Factor

1. Graham, Thomas. "Frequency of Church Attendance and Blood Pressure Elevation." *Journal of Behavioral Medicine* 1.1 1978.

2. Redaksie, Van Die. "Church Attendance and Coronary Heart Disease." Editorial. *South African Medical Journal* 47.29 1973: 1267.

3. Levin, Jeff. God, Faith, and Health. NY: John Wiley & Sons, 2001.

4. Kalb, Claudia. "Faith Healing." *Newsweek on the Web* 10 Nov. 2003.

5. Levin, Jeffrey S. "Is Religion Therapeutically Significant for Hypertension?" *Social Science Medicine* 29.1 1989: 69-78.

6. Levin, Jeffrey S. "How Religion Influences Morbidity and Health: Reflections on Natural History, Salutogenesis, and Host Resistance." *Social Science Medicine* 43.5 1996: 849-864.

7. Levin, Jeffrey S. "Religion and Spirituality in Medicine: Research and Education." *JAMA* 278.1 1997: 792-793.

Longer Living Populations

1. "New Book Promotes Japan's Long-life Island." http://archives.cnn.com/2001/WORLD/asiapcf/east/05/15/japan.okinawa.healthbook/. 15 May 2001.

2. Fackelmann, Kathleen. "The Secrets of Longevity." *USA Today on the Web* 22 Feb. 2004.

3. Takayama, Hideko. "The Grandparents Lived Past 100, but After Too Many Burgers, the Islands' Next Generation May Not Make It to Middle Age." *Newsweek* 13 Jan. 2003.

4. "Health after 100: Secrets of Centenarians." *Johns Hopkins Medical Letter* Nov. 2001.

5. Pascucci, Mary Ann. "Ingredients of an Old and Healthy Life; A Centenarian Perspective." *Journal of Holistic Nursing* 1997: 199-213.

Primary Care and Alternative Medicine in the Life Ecology Factors Light

1. Arvantes, James. "Patient-centered Medical Home is Key to Health Care." *AAFP.org* 14 May 2007.

2. Ruggie, Mary. "Mainstreaming Complementary Therapies: New Directions in Health Care." *Health Affairs* 24.4 2005.

3. "Alternative Advances: Beat the Bean Counters." *Ivanhoe Newswire* 13 May 2005.

4. Thorpe, Kenneth E. "The Rise in Health Care Spending and What To Do About It." *Health Affairs* 24.6 2005. (most spending is related to *modifiable* population risk factor, he recommends that rather than focus on insurance models, we should focus on prevention, public health, and cost-effective healthcare)

Part III Root Cause #3—Modern Medicine is Harmful

Chapter 5
THE PROBLEMS OF COMPLEXITY, ERRORS, AND WASTE

Adverse Drug Events/Medical Injuries

1. Lazarou, Jason. "Incidence of Adverse Drug Reactions in Hospitalized Patients: Meta-analysis of Prospective Studies." *JAMA* 279.15 1998: 1200-1205.

2. "Leading Hospitals under Fire for Errors." *USA Today on the Web* 29 Sept. 2003.

3. Friedman, Richard A. "ESSAY; Curing and Killing: the Perils of a Growing Medicine Cabinet." *NYTimes.com* 17 Dec. 2002.

4. Kaushal et al. "Medication Errors and Adverse Drug Events in Pediatric Inpatients." *JAMA* 25 April 2001.

5. Douglass, Elizabeth. "Child's Death Highlights Need for Drug Error Prevention." *ASA News* 2002:a 341.

6. Leape, Lucian L. "Counting Deaths Due to Medical Errors." *JAMA* 288.19 2002: 2405.

7. "Report Says 195,000 Deaths Due To Hospital Error." *Reuters* 27 July 2004.

8. "Scant Progress Seen On Cutting Medical Errors." *American Medical Network on the Web* 4 Nov. 2004.

9. Woznicki, Katrina. "US Hospitals Called Little Better on Patient Safety." *Medpage Today on the Web* 3 May 2005.

10. Gandhi, Tejal K. "Adverse Drug Events in Ambulatory Care." *New England Journal of Medicine* 348.6 2003: 1556-1564.

11. O'Neill, John. "PATTERNS: Medical Errors, for Outpatients." *NYTimes.com* 4 Feb. 2003.

12. Gandhi, Tejal K. "Drug Complications in Outpatients." *Journal of General internal Medicine* 15.3 2000: 149.

13. Zhan, Chunliu. "Excess Length of Stay, Charges, and Mortality Attributable to Medical Injuries during Hospitalization." *JAMA* 290.14 2003: 1868-1874.

14. Paul, Maria. "Study Finds Surprisingly High Rate of Patients Readmitted to Hospital Within a Month." *Eurekalert.org* 1 April 2009.

Infections

1. Allen, Scott. "A Death Underscores Unsettling Surgical Truths: Family Ties Doctor to Fatal Infection." *Boston Globe on the Web* 9 Nov. 2005.

2. McCaughey, Betsy. "Hospital's Dirty Little Secret: Infections Now Are Rampant." *Investor's Business Daily on the Web* 2 Aug. 2002.

3. Roberts, Rebecca R. "The Use of Economic Modeling to Determine the Hospital Costs Associated with Nosocomial Infections." *Clinical Infectious Diseases* 36 2003: 1424-1432.

4. "CDC Finds Lapses in Hospital Hygiene; Only Half of Doctors, Nurses wash Hands after Patient Contact." *Associated Press/MSNBC* 21 Feb 2003 (this includes the estimate of 2 million infections per year in hospital as well as 90,000 deaths per year)

Administrative Waste

1. Zhang, Jane. "Why We Need 1,170 Codes for Angioplasty." *WSJ.com* 11 Nov. 2008.
2. Woolhandler, Steffie. "Costs of Healthcare Administration in the United States and Canada." *New England Journal of Medicine* 349.8 2003: 768-775.
3. Levin, Stephanie. "Study Finds Billions of Health Insurance Dollars Used for Administrative costs." *EurekAlert.org* 12 Nov. 2005.
4. Himmelstein, David U. "Administrative Waste in the US Healthcare System in 2003: The Cost to the Nation, the States, and the District of Columbia, Would State Specific Estimates of Potential Savings." *International Journal of Health Services* 34.1 2004: 79-86.
5. List, Barry. "Diagnosis: Mismanagement - Operations Researcher Argues Healthcare Industry Could Trim Costs More Than 10%." *Informs on the Web* 13 Oct. 2003.

BATTLE FOR PAYMENT/NONPAYMENT RESULTS IN MORE WASTE

6. Baisden, Harry. "AHA Criticizes BCBSA on Cost Research Content, Interpretation." *AHA News* 28.42 2002: 1-2.
7. Scheffey, Daniel. "Rising Hospital Costs: The Value Quandary." *US newswire on the Web* 11 Dec. 2002.
8. Cook, Bob. "Clash of the Titans: Hospitals vs. health plans." *AMNews on the Web* 23 Dec. 2002.

WASTE OF DEFENSIVE MEDICINE INCLUDING UNNECESSARY MALPRACTICE CRISES

1. Nader, Ralph. "Statement by Ralph Nader on the Occasion of President Bush's Address in Scranton, Pennsylvania on Medical Malpractice." *USA newswire on the Web* 17 Jan. 2003. (The risk from being sued is highly overstated and yet the response to this fear results in substantial waste.)
2. Hunter, Robert. "New Study Shows Insurance Industry, Not Lawsuits, Causing Insurance Rates to Skyrocket for West Virginia Doctors." *US Newswire on the Web* 5 Jan. 2003. < http://www.findarticles.com>
3. "Doctors in Florida, Mississippi Protest Insurance Rates" *Washington Post on the Web* 28 Jan. 2003.
4. "New Jersey Hospitals Cancel Surgeries to Prepare for Doctors Strike." *Associated Press* 3 Feb. 2003.
5. "New Jersey Doctors Staged a Work Slowdown, More than 1300 New Jersey Doctors Protest Malpractice Insurance Premiums with Work Slowdown, Rallies." *Associated Press* 3 Feb. 2003.
6. "Pennsylvania Hospitals Brace for Dr. Walkout." *Associated Press* 31 Dec. 2002:A258

7. Goldstein, Josh. "Pennsylvania Warns Doctors Not to Quit." *Philadelphia Inquirer* 28 Dec. 2002.

8. "18 States Now in Deep Liability Crisis." *AMENews on the Web* 17 Mar. 2003.

9. Sack, Kevin. "New Florida Law Allows Low-Cost Health Policies." *NYTimes.com* 22 May 2008.

HUMAN RESOURCES STRETCHED THIN MEANS ERRORS

1. "Study: Nursing Education, Death Rates Linked." *Associated Press* 24 Sept. 2003.

2. Aiken, Linda H. "Education Levels of Hospital Nurses and Surgical Patient Mortality." *JAMA* 290 2003: 1617-1623.

3. Pear, Robert. "Report Cites Danger in Long Nurses Hours." *NYTimes.com* 5 Nov. 2003.

4. Gerretson, Sharon. "Nurse to Patient Ratios in American Health Care." *Nursing Standard* 19 2004: 14-16.

5. Costello, Mary Ann. "Study Links Patient-nurse Ratios to Mortality Rates, Staff Unrest." *JAMA* 38.42 2002: 8.

6. Aiken, Linda H. "Hospital Nurse Staffing and Patient Mortality, Nurse Burnout, and Job Dissatisfaction." *JAMA* 288 2002: 1987-1993.

7. "California Issues Proposed Regulations for First US Nurse-patient Ratios." *AHA News* 38.39 2002: 8.

8. Carlson. "Study Reveals Nurses' Dissatisfaction with Quality of Current Hospital, Healthcare Systems." *Modern Healthcare* 6 July 2009.

DIFFICULT TO OVERCOME SYSTEM COMPLEXITY

1. Woznicki, Katrina. "US Hospitals called Little Better on Patient Safety." *Medpage Today on the Web* 3 May 2005.

WASTED OPPORTUNITY PER THE "DANGERS OF DOING TOO MUCH"

1. McGlynn, Elizabeth A. "The Quality of Health Care Delivered to Adults in the United States." *New England Journal of Medicine* 348.26 2003: 2635-2645.

2. Fackelmann, Kathleen. "Health Systems Fails Seniors Half the Time." *USA Today on the Web* 3 Nov. 2003.

3. Wenger, Neil S. "The Quality of Medical Care Provided to Vulnerable Community-Dwelling Older Patients." *Annals of Internal Medicine* 139.9 2003: 740-747.

4. Murphy, Amy. "Hospitals that Follow Guidelines Save Lives." *Bio Medicine on the Web* 28 Sep. 2005.

5. "Doctors Ignoring Guidelines, Study Says." Associated Press 25 June 2003.

6. "Poor Compliance with Rx Medicines Bedevils Health Care." *Pharmacy Times* 1 Sept. 2007.

7. Buckley, Anne. "Access to Existing Medical Treatments Could Save More Lives than Spending to Improve the Treatments." *Bio Medicine on the Web* 6 Dec. 2005.

8. Hawryluk, Markian. "California Emergency Departments Close after Hemorrhaging Money." *AMedNews on the Web* 24 March 2003.

9. Institute of Medicine. "Crossing the Quality Chasm, Executive Summary." National Academies Press, 2001.

10. "IOM Notes Shift to Chronic Care Management: Health Care Doesn't Use The Information Technology and Training and Coordinating Techniques That Other Sectors Use." *Managed Care Magazine on the Web* 12 March 2003.

11. Robeznieks, Andis. "IOM Quality Study Targets 20 Priority Areas: The Revolutionary Report is the Latest from the Institute of Medicine Aimed at Improving Patient Care. *AMNews on the Web* 17 Feb. 2003.

12. Marinker, Marshall. "Not to be Taken as Directed." *British Medical Journal* 326 2003: 348-349. (We are quite unsuccessful in causing patient compliance with medical plans. Again coaching and time are the keys but lack of resources prevents this, a source of indirect harm by wasting resources)

13. Kavilanz, Parija B. "Insurers Not Improving Nation's Healthcare." *CNN.com* 22 Oct. 2009.

Part IV Putting it All Together

Chapter 6

THE PROBLEMS CREATED BY POOR ACCOUNTABILITY AND INCENTIVES

Poor Accountability and Incentives—How the Healthcare Mess Developed

POOR ACCOUNTABILITY

1. Hartocollis, Anemona. "Reporting of Mistakes by Hospitals is Faulted." *NYTimes.com* 10 March 2009.

2. Berenson, Alex. "Weak Oversight Lets Bad Hospitals Stay Open." *NYTimes.com* 8 Dec.2008.

3. Glendinning, David. "Medicare Could Start Comparing Resource Use Among Doctors in 2008. A GAO Report Prompts Warnings From Physicians Against the Government Using the Information to Penalize Doctors Deemed 'Overutilizers'." *AMNews* 25 June 2007. (How can we maintain fee for service with no accountability for spending?!)

4. Meyers, Susan. "The Road to Transparency." *Trustee* 58.5 2005: 18, 20-2. (Nice summary of how far we must travel in order to truly establish health outcomes accountability)

5. "Blues Plans Ready Consumer Cost Data." *Health Data Management* 1 Feb. 2009.

6. Kavilanz, Parija B. "Biggest Medical Mystery: The Bill." *CNNMoney.com* 22 April 2009.

7. Editorial. "Our Pen-and-Paper Doctors." *NYTimes.com* 24 June 2008.

Correlations Between the American Healthcare and Financial System Crises

1. Fons, Jerome S. and Partnoy, Frank. "Rated F for Failure." *NYTimes.com* 16 March 2009. (Regarding the failure of credit ratings agencies to accurately judge risk)
2. Friedman, Thomas L. "All Fall Down." *NYTimes.com* 26 Nov. 2008.

So How in the World Did We Allow this Healthcare System Mess to Develop? The Perfect Storm of Lost Checks and Balances

3RD PARTY PAYMENT

1. "History of Taxation in the United States." www.eoearth.org/article/History_of_taxation_in_the_United_States
2. Wolff, Rick. "The Fallout from Falling U.S. Wages." *MRZine* 6 Dec. 2006. (Stagnant wages for the past 40 years!) http://mrzine.monthlyreview.org/wolff120606.html
3. Tanne, Janice Hopkins. "US Healthcare Lobbyists Outspend Other Pressure Groups." *British Medical Journal* 328 2004: 786.
4. Blumenthal, David. "Employer-Sponsored Health Insurance in the United States-Origins and Implications." *NEJM* 6 July 2006.
5. Samuelson, Robert J. "Let's Not Hide Health Costs." *Newsweek MSNBC* Jan. 2007.
6. Editorial. "Medicare's Bias." *NYTimes.com* 14 July 2008. (The broken promise of private plans creating competition and driving down Medicare costs)

WRONG INCENTIVES INCLUDING THE QUESTIONABLE IMPACT OF QUALITY MEASURES AS CURRENTLY DEFINED

1. Urbina, Ian. "In the Treatment of Diabetes, Success Often Does Not Pay." *NYTimes.com* 11 Jan. 2006.
2. Ginsburg, Paul B and Grossman, Joy M.. "When the Price Isn't Right: How Inadvertent Payment Incentives Drive Medical Care." *Health Affairs* 9 2005.
3. Teutschet, Steven M. "Misaligned Incentives in America's Health: Who's Minding the Store?" *Annals of Family Medicine* 3 2005: 485-487.

POOR MARKET FUNCTION

1. Lange, Mark. "A Tumor at the Heart of Medicare." *NYTimes.com* 21 March 2009. (The Medicare Part D example of good intentions for competition being undermined by lobbyists and poor existing marketplace structure)
2. Leonhardt, David. "High Medicare Costs, Courtesy of Congress." *NYTimes.com* 25 June 2008.

System Crisis

LOBBYING POWER/INFLUENCE

1. Tanne, Janice Hopkins. "US healthcare Lobbyists Outspend Other Pressure Groups." *British Medical Journal* 328 2004: 786.
2. Editorial. "Medicare Savings vs. The Lobbyists." *NYTimes.com* 25 June 2008.

POTENTIALLY FRAUDULENT IF NOT UNETHICAL BEHAVIOR INCLUDING CONFLICT OF INTEREST

1. Frieking, Kevin. "Medicare Fraud Rampant in LA, Miami." *Time magazine* July 2007.
2. Meier, Barry. "Guidant Didn't Disclose a Flaw in Defibrillator for 3 Years." *NYTimes.com* 24 May 2005.
3. Moynihan, Ray. "Another US Healthcare Giant is Hit by Scandal." *British Medical Journal* 327 2003:1128.
4. Vogt, Katherine. "First HealthSouth Sentences Handed Down." *AMNews on the Web* 5 Jan. 2004.
5. Freudenheim, Mill. "Hospital Chain Accused of Accounting Fraud." *NYTimes.com* 20 Mar. 2003.
6. Sullivan, Kip. "Minnesota Fat Cats." *In These Times on the Web* 8 July 2002.
7. Hunter, Robert. "New Study Shows Insurance Industry, Not Lawsuits, Causing Insurance Rates to Skyrocket for West Virginia Doctors." *US Newswire on the Web* 5 Jan. 2003.
8. Eichenwald, Kurt. "Guidant Admits that it Hid Problems of Artery Tool." *NYTimes.com* 13 June 2003.
9. Kristof, Nicholas D. "Dad's Life or Yours? You Choose." *NYTimes.com* 4 Oct. 2009. (Another example of the ridiculous trade-offs people need to make because of the ridiculous cost of coverage and threat of being excluded from coverage by pre-existing conditions)
10. "Guidant Sued Over Handling of Aortic Graft." *Associated Press* 14 June 2003.
11. "US Sues For-profit Hospital Company Over Medicare Bills." *Reuters* 10 Jan. 2003.
12. Berry, James. "Aetna Settles Suit With Physicians." *ADA News on the Web* 29 March 2003.

SUPPLIES PURCHASING CONFLICT OF INTEREST

1. Meier, Barry. "A Regions Hospital Supplies: Costly Ties." *NYTimes.com* 8 Oct. 2002.
2. Walsh, Mary Williams. "More Hospitals Change the Way They Buy Drugs and Supplies." *NYTimes.com* 28 Dec. 2002.
3. Walsh, Mary. "Wide US Inquiry into Purchasing for Healthcare." *NYTimes.com* 21 Aug. 2004.

PHYSICIANS

1. Carey, Benedict and Harris, Gardiner. "Psychiatric Group Faces Scrutiny over Drug Industry Ties." *NYTimes.com* 12 July 2008.

2. Becker, Jo and Snyder, David. "Maryland Lawmakers Take Aim at Medical Board." *Washington Post on the Web* 21 March 2003.

3. Wilson, Duff. "Harvard Medical School in Ethics Quandary." *NYTimes.com* 3 March 2009.

4. Harris, Gardiner. "Top Psychiatrist Didn't Report Drug Makers' Pay." *NYTimes.com* 4 Oct. 2008.

5. Editorial. "Drugs and Disclosure." *NYTimes.com* 11 Oct. 2008.

6. Public Citizen's Health Research Group. "20,125 Questionable Doctors.". http://www.citizen.org/hrg/qdsite/introduction.htm. (half of hospitals not reporting discipline against physicians as they should)

PHARMACEUTICAL INDUSTRY (Also see Chapter 3 References)

1. Harris, Gardiner. "FDA Says Bayer Failed to Reveal Drug Risk Study." *NYTimes.com* 30 Sep. 2006.

2. Berenson, Alex. "Despite Warnings, Drug Giant Took Long Path to Vioxx Recall." *NYTimes.com* 14 Nov. 2004.

3. Harris, Gardiner. "Judge Says Maker of OxyContin Misled Officials to Win Patents." *NYTimes.com* 6 Jan. 2004.

4. Jewell, Mark. "Express Scripts to Pay $9.5 Million in Settlement." *Associated Press* 27 May 2008.

5. "Pfizer Settles with Maryland, 18 Other States, It Must Change How It Promotes Antibiotic for Child Ear Infections." *Associated Press* 7 Jan. 2003.

6. Lavoie, Denise. "Whistle-blower to Get $24.6 Million, Pfizer Also Will Pay Civil, Criminal Fines." *CBS News on the Web* 13 May 2004.

7. Abelson, Reed. "How Schering Manipulated Drug Prices and Medicaid." *NYTimes.com* 31 Jul. 2004.

8. Pear, Robert. "Investigators Say Drugmakers Repeatedly Overcharged." *NYTimes.com* 30 June 2004.

9. "Drug Makers to Pay Medicaid Settlement; Bayer, Glaxo, Smith Kline to Pay Record Medicaid Fraud Settlements to Resolve Alleged Overcharges." *Associated Press* 16 April 2003.

10. Berenson, Alex. "Merck Admits a Data Error on Vioxx." *NYTimes.com* 31 May 2006.

OVERVIEWS OF AN AMERICAN HEALTHCARE SYSTEM IN CRISIS

1. Abramson, John. "Overdosed America: The Broken Promise of American Medicine." New York: HarperCollins, 2004.

2. McCanne, Don. "Nationalize Health Care." *USA Today on the Web* 5 March 2003.

3. Genuis, Stephen J. "Diagnosis: Contemporary Medical Hubris; RX: a Tincture of Humility." *Journal of Evaluation in Clinical Practice* 1 Dec. 2005.

4. Welch, Charles A. "Making Healthcare Better, Cheaper, Safer." *The Boston Globe* 12 May 2003. (A nice summary of IOM's report on American healthcare system problems and goals for improvement)

5. Cutler, David M. Your Money or Your Life: Strong Medicine for America's Health Care System. New York: Oxford University Press, 2004.

6. Foreman, Judy. "Heal Health Care System? Start Anew." *New York Times on the Web* 2 Dec. 2003.

7. Clinton, Hillary. "Now Can We Talk About Health Care?" *New York Times on the Web* 18 April 2004.

8. Lewis, Sandy G. "Homeostasis without Reserve." *New England Journal of Medicine* 347.24 2002: 1971-1975.

9. Mongan, James J. "Options for Slowing the Growth of Health Care Costs." *New England Journal of Medicine* 358 2008:1509-1514.

10. Institute of Medicine. Crossing the Quality Chasm, Executive Summary. National Academies Press, 2001.

11. Krugman, Paul. "A Private Obsession." *NYTimes.com* 29 April 2005.

12. Sanfilippo, Fred. "Pull the Plug on the Current Healthcare System." Dec. 2004. <http://www.aamc.org/newsroom/reporter/dec04/viewpoint.htm>

13. Goldstein, Warren. "Unspeakable Truths No One Will Admit." *Philadelphia Inquirer* 29 June 2003.

14. Radford, Tim. "Top Scientist Warns of 'Sickness' in US Health System." *British Medical Journal* 326 2003: 416.

15. Krugman, Paul. "Pride, Prejudice, Insurance." *NYTimes.com* 7 Nov. 2005.

16. Kristof, Nicholas D. "Health Care Fit for Animals." *NYTimes.com* 27 Aug. 2009. (Former insurance executive has an awakening and reveals the many tactics employed by healthcare insurance companies to maintain their profits.)

17. DerGurahian, Jean. "A Long Way to Go." *Modern Healthcare* 7 Dec. 2009. ("Nation's progress in improving quality of care said to be slower than anticipated")

18. Sack, Kevin. "From the Hospital to Bankruptcy Court." *NYTimes.com* 25 Nov. 2009. (Healthcare costs as the number one cause of bankruptcies including many tragic stories of working, insured people being hurt unexpectedly. Also many stories of tragic domino effect of illness leading to bankruptcy and job loss at the same time)

19. Wilson, Duff. "Research Uproar at a Cancer Clinic." *NYTimes.com* 23 Oct. 2009. (The poor state of clinical research checks and balances)

Chapter 7

TRANSFORMATIONAL HEALTHCARE REFORM, POWERFUL ACCOUNTABILITY AND INCENTIVES

Building Block#2: Accountability for Health Outcomes and Costs

HEALTH OUTCOMES (QUALITY) AND PRICE TRACKING INCLUDING DATABASES/ ELECTRONIC HEALTH RECORD

1. Lohr, Steve. "Who Pays for Efficiency?" *NYTimes.com* 11 June 2007. (The need to make an electronic health record investment)

2. Stencel, Christine. "Institute of Medicine News: Report on Healthcare Performance." *Eurekalert.org* 1 Dec. 2005.

3. Zwillich, Todd. "Government Touts Its Web Site That Allows Users to Compare the Quality of Hospitals." *WebMD Medical News* 21 May 2008. (Interesting that they acknowledge that these "quality" measures focus on process measures NOT how well patients are actually doing! We have a long way to go in establishing health outcomes accountability)

4. O'Reilly, Kevin B. "…AMA-convened Physician Consortium for Performance Improvement…" *AMNews* 2 July 2007. (An example of efforts to produce health outcomes indicators)

5. O'Reilly, Kevin B. "Surgical Quality Program Cuts Complications, Patient Deaths." *AMNews* 21 Sept. 2009.

6. O'Reilly, Kevin B. "Study Questions Impact of Quality Report Cards." *AMNews* 18 Feb. 2008. (Must create accountability AND correct incentives simultaneously)

7. Hall, Jim. "First, Make No Mistakes." *NYTimes.com* 29 July 2009

8. Hagland, Mark. "When It Comes to Quality Improvement Methodologies, CIO Leadership Will Be Essential." *Healthcare Informatics* Jan. 2007.

9. Berry, Emily. "Web Site Shows What Health Insurers Pay Minnesota Doctors, Clinics." *AMNews* 17 Sept. 2009.

10. Burton. "Publishing Hospitals' Outcomes May Augment Quality, Drive Pricing Down." *The Wall Street Journal* 6 Oct. 2009. (The Pennsylvania example of system-wide price/ quality transparency and resulting improvement in costs and outcomes)

11. Groopman, Jerome and Hartzband, Pamela. "Why 'Quality' Care Is Dangerous." *The Wall Street Journal* 8 April 2009. (A critique of the quality movement in its current form)

12. Mosquera, Mary. "Consumer Technology May Improve Health Outcomes." *Government Health IT* 23 Oct. 2009.

HEALTHCARE SCIENCE FOR THE FUTURE

1. Perrin, Edward B. "Some Thoughts on Outcomes Research, Quality Improvement, and Performance Measurement." *Medical Care* 20.6 2002: 89-91.

2. Abaid, Lisa N. "Reducing Publication Bias through Trial Registration." *Obstetrics & Gynecology* 109 2007:1434-1437.

3. Edwards, Adrian, and Gigerenzer, Gerd. "Simple Tools for Understanding Risks: from Innumeracy to Insight." *British Medical Journal* 327 2003: 741-744.

4. Tunis, Sean R. "Increasing the Value of Clinical Research for Decision-making in Clinical and Health Policy." *Journal of the American Medical Association* 290 2003:1624-1632.

5. Ganz, Patricia A. "What Outcomes Matter to Patients. A Physician-researcher Point of View." *Medical Care* 40.6 2002: 11-19.

6. Stryer, Daniel. "Step Across the Gap: Tools, Trials and Data." *Medical Care* 41.8 2003.

7. Editorial. "Evidence and Healthcare Reform." *NYTimes.com* 28 Feb. 2009.

8. Pearlstein, Steve. "Fixing Health Care Starts With the Doctors." *Washingtonpost.com* 10 June 2009.

9. Neumann, Peter. "A Strategic Plan for Integrating Cost-Effectiveness Analysis into the US Healthcare System." *The American Journal of Managed Care* April 2008.

10. Currie, Colin. "Clinical Arithmetic, an Enlightenment Legacy Still Needs Defending-Against More Subtle Adversaries." *British Medical Journal* 327 2003: 1418-1419.

11. Buckley, Anne. "Access to Existing Medical Treatments Could Save More Lives than Spending to Improve the Treatments." *Bio-Medicine on the Web* 6 Dec. 2005.

12. Chalmers, Iain. "Descriptive Survey of Non-Commercial Randomized Controlled Trials in the United Kingdom, 1980-2002." *British Medical Journal* 327 2003: 1017.

13. Kelly, William N. "Careers in Clinical Research: Obstacles and Opportunities." *JAMA* 273.1 1995:12.

14. Thompson, James's N. "Preventing the Extinction of the Clinical Research Ecosystem." *JAMA* 278.3 1997: 241-245.

15. Genel, Myron.1995 "Public-Policy Plenary Symposium: 'The Crisis in Clinical Research'." *Pediatric Research* 39.5 1996: 902-913.

16. "Closing the Gap between Proof in Practice." *Health Affairs* 41.8 2003.

17. Iglehart, John K. "The New Imperative: Producing Better Evidence." *Health Affairs* 24.1: 7.

18. O'Reilly, Kevin B. "House Bill Earmarks $3 Billion in Funds for Comparative Research." *AMNews* 18 June 2007. (Remember this would force treatments and tests over the relative benefit hurdle which is rarely done currently but an obvious must)

19. Kravitz, Richard L. "Doing Things Better vs. Doing Better Things." *Annals of Family Medicine* 3 2005:483-485.

20. AAMC Reporter. "Setting Priorities: Transforming Scientific Research into Better Health Care." April 2003.

21. Meier, Barry. "New Efforts Reopens a Medical Minefield." *NYTimes.com* 7 May 2009. (An example of the power of real science in exposing the pure value of new treatment options and how the establishment attempts to block this information)

22. Pear, Robert. "U.S. to Compare Treatments." *NYTimes.com* 16 Feb. 2009. (Some movement at the federal level to fund comparative effectiveness trials. This is what we call relative benefit which is a much more powerful method of demonstrating the true value of new treatments)

23. Juhn, Peter, et al. "Balancing Modern Medical Benefits and Risks." *Health Affairs* 26.3 2007. (Still amazing to see titles like this after we have been "modern" for 50 years! NOW we're going to balance the risks?!)

24. Rubin, Rita. "Panel Pinpoints 100 Areas to Yield Most Bang for Health-Care Buck." *USA Today* 1 July 2009. (The IOM recommends 100 areas that should be studied more systematically and with cost-effectiveness research)

25. Institute of Medicine. Initial National Priorities for Cost-effectiveness Research. June 2009.

26. Pearson, Steven D. "Quality, Innovation, and Value for Money." *JAMA*. 23/30 Nov. 2005. (The British example of intelligent healthcare decision making on a large scale)

27. Kravitz, Richard L. "Doing Things Better vs. Doing Better Things." *Annals of Family Medicine* 3 2005:483-85. (The title tells it all and points to our idea within Root Cause #1 that we should seek scientific advancement before technological advancement. The opposite has happened to this point)

28. Meier, Barry. "Panel Suggests U.S. Medical Priorities." *NYTimes.com* 1 July 2009. (Nice summary of the lack of scientific accountability in healthcare decision making)

SPECIFIC MEASURES AND KEY CONCEPTS

1. Sloan, Jeff. "Practical Guidelines for Assessing the Clinical Significance of Health-related Quality-of-life Changes within Clinical Trials." *Drug Information Journal* 37 2003: 23-31.

2. Timble, Justin. "A Cost-Effectiveness Framework for Profiling the Value of Hospital Care." *Medical Decision Making* 1 June 2008.

3. Schiffner, R. "Willingness to Pay and Time Trade-off: Sensitive to Changes the Quality of Life in Psoriasis Patients?" *British Journal of Dermatology* 148.6 2003:1153.

4. Wilson, Edward. "Priority Setting In Practice: What Is the Best Way to Compare Costs and Benefits?" *Health Economics* 17 June 2008.

5. Hutubessy, Raymond. "Generalized Cost-effectiveness Analysis for National-level Priority Setting in the Health Sector." *Cost-effectiveness and Resource Allocation* 19 Dec. 2003.

6. Woolf, Stephen. "The Breakeven Point: When Medical Advances Are Less Important Than Improving The Fidelity With Which They Are Delivered." *Annals of Family Medicine* 3 2005: 545-552.

7. Neunamm, Peter J, et al. "A Strategic Plan for Integrating Cost-Effectiveness Analysis into the Healthcare System." *The American Journal of Managed Care* April 2008.

8. Fritze, John. "Health Care Comparisons Help Show Best Practices, Prices." *USA Today* 28 Sept. 2009. (Cost-effectiveness research in action with healthcare systems such as Kaiser)

Building Block #3: Incentives

INDIVIDUAL AND FAMILY INCENTIVES to be value conscious shoppers including Healthcare Savings Accounts and the difficult matter of motivating consumers to improve their Life Ecology Factors.

1. Scandlen, Greg. "Consumer-Driven Health Care: Just A Tweak or A Revolution?" *Health Affairs* 24.6 2005.

2. Rosenthal, Meredith, et al. "A Report Card on the Freshman Class of Consumer-Directed Health Plans." *Health Affairs* 24.6 2005. (Nice summary of marketplace deficiencies that need to be corrected before the consumer can cause a revolution akin to Building Blocks 2 and 3)

3. Robinson, James C. "Health Savings Accounts-The Ownership Society in Health Care." *New England Journal of Medicine* 22 Sept. 2005. (Nice summary of the pros and cons of HSAs by one the premier healthcare economists in the United States)

4. Editorial. "Healthy Trend." *Investor's Business Daily* 26 Oct. 2005. (A pro-HSA opinion from a business newspaper)

5. Reuters. "Report: Medicine Use Falls with High Copays." *HEALTHonline* 19 May 2004. (The downside of HSAs are consumer irresponsibility and thus the argument by some to force HSAs in to a managed care type of arrangement so there are still cost savings that can go to the consumer but responsible healthcare and health behaviors will still be supported and promoted)

6. Pear, Robert. "New Medicaid Rules Allow States to Set Premiums and Higher Co-Payments." *NYTimes.com* 27 Nov. 2008. (Again, a push to transfer some costs to individuals but then the risk of delaying necessary care. Some HSA plus solution will be the best of both worlds as presented in this book. HSA allowing cash savings as an incentive to become an active consumer while purchasing packages that cover total care not coverage for fee for service)

7. Dowd, Bryan E. "Coordinated Agency Versus Autonomous Consumers in Health Services Markets." *Health Affairs* 24.6 2005. (Nice summary of the various innovative consumer empowerment healthcare packages ranging from catastrophic coverage only vs HSA and managed care if ala carte purchasing is too difficult)

8. Pear, Robert. "Congress Plans Incentives for Healthy Habits." *NYTimes.com* 10 May 2009.

9. Douthat, Ross. "The Catastrophic Option." *NYTimes.com* 19 Oct. 2009.

HEALTHCARE SYSTEM INCENTIVES—Flat fee for total care and other ideas to reduce/ eliminate fee-for-service. Innovators that would flourish in a flat fee environment and therefore deliver value to consumers.

1. Galewitz, Phil. "Can 'Bundled' Payments Help Slash Health Costs?" *USA Today* 26 Oct. 2009.

2. Harris, Gardiner. "Hospital Savings: Salaries for Doctors, Not Fees." *NYTimes.com* 25 July 2009.

3. Hall, Mark A. and Havighurst, Clark C. "Reviving Managed Care with Health Savings Accounts." *Health Affairs* 24.6 2005.

4. Kowalczyk, Liz. "Hospitals Attack State Pay Proposal." *Boston Globe* 4 Oct. 2009. (Push back regarding the first-in-the-nation proposal for fixed annual per-person budget versus fee for service in Massachusetts)

5. Bach, Peter B. "Paying Doctors to Ignore Patients." *NYTimes.com* 24 July 2008. (The perverse incentives to do things rather than spend time with patients)

6. Freudenheim, Milt. "Trying to Save by Increasing Doctors' Fees." *NYTimes.com* 21 July 2008. (The medical home concept to improve primary care including better coordination, better prevention, and reducing unnecessary care. Paying doctors to spend more time with their patients in the hopes of reducing costs!)

7. Editorial. "Mere Criticism Won't Fix Costs." *Boston Globe* 8 Oct. 2009. (Massachusetts healthcare system pushes back against flat annual fees and the Globe itself pushes back by asking for tangible solutions to cost control. An excellent summary.)

8. Kowalczyk, Liz. "State Plan May Place Limits on Patients' Hospital Options." *Boston Globe* 11 Oct. 2009. (Even more thorough discussion of the Massachusetts debate regarding the move to eliminate fee for service)

9. Neergaard. "Health Systems Trying to Reduce Healthcare Overuse are Obama's 'Islands of Excellence'." *Associated Press* 8 Sept. 2009.

10. Verghese, Abraham. "Mending the Hospital Safety Net." *The Wall Street Journal* 7 Aug. 2009. (Even public hospitals dependent on Medicare and Medicaid funding are capable of becoming successful given the amount of waste in the system)

11. Boulton, Guy. "ThedaCare among U.S. Leaders in Efficiency Efforts." *The JournalSentinel.com* 30 March 2008. (Another example of the types of efficiency that can be extracted from healthcare systems with available industrial engineering techniques. A flat fee system would reward such innovative hospitals)

12. Sack, Kevin. "Massachusetts Faces Costs of Big Health Care Plan." *NYTimes.com* 16 March 2009. (Massachusetts dipping toe in flat-fee waters because of cost overruns)

13. Sachs, Michael. "Disruptive Innovation Is Occurring-Don't be Left Behind!" *SG2 Healthcare Intelligence* 28 April 2009.

14. Kane, Nancy. "Keep Hospitals Whole." *NYTimes.com* 12 July 2009. (Nice detailed ideas about moving to a bundled payment system for Medicare)

15. Berry, Emily. "Mass. Physicians Urge Caution on Payment Overhaul." *AMNews.com* 29 Oct. 2009.

16. Alonso-Zaldivar, Ricardo. "Could 'Medical Homes' Bring Order to Health Care?" *The Associated Press* 3 Nov. 2009. (The type of healthcare innovation that global or flat-fee payments would support)

OPENING THE HEALTHCARE INSURANCE MARKETPLACE

1. Editorial. "Reform and Your Premiums." *NYTimes.com* 15 Oct. 2009. (insurance industry report draws widespread criticism as a scare tactic to block reform of the insurance industry including allowance for insurance coops and a public insurance option)

2. Editorial. "Out-of-Network Payment Practices." *NYTimes.com* 8 April 2009. (The lack of fluidity in the healthcare insurance marketplace means no *functional* marketplace. Also highlights unethical practices by the healthcare insurance industry)

3. Murray, Shallagh. "Pelosi Joins Fellow Democrats in Tough Talk for Health Insurers." *Washington Post* 15 Oct. 2009. (Very nice summary of the types of protections the healthcare insurance industry enjoys and the threats made by Democrats against these protections in return for gamesmanship on the part of the insurance companies. *These protections are a major impediment to a functional marketplace in American healthcare*)

4. Editorial. "Not So Reasonable and Customary." *NYTimes.com* 17 Jan. 2009. (Incredible conflict of interest in price setting by insurance companies especially regarding out-of-network care, the very thing required to make the marketplace functional!)

5. Editorial. "Insurance Company Schemes." *NYTimes.com* 29 June 2009. (The shameful healthcare insurance industry practice of "rescission" meaning cancellation of policies for "pre-existing" conditions "discovered" after the fact when patients required expensive care)

6. Frum, David. "Healthcare: Give Insurers More Power." *LATimes.com* 20 Sept. 2009. (Excellent list of ideas to cause the healthcare insurance marketplace to function properly)

7. Ginsburg, Paul B. "Cut Medicare With a Scalpel." *NYTimes.com* 12 July 2009. (Why hospitals' growing power will be a significant impediment to reform, especially cost containment)

8. Robinson, James C. "Consolidation and the Transformation of Competition in Health Insurance." *Health Affairs* 23.6 2004. (Evidence of healthcare insurance sector consolidation and effective monopolization. Reduced competition means a non-functioning marketplace. Interesting to note the significant drop in healthcare insurance premiums in the early-mid 90s with the entry of new competitors i.e. HMOs. Once these started leaving, prices took off again)

THE PUBLIC OPTION AS ONE ADDITIONAL COMPETITOR

1. Werner, Erica. "Pelosi Makes Case for Government-run Health Option." *Associated Press* 16 Oct. 2009. (Rep. Pelosi makes the argument that healthcare insurance industry misbehavior is another rationale for a public option to offer competition to keep them honest)

2. Kuttner, Robert. "Facing Down the Private Insurance Industry." *The Boston Globe* 4 June 2009. (The public option as a valuable tool for keeping the healthcare insurance honest)

3. Editorial. "A Public Health Plan." *NYTimes.com* 21 June 2009.

4. Editorial. "The Public Plan Continued." *NYTimes.com* 18 Oct. 2009.

5. Stolberg, Sheryl Gay. "Public Option Is Next Big Hurdle in Health Debate." *NYTimes.com* 15 Oct. 2009.

6. Thaler, Richard. "A Public Option Isn't a Curse, or a Cure." *NYTimes.com* 16 Aug. 2009. (The belief that the public option will not be a serious threat because of the tendency of government-run entities to be inefficient. This overlooks that ANY real *national* competition will improve marketplace function significantly)

7. Dow, William H. et al. "A Public Option that Works." *NYTimes.com* 22 Aug. 2009. (The first large-scale public healthcare option in action with initial positive results, San Francisco)

8. Pear, Robert. "Doctors' Group Opposes Public Insurance Plan." *NYTimes.com* 11 June 2009.

9. Cohen, Roger. "Get Real on Health Care." *NYTimes.com* 14 Sept. 2009. (Do NOT be fooled by the "we're going to become socialists with the public option. The French DO have private insurance *on top of* basic coverage and half the American coverage is government based! **Either fix the market or go to a more government driven system. Americans are crazy to stay in between as they are currently**)

10. Krugman, Paul. "Health Care Showdown." *NYTimes.com* 22 June 2009. (Thoughts on the politics of blocking the public option)

THE NATIONAL CO-OP (ALSO CALLED AN EXCHANGE) OPTION as another competitor including putting money in individual's hands to purchase healthcare insurance, driving up value sensitivity and therefore market function.

1. Sack, Kevin. "Health Co-op Offers Model for Overhaul." *NYTimes.com* 7 July 2009.

2. Kranish, Michael. "Health Co-ops' Fans Like Cost and Care." *Boston Globe* 19 Aug. 2009

3. Mufson, Steven. "Cooperatives' Record Weighed in Health-Care Debate." *Washington Post* 27 Aug. 2009.

4. Pear, Robert and Harris, Gardiner. "Alternate Plan as Health Option Muddies Debate." *NYTimes.com* 18 Aug. 2009.

5. Abelson, Reed. "Health Insurance Exchanges: Will They Work?" *NYTimes.com* 6 Oct. 2009.

6. McGarr, Cappy. "A Texas-Sized Health Care Failure." *NYTimes.com* 6 Oct. 2009. (Lessons described for an unsuccessful healthcare insurance coop)

7. Enthoven, Alan C. "Employment-based Health Insurance is Falling: Now What? A Strategy, Based on Managed Competition, to Free Employers from the Health Care Costs Spiral and Produce Effective Managed Care." *Health Affairs Web Exclusive* 28 May 2003.

8. Enthoven, Alain and Riemer, David. "The Only Public Health Plan We Need." *NYTimes.com* 25 June 2009. (Excellent article on a valuable solution although it lacks the Building Block #1 that we feel is necessary. It does address Building Block #2 if structured to encourage flat-fee models and interstate competition. Exchanges need three critical elements to be powerful: 1) a critical mass of subscribers to entice healthcare insurance vendors, 2) vouchers for an amount only up to the lowest cost qualified plan (encouraging a value competition), 3) a federal exchange mechanism to encompass this program)

COMPREHENSIVE SOLUTIONS A MUST

1. Kahn, Charles N. "Payment Reform Alone Will Not Transform Health Care Delivery". *Health Affairs* 27 Jan. 2009.

2. Harris, Gardiner. "Maine Finds a Health Care Fix Elusive." *NYTimes.com* 11 Nov. 2009. (The Maine example of decades of frustration with reform attempts to no avail. It is vital for comprehensive reform with all the key Building Blocks)

3. Perrott, David. "The Dutch Health Care System: Possible Model for American?" *The Physician Executive Journal* Nov/Dec. 2008.

4. Reid, T.R. and PBS. "Sick Around the World." *Frontline* 2009.

Chapter 8

THE FINAL SUMMARY—WHAT CAN YOU DO?

1. "American Values Blamed for U.S. Health-care Crisis." *ScienceDaily* 8 Dec. 2008.

2. Woolf, Steven H. "Promoting Informed Choice: Transforming Health Care To Dispense Knowledge for Decision Making." *Annals of Internal Medicine* 16 August 2005.

3. Vesely. "Group Signs Joint Statement Calling for Better Consumer Health IT Tools." *Modern Healthcare* 25 June 2009.

4. Tu, Ha T. "Striking Jump in Consumers Seeking Health Care Information." *HSChange. org* Aug. 2008.

5. Fraenkel, Liana. "Participation in Medical Decision Making: The Patients' Perspective." *Medical Decision Making* Sept-Oct 2007.

Why Rationing is OK

1. "Should Benefit to Individuals Outweigh Good for Groups?" *Managed Care Magazine* Sept. 2003.

2. Harris, Gardiner. "British Balance Gain Against the Costs of the Latest Drugs." *NYTimes. com* 3 Dec. 2008.

3. Kinsley, Michael. "Health Care Faces the 'R' Word." *The Washington Post* 26 June 2009.

4. Leonhardt, David. "Health Care Rationing Rhetoric Overlooks Reality." *NYTimes.com* 17 June 2009.

Appendix

THE ROLE OF THE VARIOUS ACTORS IN THIS TRANSFORMATION

Healthcare Providers

1. Lohr, Steve. "Health Care That Puts a Computer on the Team." *NYTimes.com* 27 Dec.2008.

2. Davis, Ronald M. "Autonomy vs. Accountability: A Delicate Balance." *AMNews* 20 Aug. 2007. (The battle *against P4P and the refusal to relinquish autonomy*)

3. "Transparency Is 'Inevitable,' Healthcare Futurist Joe Flower Predicts." *ACPE.org* Sept. 2008.

4. Larson, Laurie. "Physician Autonomy vs. Accountability: Making Quality Standards and Medical Style Mesh." *Trustee* July 2007.

5. Reinertsen, James L. "Zen and the Art of Physician Autonomy Maintenance." *Annals of Internal Medicine* 17 June 2003. (This author also recommends the giving up of *individual* autonomy to maintain the *collective* autonomy of physicians, a kind of accountability)

6. Gingrich, Newt, Beane, Billy, and Kerry, John. "How to Take American Health Care from Worst to First." *NYTimes.com* 24 Oct. 2008. (A very nice article by former and current congressman from the Left and Right regarding the need for more evidence to drive decision-making including actual decision-making guidelines and systems)

The Healthcare Insurance Companies (Please also Refer to the References in Chapter 7, Building Block #3)

1. Moran, Donald W. "Whence and Whither Health Insurance? A Revisionist History." *Health Affairs* 24.6 2005.

2. O'Connor, Patrick. "Dems Launch Attack on Insurers Exemption." *Politico.com* 14 Oct. 2009. (Significant call for ending the insurance industry's anti-trust exemption. Very strong language against the exemption of the healthcare insurance industry as anti-competitive. The original exemption bill was called McCarran Ferguson)

Employers

1. Smith, Donna. "U.S. Business Leaders Say Hobbled by Healthcare Costs." *Reuter* 13 March 2009.

2. Galvin, Robert S. "Why Employers Need to Rethink How They Buy Health Care." *Health Affairs* 24.6 2005.

ABOUT THE AUTHOR |

Niraj Nijhawan, a physician practicing in Wisconsin, is a 1992 graduate of the University of Wisconsin Medical School. Dr. Nijhawan completed his medical residency in anesthesiology at the Medical College of Wisconsin; acquired a Master's Degree in clinical research; has conducted and constructed multiple clinical trials; and has held several healthcare leadership roles. For over a decade, Dr. Nijhawan has passionately pursued, researched, and presented solutions to many fundamental and frequently misperceived matters related to healthcare reform.

Join the conversation at
MMKILLS.COM

- Become a member and gain access to an everexpanding list of pertinent articles, books, and website links

- Be part of the mmkills blog

- Learn about additional opportunities to become healthier and save money

- Learn about opportunities to make the healthcare system work better for you through reform efforts